PRENTICE-HALL ELECTRONIC TECHNOLOGY SERIES

under the editorship of Dr. Irving L. Kosow

Electronic Precision Measurement
Techniques and Experiments

by MEMBERS OF THE STAFF OF PHILCO TECHNICAL INSTITUTE

PRENTICE-HALL, INC.

Electronic Precision Measurement Techniques and Experiments

Englewood Cliffs, New Jersey

PRENTICE-HALL INTERNATIONAL, INC., London
PRENTICE-HALL OF AUSTRALIA, PTY., LTD., Sidney
PRENTICE-HALL OF CANADA, LTD., Toronto
PRENTICE-HALL OF INDIA (PRIVATE) LTD., New Delhi
PRENTICE-HALL OF JAPAN, INC., Tokyo

Current printing (last digit):

11 10 9 8 7 6 5 4 3 2

ELECTRONIC PRECISION MEASUREMENT
TECHNIQUES AND EXPERIMENTS

Printed in the United States of America

Preface

This manual has been prepared by members of the staff of the Philco Technological Center to fill a void in technical literature on the subject of precision measurement techniques. During the past decade, electronic equipment has become increasingly complex and the measuring accuracies needed to test and calibrate this new equipment have become increasingly stringent. Unless proper precision measuring techniques are employed, it is impossible to satisfy these accuracy requirements.

This manual is designed to provide a broad source of information on precision measurement techniques, with primary emphasis on electrical and electronic equipment. Since, in standard measurements, accuracy is of utmost importance, a large part of the manual is devoted to the special techniques required in calibrating test equipment. It includes numerous exercises in the use and calibration of typical precision measuring instruments.

Contents

x

Electronic Precision Measurement
Techniques and Experiments

Introduction to Standardized Calibration

1

THE NEED FOR INSTRUMENT CALIBRATION

"I often say that when you can measure what you are speaking about, and express it in numbers, you know something about it; but when you cannot measure it, when you cannot express it in numbers, your knowledge is of a meagre and unsatisfactory kind; it may be the beginning of knowledge, but you have scarcely, in your thoughts, advanced to the stage of science, whatever the matter may be."—Lord Kelvin, 1883.

Lord Kelvin thus stated the basic maxim of science—that little progress is possible in any field of investigation without the ability to measure. The dependability of present-day mass production, the interchangeability of parts, worldwide travel and communication, scientific and technological progress, and even international economics could not exist without precision measurement techniques.

The need for precision measurements is particularly acute in the field of electronics. From the tremendous expansion of the electronics industry, to meet the needs of World War II, have come postwar developments affecting every phase of living. An overwhelming variety of electronic equipment is in use today. In order that this equipment may function properly and be adequately maintained, precision measurements must be made either continuously or periodically.

UNIVERSAL STANDARDS REQUIRED

The ability to measure is not sufficient in itself. In order to provide universal application, accurate measurements must be based upon internationally accepted standards. Moreover, measuring instruments must be frequently calibrated against these standards.

The manufacture of automotive engines requires standard gage blocks for the production of cylinders and pistons to fine tolerances. Buyers and sellers of grain and other commodities depend upon standard weights for accuracy of railway track scales. Space-probing rockets depend upon precise guidance mechanisms, which, in turn, depend upon astronomical and electrical standards for their accuracy.

In one instance, the performance of approximately 100 different radar sets was carefully measured with test equipment of known accuracy. The test revealed that on the average the maximum effective range of the sets under test was only one-half the maximum range possible. In fact, five sets were found to be operating at less than 10% of their possible maximum range, which means, in effect, that these radars were protecting less than 1% of their assigned tactical areas. Yet, in each case, the set under test was thought to be in normal operating condition, or better, by the radar personnel concerned.

Such poor performance, which might have had serious military consequences, demonstrates the importance of precise measurements made with test instruments of known accuracy and reliability. Standardized calibration—the art of calibrating test instruments against primary or secondary standards —is essential to this accuracy and reliability.

1

PURPOSE OF THIS MANUAL

This manual is intended to serve as a broad source of general information on the subjects of precision measurement techniques and test equipment calibration. Primary emphasis is on electrical and electronic equipment. Introductory material on standards, systems of measurements, and evaluation of experimental data is included. The reader, however, is assumed to have a detailed knowledge of the operation and use of the field test instruments (voltmeters, wave analyzers, etc.) which are to be calibrated. Since, in standards measurements, accuracy is of utmost importance, most of this manual is devoted to the special techniques required in calibrating field test equipment. Sources of error are given due space.

HISTORY OF STANDARDS

Weights and measures can be traced back to prehistoric times, although there is considerable uncertainty about many origins. Units of length were probably the earliest standards used. These were given in terms of human appendages: the length of the foot and forearm, and the width of the palm. Units of weight were given in terms of shells and of kernels of grain.

Such a system did not provide a very exact definition of units. Later, the units were given a slight degree of standardization by letting the foot be the length of some tribal chieftain's foot.

Eventually, the units of measure became embodied in physical standards of crude construction, kept in the safe confines of religious temples. The term *crude* is used because such standards seem crude today; actually, however, those standards were as well suited to the needs of their day as our present standards are for our more exacting requirements.

The units and standards were modified down through the ages, and eventually were grouped into various systems: the Phileterian system of the Ptolemaic age, the Olympic system of Greece, the Roman system, the British system, etc.

It is interesting to note that one unit of measure, the degree of arc, has passed through the ages without change. This unit was originated by the early Babylonians. Since their year was divided into 360 days, they also divided the circle into 360 parts, or degrees. Since their geometric art was rather advanced, they knew that a chord equal to the radius subtends an arc of 60°. Thus the number 60 became the basis of their sexagesimal number system; this accounts for the division of the degree into 60 minutes, and the minute into 60 seconds.

Changes have been more gradual with the passing of time.

The metric system developed as the international decimal system based on the meter and the kilogram. Early standards for these units of measure were determined in terms of natural phenomena. The meter was one ten-millionth of a meridianal quadrant of the earth, and the kilogram was the mass of 1 cubic decimeter of water at maximum density.

Later, however, the trend toward defining units in terms of physically reproducible objects developed. The meter became the length of a standard metal bar, and the kilogram became the mass of a metal cylinder.

Presently, the trend seems to be based on a return to natural phenomena. The meter was recently (1960) defined in terms of the wavelength of the light produced by a krypton standard. Time measurement will soon be based on the vibrations of submolecular structures.

The commonly employed system of weights and measures in the United States developed from the British system, the British system having come from the Roman. The present units in the United States, Great Britain, and all agreeing nations are, however, derived in terms of the internationally accepted legal standards of the metric system.

NBS PRIMARY STANDARDS LABORATORY

The National Bureau of Standards was established to provide essential scientific services to the government, business, industry, and science. These services are primarily related to standards and methods for accurate measurement of natural phenomena.

The Bureau, however, does not stop at merely maintaining absolute standards. It also provides the methods and instruments required to utilize these standards. Then, through calibration services, it insures the accuracy of a myriad of industrial and scientific instruments by comparing them with the national standards. Research is continually conducted to meet the increasing needs for more precise measurements.

Closely related to the standards program is the Bureau's work on the basic properties of matter and materials. The Bureau deter-

mines fundamental physical constants, such as the acceleration of gravity, to provide the accurate values needed by scientists and engineers. The properties of materials, such as metals and plastics, are studied and evaluated so that these items may be fully utilized in industry.

In response to the Armed Services' urgent need for accurately calibrated electronic equipment to be used in radar, aircraft control, and missile guidance, an Electronic Calibration Center was opened in Boulder, Colorado, in 1958. At this installation, the master working standards used to calibrate production line and research laboratory instruments in this country, as well as others, are calibrated against the nation's primary electronic standards.

Robert C. Sprague, Chairman of the board of the Sprague Electric Company, stated,

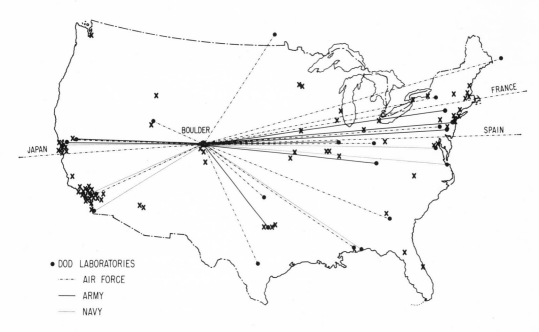

● DOD LABORATORIES
---- AIR FORCE
—— ARMY
········· NAVY

× INDUSTRIAL LABORATORIES

Fig. 1-1 World utilization of NBS electronic services. World-wide measurements and calibrations are made with reference to the standards maintained by the National Bureau of Standards. This insures that measurements made by manufacturer, repairman, and user will be consistent. (Courtesy, National Bureau of Standards.)

Fig. 1-2 National Bureau of Standards Research Center in Boulder, Colorado. Here basic research and development of new standards and new measurement techniques in the electrical sciences are conducted. (Courtesy, National Bureau of Standards.)

Fig. 1-3 Heredity of equipment calibration. The conduction of valid precision measurements and tests requires that records be maintained on all tests and calibration equipment. The secondary standard capacitance bridge on the left is used to calibrate "working-grade" equipment. The records associated with this device are recall notices, calibration reports, and test equipment record cards. In turn, the secondary standard bridge is calibrated with the precision variable capacitor on the right, which has been certified by the Eastern Primary Standards Laboratory.

in his address during the Boulder dedication ceremonies: ". . . our continued progress in the research and development fields depends primarily upon . . . adequate basic standards and standardized precision measuring de-vices. We cannot go forward without a firm and comprehensive foundation. To give us this foundation is the mission of the National Bureau of Standards."

A complete schedule of NBS services may be obtained by writing to the Government Printing Office for NBS Report 5589. In accordance with Government regulations, NBS must charge test fees for the calibrations it makes. Schedules of test fees may be obtained by writing to the National Bureau of Standards, Washington 25, D.C.

The NBS over-all program is broad in scope, utilizing primary knowledge in physics, mathematics, chemistry, metallurgy, and various other branches of engineering. There is, however, one predominant and unifying concept—the precise measurement of natural phenomena.

MEASURING STANDARDS AND INSTRUMENTS

The process of precision measurement always involves a succession of steps. At the source is NBS. Next in line may come a primary group of laboratory workers which maintains its basic reference standards to calibrate the apparatus used by the next lower, or secondary, group. The secondary group, in turn, calibrates the instruments used to make measurements in the plant or shop.

MEASUREMENT NOMENCLATURE *Absolute standards are devices constructed according to specifications based on the legal international definitions of the various fundamental units of measurement.* At various times, world-wide adjustments are made so that these standards will represent the basic units as nearly as possible.

Secondary reference standards are constructed from the absolute standards. They are used by secondary laboratories, and must maintain fixed values. They are periodically checked against the higher-order standards.

Interlaboratory standards are ruggedly constructed for transport between NBS and secondary laboratories. They are used as a check of accuracy between the secondary and absolute standards.

Working standards are calibrated in terms of the secondary reference standards, and are never used directly for field measurements.

Absolute measuring instruments give the value of the quantity to be measured in terms of the physical constants of the instrument and its deflection. No comparison with another instrument is necessary. Measurements with these instruments are tedious and time-consuming.

Secondary instruments are highly accurate devices, constructed so that the value desired can be read directly from the deflection of the instrument. The deflection will have no meaning, however, unless the instrument is calibrated against an absolute instrument, standard, or previously calibrated instrument.

Comparison equipment (bridges, potentiometers, etc.) are used in comparing field instruments with working standards.

Field instruments are the precision measuring devices, as well as the less accurate, nominal-value devices, used in shop and factory measurements. They are the most rug- gedly constructed of all the instruments, but are the least accurate, requiring frequent calibration as use determines.

INDUSTRIAL AND MILITARY STANDARDIZING LABORATORIES

Studies and surveys conducted by industry and the military show increasing demands for expanded calibration facilities, improved standards, and more and better measuring equipment.

The quantity of electronic calibrations required today in the design, manufacture, and adjustment of complex weapons, communication equipment, and industrial apparatus is so great that branching chains of measurement are necessary to extend the national standards to the shop or field instruments used for this work. The large number of links in each chain requires the highest predictable accuracy at each link, in order to assure sufficient accuracy of the field equipment.

For example, the air-to-air refueling of high-speed aircraft requires radar navigation equipment in order to rendezvous tanker and receiver aircraft. To assure contact between the two vehicles, their navigation equipment must be precisely calibrated against a single frequency standard. The calibration requires a total of 29 test instruments, each accurate to 0.1%. For the test instruments to be maintained at this accuracy, 25 measurement standards, each accurate to 0.01%, must be used.

In answer to such needs as these, standards laboratories have greatly increased in size and number throughout the military services and industries involved. These laboratories perform secondary calibration services guided by NBS master standards for calibration.

TYPICAL CALIBRATION LABORATORY A look inside a top-grade calibration laboratory reveals considerable differences from an ordinary room. The lighting is specially planned by

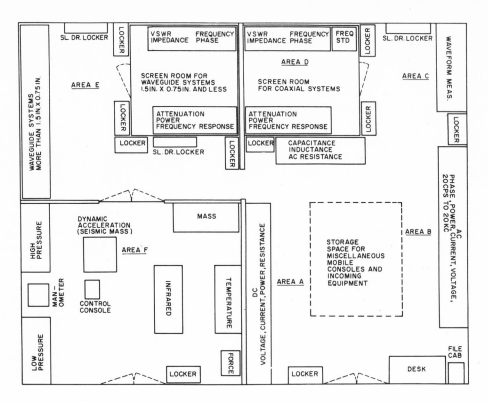

Fig. 1-4 Standards laboratory layout. Areas A and B, usually carrying the heaviest work load, provide space for a natural grouping of equipment to be used for d-c and low-frequency a-c measurements. Area C contains the equipment for waveform and frequency response measurements (note that this is conveniently located near the low a-c measurements area) although some of the frequency response equipment may have to be located in Area D. This latter area is for systems (primarily coaxial) which would be affected by radio-frequency interference. For best possible results, frequency standard equipment should also be located in this room. The microwave section (Area E) also contains a screen room—specially screened against the higher frequencies involved. The electromechanical and physical system measurements are conducted in a room completely enclosed from the rest of the laboratory (Area F). Adequate storage areas are provided as indicated.

lighting engineers to provide 100 foot-candles of light at bench level. Fluorescent lighting is normally used. The air temperature is held to within at least ±5°F of 72°F, to compensate for the heat radiated by the equipment used and under test. The relative humidity is held below 50%. Equipment must be installed to provide for the elimination of corrosive vapors such as salt air. Storage racks at opposite ends of the building, or in other convenient locations, are used for incoming and outgoing instruments, respectively.

Test benches fill the bulk of the laboratory floor space. These benches are heavily constructed to reduce vibration. Benches used for most electrical, electronic, and microwave measurements have rubberized tops to reduce vibration further and to minimize the hazards of electrical shock. Similar benches are used for electromechanical and physical measurements. However, the bench used for mass measurements is of massive wooden construction covered first with a ½-in. layer of felt and then with a ½-in. glass plate. The bench utilized for infrared and temperature measurements is covered with a *Transite* top and is equipped with an overhead vent hood to remove undesirable vapors. The dynamic shaker, used for vibration measurements, is installed on a *seismic mass* of approximately two tons minimum weight for stability purposes.

Throughout the laboratory are spaced 115-volt, 60-cycle, single phase electrical outlets (as well as a few 220-volt outlets) individually fused for 20 amperes. Test panels supplying a variety of a-c and d-c voltages and currents are available to supply regulated voltages and currents. Air supply line for dry, filtered air are also available.

Primary standards and the most accurate equipment are maintained in a separate room or in glass-enclosed racks along the walls. These storage areas are pure white, with an antiseptic-like cleanliness. Technicians in surgical gowns move about in the rigidly controlled, smokefree and dustfree atmosphere of the storage room, if such is maintained separately.

A screen room—double screened—is used for r-f measurements. Tests utilizing equipment which might create disturbing radiation-type interferences are conducted here. It is also a valuable place for making extremely small measurements which might be disturbed by stray pickup. A second similar screen room—further insulated by a 2-in. layer of black rubberized hairlike material—is used for microwave measurements.

An elaborate system of instrument log cards and calibration records is maintained to show the results of tests, out-of-tolerance conditions, repairs, and rechecks. This will aid in future troubleshooting, as well as point out recurring problems which may have to be referred to the manufacturer. Little confidence can be placed in the results of field tests unless calibration records for the test equipment show that the equipment is worthy of the measurements being made.

When the laboratory personnel are satisfied that the equipment they are calibrating meets specifications, a certificate of calibration is issued and the equipment is wire-sealed to insure against tampering. The certificate indicates the next date when calibration is normally due. Should the wire seal be broken at any time, the calibration is considered invalid.

There are many variations in arrangement and procedure employed by secondary standardizing laboratories. Although the particular problems that confront the various facilities differ greatly, all the facilities have a common function—maintaining and disseminating the instruments of measurement.

SUGGESTED PRACTICES

The vast experience of NBS in the field of precision measurements and standards maintenance has enabled the Bureau to set up a list of general principles for any program in calibration service. (These suggested practices are detailed in NBS Circular 578.) In addition, the Department of the Navy Office of Naval Material, recognizing the need for a coordinated program of standardized calibration, has compiled and distributed* the *Standards Laboratory Information Manual* (SLIM) to insure that all Naval laboratories, as well as contracting industries, will meet certain minimum requirements. A brief discussion of the general practices suggested by both organizations follows.

Of primary importance in any standardization laboratory is the competence of the personnel. The person in charge must be a qualified engineer with experience in all phases of electronic and physical measurements. Head technicians should be of the highest possible caliber, with subordinate technicians assigned according to a descending proficiency scale. Whenever possible, standards technicians should receive specialized training at a higher-level laboratory or at a special training center. The number of personnel required depends upon the volume of work which can be accomplished per unit time. This, of course, varies according to the num-

* Naval Inspector of Ordnance, 1675 W. 5th Street, Pomona, Calif.

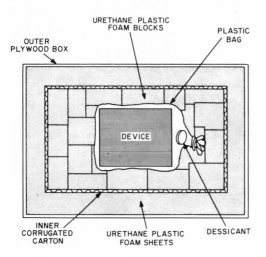

Fig. 1-5 Standard instrument packing.

ber of tedious and complex calibrations which must be made in comparison to the volume of straightforward, quickly obtained calibrations. A second factor to consider in determining the required number of personnel is the inventory of laboratory-operated equipment which must be maintained and calibrated.

In order to maintain definite responsibility for accuracy, NBS suggests that standardizing laboratories be kept separate from the rest of the organization. This also helps to establish pride in workmanship. In addition to organizational separation, the laboratory facility itself should be kept as far removed as possible from heavy vibration machinery, rotating machinery, large transformers and other saturable-core devices, and high-energy electrical or electronic installations.

In designing a new laboratory, the atmospheric conditions specified by the American Society for Testing Materials is recommended. This calls for a relative humidity of $50 \pm 2\%$ and a temperature of $73.4°F \pm 2°F$. Freedom from dust and corrosive vapors is important; hence primary consideration should be given to effective air filtering and electrostatic precipitation.

Actual laboratory layout depends upon size as well as volume and type of work to be performed. Numerous—and often, conflicting —factors must be considered. Figure 1-4 shows the ideal general standards laboratory layout recommended by the Department of the Navy.

The shipping of primary and working standards and comparison equipment should be held to a minimum, since deterioration occurs most rapidly with handling and shipping. Figure 1-5 shows a desirable packing technique used by Naval laboratories. Records of reference standards should be maintained. In general, these standards should not be readjusted since such adjustments may initiate a progressive drift in value.

Choice of measuring equipment, as well as the frequency for comparisons of measuring equipment, varies, depending upon the volume of equipment to be tested, the delicacy of the apparatus, and the type of personnel handling the equipment. When abnormal standards occur, a check should be made with a higher calibrating service, regardless of formally scheduled check time.

ROUTINE CALIBRATION PROCEDURES

Valuable time can be saved if a standards lab will adopt routine and "standard" procedures for the accomplishment of all measurements and calibrations. Examples of these procedures are the Department of the Navy's *Measurement System Operation Procedures* (MSOP's) and the 33K-series of Technical Orders (TO's) published by the United States Air Force.

Whatever the actual calibration procedure to be followed, preliminary steps should always include (1) visual inspection for obvious physical defects, (2) operational test to point out major defects, (3) preliminary maintenance pointed out by the previous steps, (4) cleaning and lubrication according to manufacturer's specifications, (5) zero-setting of all indicators, (6) leveling of devices which require this precaution, (7) determination of "intended-use" position of the various instruments, (8) sufficient warm-up time for electronic devices.

CALIBRATION AND CERTIFICATION

Primary standards laboratories directly relate their measurements to the National Bureau of Standards. Only the primary labs and NBS can *certify* equipment and standards, since the calibration procedures, measuring devices, and reference standards of only these two laboratory classes have the necessary accuracy for certification.

Secondary standards laboratories relate their measurements to primary standards laboratories, or to NBS if the required accuracy so demands.

Industrial standards laboratories (shop and field) relate their measurements to any of the foregoing three laboratory classes, depending upon the accuracy required. The bulk of their work is related to the secondary standards laboratory, however, although, quite frequently, shop and field calibrations may require such an accuracy that the industrial laboratory is, itself, a secondary standards laboratory.

In performing the various levels of calibration, certain checkpoints are designated at the values to be compared to an appropriate standard. The discussion which follows outlines *minimum requirements.*

CALIBRATION CHECK POINTS *At least three independent determinations of the absolute value of a fixed standard (gage block mass, resistor, capacitor, etc.) must be used in order for this device to be certified.* The calibration record should include the results of all three determinations along with the *arithmetic average* of the three as well as their deviation, or range—the largest recorded value minus the smallest recorded value.

Variable standards must be measured at each step in their increment controls. Each step usually includes the value of the previous step(s) as a part of the new value.

A linearity check should be made through all the major scale divisions of a single range linear scale indicator. After the completion of this calibration a recheck of the full- and half-scale divisions should be made.

The linearity check for single-range non-linear scale indicators should be restricted to the major divisions located in the portion of the scale where the distance between scale divisions is equal to, or greater than, the size it would be if the scale were divided evenly (linearly).* After completion of this calibration, the full- and half-scale divisions should be rechecked as above.

If the various ranges of multiple-range indicators vary by a fixed-element multiplier, the linearity check may be performed for only one range. The half- and the full-scale divisions of the other ranges should be checked. If the range multiplier is a variable element, the linearity check should be performed for each range.

* Naval Inspector of Ordnance, 1675 W. 5th Street, Pomona, Calif.

QUESTIONS

1 In the design of a calibration laboratory, what environmental considerations must be regarded?

2 How important are records in the calibration of an instrument?

3 Describe the organizational structure of the National Bureau of Standards.

4 Define the terms:
(a) Absolute standards
(b) Secondary reference standards
(c) Interlaboratory standards
(d) Working standards

(e) Absolute measuring instruments
(f) Secondary instruments
(g) Comparison equipment
(h) Field instruments

5 What would be the calibration check points for the d-c volts function of a Simpson 260 multimeter?

Mathematical Evaluation of Errors 2

When performing precision measurements, it is advisable to record a series of observations rather than to be content with one specific value. Errors of one magnitude or another will enter into all observations. With a sufficient number of readings, mathematical techniques may be employed to minimize the effects of error. These techniques consist of finding the average value of a given set of data and computing its probable error.

Errors, in general, are classified as personal, accidental, systematic, and instrumental.

Personal errors occur by pure chance and depend primarily on the observer's experience. A common form of error which can be eliminated because of its consistency is the tendency of an observer to judge readings on the high or low side of the actual value. The elimination process consists of deliberately setting an instrument at some random initial reading other than zero whenever possible. This initial reading should be subtracted from all subsequent readings. Consistent high or low tendencies will be canceled by the subtraction process. Another method of overcoming personal errors is to have readings made by more than one observer.

Systematic errors often come from sources unknown to the observer and, for this reason, may be extremely difficult to detect. One method of overcoming systematic errors is to make observations using two different sets of standards. This is not always practical, however. Observations with reversible instru-

ments should always be made in both directions.

Accidental errors are due to any number of small factors which change from one observation to another. The fluctuations may occur in the positive or negative direction and may be distributed in any manner within certain maximum and minimum values. Evaluation of accidental errors, then, becomes a study of the distribution of data. For example, Fig. 2-1 is a plot of magnitude of observed data (x) against the frequency of occurrence of these magnitudes (y). In the distribution plot, any value has an equal probability of being the true value. This includes the minimum value, x^1, the maximum, x^2, the mean, x^0, or any value between.

Another type of distribution is shown in Fig. 2-2. Here the value, x^0, is the most probable value since it occurs the most number of times. Since the distribution plot is an isosceles triangle, x^0 also represents the average value. The minimum and maximum values are again given by x^1 and x^2. There is no absolute certainty that x^0 is the true value; however, it has the greatest probability of being the true value. This distribution allows a more definite evaluation than the distribution shown in Fig. 2-1.

ACCURACY AND PRECISION OF NUMERICAL VALUES

Precision refers to the degree of agreement of a group of measurements among themselves.

Accuracy refers to the true value of the quantity being measured. The voltage of a dry cell may be read 10 times. The maximum deviation within the 10 readings may be only 0.001 volt from any one of the readings. This would represent a high degree of precision. The voltmeter may not have been calibrated before the observations, however, so that its indications are really 0.5 volt in error of the true value impressed upon it. This, then, would represent a very poor accuracy.

It is up to the observer, himself, to take the necessary precautions to insure that his instruments are functioning properly and that no controllable outside phenomenon is influencing the accuracy of his measurements.

SOURCES OF ERROR IN INSTRUMENTS

Some of the controllable errors which must be taken into consideration are the errors inherently present in measuring instruments because of their mechanical structure.

Friction of various moving components is an important example of a controllable error. Designers of precision equipment always take measures to reduce this ever-present physical property. Dampness and dust, however, may destroy the effectiveness of the precautionary measures. Undue friction can be detected by causing the mechanical component to move slowly throughout its entire range, stopping at several points along the way. If the instrument appears to drag and stick at certain spots, friction is undoubtedly the cause.

Springs are almost always used in deflection-type instruments. If an instrument is kept at a large deflection for a considerable amount of time, the spring may "stretch" slightly. This will cause the instrument gradually to shift away from its zeroing position. Temperature changes cause an inverse change in spring elasticity on the order of 0.04% per °C.

The physical position in which an instrument was designed to be used should always be determined, and the instrument should be used only in this position.

The primary points on precision instrument scales are marked by comparison with a reference or primary standard. The subdivisions, however, are laid out on a basis of proportionality. This often introduces error.

In making electrical measurements, simplicity is the key to excluding errors. Short leads reduce stray capacitance and inductance effects. The experimental setup must be shielded from stray fields. Additional cooling apparatus may be required to prevent excessive internal heating in larger instruments.

Always make certain that the instruments

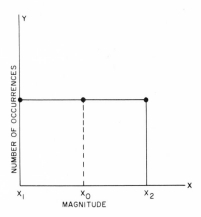

Fig. 2-1 Distribution plot showing equal probability of occurrence.

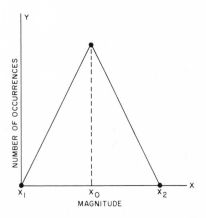

Fig. 2-2 Distribution plot showing the "most probable" occurrence of the value k_0.

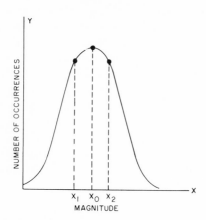

Fig. 2-3 Normal, or gaussian, distribution plot.

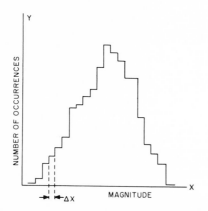

Fig. 2-4 Practical "step" distribution curve due to finite distances between values.

used are meant to be used for the frequency and wave form being investigated.

NORMAL MEASUREMENT DISTRIBUTION

The normal, or gaussian, distribution of values is given in Fig. 2-3. This type of distribution is based on the fact that if an infinite number of small errors were to occur, they would have an equal chance of being distributed about the mean value, x_0. Thus, for each value x_1 below x_0 there is an equally probable value, x_2, the same distance above x_0. The more peaked this distribution curve becomes,

the more definitely an observer may state that the most probable reading is the true reading. In this distribution the most probable value, x_0, is also the mean value of the distribution.

In actual practice, it is often impossible to represent distribution by a smooth curve, because of the finite distance between some value x and the next value $x + \triangle x$. This is shown in Fig. 2-4. The smaller the increments of $\triangle x$, however, the more closely the steps will approximate the slope (dy/dx) of the gaussian curve.

THE AVERAGE OR ARITHMETIC MEAN VALUE

The average, or arithmetic mean, of a collection of values is given by

$$x_0 = \frac{\text{sum of recorded values}}{\text{number of recorded values}}$$

The deviation of each reading is found by obtaining the difference between each recorded value and the mean value x_0. The average error is then found by

$$\text{avg error} = \frac{\text{sum of deviations}}{\text{number of recorded values}}$$

It is often desirable to express the error as a percentage of the mean value, as follows:

$$\% \text{ error} = \frac{\text{average error}}{\text{arithmetic mean}} \times 100 \%$$

ACCUMULATION OF ERRORS

When computations must be made with various observed quantities, the error of each individual quantity influences the error of the final result. The following is given as a general rule for most field-type calibrations.

In performing an addition or subtraction, the error of the result is the largest numerical error appearing in any one of the quantities. For multiplication and division, retain the largest *percent error* of any one of the terms as the percent error of the final value.

PROBABILITY DISTRIBUTION

Occasionally it is necessary to be more definite about how closely an observed reading approaches the true value being measured. That is, if the true value is M and the mean value of the observed data is x_0, what degree of uncertainty is involved in the statement:

$$M = x_0 \pm x'$$

where $\pm x'$ represents some segment about the mean (Fig. 2-5)?

The usual method of expressing this uncertainty is in terms of probable error, which is defined so that there is a 50% chance (equal probability) that the true value M lies somewhere in the segment bounded by $x_0 - x'$ and $x_0 + x'$.

The gaussian distribution curve can be theoretically expressed by the equation:

$$y = \frac{h}{\sqrt{\pi}} e^{-h2x2}$$

Here e is the natural logarithmic base and x is the deviation from the mean. The symbol, h, is the "modulus of precision" found from the relation:

$$h = \frac{y_0 \sqrt{\pi}}{n \; \triangle x}$$

where y_0 is the number of occurrences of the mean value, $\triangle x$ is the width of an interval between readings (see Fig. 2-4), and n is the total number of readings taken.

The limits within which the true value M has a 50% chance of occurring in the vicinity of *any one particular reading* (see Fig. 2-6) are given by

$$x'' = \pm \; \frac{0.477}{h}$$

The limits within which the true value M has a 50% chance of occurring in the vicinity of the *mean value, x_0* (see Fig. 2-5) are given by

$$x' = \frac{0.477}{h \sqrt{n}}$$

As an example, assume that 25 coins were tossed simultaneously on 200 different occasions. The recorded data are given in Table 2-1. The column labeled x shows the number of times that heads appeared in each group of 25 coins. The column labeled y shows the total number of times that a specific number of heads (x) appeared during the 200 tosses.

A coin has two sides. Assuming that the coin is symmetrical, either heads or tails has an equal opportunity of appearing. In other words, if 25 coins are tossed simultaneously, heads should appear 12.5 times.

The experimental mean value is given by:

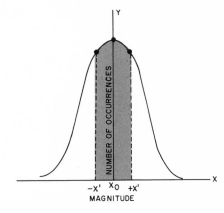

Fig. 2-5 Gaussian distribution showing limits of probable error about the mean.

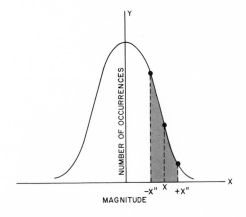

Fig. 2-6 Gaussian distribution showing limits of probable error about any point (measurement) X.

$$x_0 = \frac{\text{sum of } xy}{\text{total number of tosses}} = \frac{2483}{200} = 12.42$$

This mean value is not represented by any reading in the recorded data. The gaussian distribution plot is given in Fig. 2-7. The occurrence (y_0) of the mean value is established by interpolation. The procedure consists of computing the value of y based on the fact that x_0 occurs at 0.41 of the increment between $x = 12$ and $x = 13$:

$$y_0 = 28 + \left[\frac{34 - 28}{100} \times 41 \right] = 30.5$$

This point is also shown in Fig. 2-7.

Before evaluating the probable error of x_0, the modulus of precision must be determined,

$$h = \frac{y_0 \sqrt{\pi}}{n \quad \triangle x} = \frac{30.5 \sqrt{\pi}}{200 \, (1)} = 0.27$$

The probable error is then given by

$$x' = \frac{0.477}{h \sqrt{n}} = \frac{0.477}{(0.27) \sqrt{200}} = \pm 0.12$$

Therefore, the number of heads which can be expected to occur in 25 coins is 12.41 ± 0.12 as determined by the experiment. The theoretical value (12.5) falls within this range.

The mean value and the most probable value do not correspond in Fig. 2-7 because a large enough number of observations was not taken. The ideal gaussian distribution, remember, is based on an infinite number of observations.

Table 2-1 Data Recorded During Coin-Tossing Experiment

x	y	xy
5	1	5
6	1	6
7	4	28
8	8	64
9	10	90
10	18	180
11	26	286
12	28	336
13	34	442
14	24	336
15	22	330
16	13	208
17	8	136
18	2	36

| * $\triangle x = 1$. | | n = 200. |

USE AND REJECTION OF DATA

Occasionally, and perhaps too frequently where inexperienced observers are concerned, one or more readings appear "way out of line" with the rest of the readings. There are several trends of thought about dealing with extremely large deviations. Some observers prefer to reject all data that exceed certain limits of deviation. *All values regardless of their deviation, however, should be recorded.*

A preferred method of handling large deviations is to give these readings a "relative weight" as compared to the other readings. This process is called the *weighting of data* and gives any individual reading a value in terms of its trustworthiness. Establishing a system of relative weights is rather arbitrary and depends on the judgment of the observer. Thus, this system may be advantageous or disadvantageous, depending on the observer's experience.

One method of assigning relative weights is based on probable error. If one particular

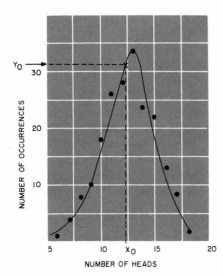

Fig. 2-7 Distribution plot for coin-tossing experiment.

reading has a probability of $x'' = 0.075$ and if 10 readings are taken, the relative weight of the reading in question may be assigned as 0.75 that of the other readings.

SIGNIFICANT FIGURES

In writing a measured value as a series of digits, certain of these digits will have an element of doubt associated with them. It is advisable to consider any digits interpolated between actual scale graduations as "doubtful digits."

The total number of significant digits—those that should be retained—is directly dependent on the probable error associated with the reading. If the reading is interpreted by the observer as being 2.6835 and the probable error of this particular reading is ± 0.05, then the reading should be taken as 2.68 ± 0.05.

In general, two doubtful figures may be retained as part of the significant figures of a measurement unless the observer is very inexperienced.

CALIBRATION TOLERANCES*

TEST INSTRUMENT CALIBRATION Three tolerance limits must be applied to the arithmetic average (mean) reading obtained during a calibration process. The first is the acceptance tolerance which considers the accuracy of the mean value; the second is the repeated acceptance tolerance which considers both accuracy and precision; the final limit is the adjustment tolerance which refers to the tolerance allowed before some definite adjustment of the device should be made. Each of these tolerances is arrived at by multiplying the device's *rated accuracy* (specified by manufacturer) by an appropriate correction factor as listed in Table 2-2. These correction factors are based on the probable error principles discussed previously.

* *Standards Laboratory Information Manual*, Naval Inspector of Ordnance, Pomona, Calif.

Table 2-2 Calibration Tolerance Correction Factors

Accuracy ratio	Accept-ance* factor	Repeated† acceptance factor	Adjust-ment* factor	Repeated† adjustment factor
Above				
4–1	1.0	1.4	0.7	1.0
4.0–1	1.0	1.4	0.7	1.0
3.5–1	1.05	1.45	0.74	1.0
2.5–1	1.1	1.55	0.77	1.1
2.0–1	1.1	1.55	0.77	1.1
1.5–1	1.4	2.0	1.0	1.4
1.0–1	1.4	2.0	1.0	1.4

* Applies to difference between test instrument mean reading and standard value at each check point.
† Applies to difference between two readings at same check point.

The manufacturer's rated accuracy for a test instrument is generally a percentage of the full-scale value. However, there are exceptions to this. If the zero point lies between the ends of the scale, the rated accuracy is a percentage of the arithmetic sum of the end-scale values. If the scale is nonlinear, the rated accuracy is a percentage of the portion of the scale where the scale divisions are greater than, or equal to, two-thirds of the width they would be if the scale were linear (divided evenly). Other special considerations can be found by consulting the manufacturer's specifications for a particular instrument.

The *accuracy ratio* referred to in column one of Table 2-2 is the ratio of the rated accuracy of the test instrument to the accuracy of the calibration *system*. Thus, this ratio takes into consideration the errors of both the test instrument and the calibration system. The calibration system accuracy is determined by arithmetically adding the accuracies of the system components. For ratios of 4 to 1, or better, the acceptance correction factor (column two) is equal to 1—there is no correction—and the instrument will be calibrated within the limits of its rated accuracy. The difference between repeated measurements (any two of the over-all number) must fall within the limits given by multiplying the rated accuracy by the correction factor in column three.

If the difference between the mean test instrument reading and the standard value is greater than the tolerance obtained by multiplying the rated accuracy and the adjustment correction factor (column four), adjustment of the instrument must be made in order to insure that it will operate within the acceptance tolerance limit during the interval until the next calibration. The adjustment correction factor is 70.7% of the acceptance factor.

As an example of what has been discussed, assume that a multirange d-c milliammeter with a rated accuracy of 3% is to be calibrated by a system with an accuracy of 1%. The rated accuracy of the test instrument is based on full-scale reading and the instrument has five ranges; 3 ma, 10 ma, 30 ma, 100 ma, and 1 amp. The 1-amp range is chosen for the linearity test. The accuracy ratio is given by

$$\frac{3\% \times 1\ \text{amp}}{1\% \times 1\ \text{amp}} = 3\ \text{to}\ 1$$

Consulting Table 2-2, the acceptance, repeated acceptance, adjustment, and repeated adjustment factors are 1.05, 1.45, 0.74, and 1.0, respectively. The tolerances for the linearity test are found by multiplying the rated accuracy of the test instrument by these factors; i.e., for the 1-amp range:

$$1\ \text{amp} \times 3\% \times 1.05 = 0.0315\ \text{amp}$$

which is the acceptance tolerance. The other tolerances are similarly arrived at; all are listed in Table 2-3.
For the calibration of the other ranges, it will be necessary to check only the full- and half-scale divisions.

Table 2-3 Calibration Tolerances for Linearity Check Multi-Range D-C Milliammeter

Check points (amp)	Acceptance tolerance (amp)	Repeated acceptance tolerance (amp)	Adjustment tolerance (amp)	Repeated adjustment tolerance (amp)
1	±0.0315	±0.0435	±0.0222	±0.03
0.8	±0.0315	±0.0435	±0.0222	±0.03
0.6	±0.0315	±0.0435	±0.0222	±0.03
0.4	±0.0315	±0.0435	±0.0222	±0.03
0.2	±0.0315	±0.0435	±0.0222	±0.03

Table 2-4 Calibration Tolerances for Multi-Range Check D-C Milliammeter

Check points (ma)	Acceptance tolerance (ma)	Repeated acceptance tolerance (ma)	Adjustment tolerance (ma)	Repeated adjustment tolerance (ma)
		900 ma range		
100	±3.16	±4.35	±2.22	±3
50	±3.16	±4.35	±2.22	±3
		30 ma range		
30	±0.945	±1.3	±0.666	±0.9
15	±0.945	±1.3	±0.666	±0.9
		10 ma range		
10	±0.316	±0.435	±0.222	±0.3
5	±0.316	±0.435	±0.222	±0.3
		3 ma range		
3	±0.0945	±0.13	±0.0666	±0.09
1.5	±0.0945	±0.13	±0.0666	±0.09

After the linearity test is completed assume that the greatest difference between a recorded value and the standard value is −0.0264. This variation is within the acceptance tolerance listed in Table 2-3. However, it is greater than the adjustment tolerance. Hence, an adjustment should be made and the linearity test re-run until the variation is within the two tolerances. Assume, also, that the largest difference between any two readings taken at any of the check points after the adjustment has been made is +0.0257. This variation is within the repeated acceptance and repeated adjustment tolerances listed in Table 2-3 so that the precision of the instrument is adequate. A similar comparison of recorded values is made for the multirange tests.

The foregoing procedure also applies for a nonlinear-scale instrument over the range specified in Chapter 1. Beyond this specific range, the tolerance is found by multiplying the total scale length by the rated accuracy (expressed as a percentage) and by a factor of (2/3).

FIXED STANDARD CALIBRATION The following discussion presupposes that a fixed standard will be calibrated by a system whose accuracy is such that the accuracy ratio will be 4 to 1 or greater.

The mean value of the measurements taken should be determined. The acceptance tolerance (accuracy), when this mean is compared to the mean of the previous calibration, is limited by the manufacturer's rated accuracy. The repeated acceptance tolerance (precision) is 1.7 times the manufacturer's rated accuracy. *Fixed standards should never be adjusted.*

If the fixed standard is new, the mean value of the measurements should not differ from the nominal value given by the manufacturer by more than the rated accuracy. The precision limits are the same as previously given.

QUESTIONS

1 What is the difference between accuracy and precision?

2 List four sources of error in instruments.

3 What are the four general classes of errors?

PROBLEMS

Assume that a multirange d-c voltmeter with a rated full-scale accuracy of 5% is to be calibrated by a system with an accuracy of 2%. The voltmeter has five ranges: 2.5 volts, 10 volts, 50 volts, 250 volts, and 1000 volts.

1 What is the accuracy ratio of the calibration setup?

2 What is the full-scale acceptance tolerance for the 1000-volt range?

3 What is the half-scale acceptance tolerance for the 1000-volt range?

4 What is the full-scale repeated acceptance tolerance for the 1000-volt range?

5 What is the half-scale repeated acceptance tolerance for the 1000-volt range?

6 What is the full-scale adjustment tolerance for the 1000-volt range?

7 What is the half-scale adjustment tolerance for the 1000-volt range?

8 What is the full-scale repeated adjustment tolerance for the 1000-volt range?

9 What is the half-scale repeated adjustment tolerance for the 1000-volt range?

10 What is the half-scale acceptance tolerance for the 250-volt range?

11 What is the full-scale repeated acceptance tolerance for the 250-volt range?

12 What is the half-scale repeated acceptance tolerance for the 250-volt range?

13 What is the full-scale adjustment tolerance for the 250-volt range?

14 What is the full-scale repeated adjustment tolerance for the 250-volt range?

15 What is the half-scale repeated adjustment tolerance for the 250-volt range?

16 What is the half-scale acceptance tolerance for the 50-volt range?

17 What is the full-scale acceptance tolerance for the 50-volt range?

18 What is the full-scale repeated acceptance tolerance for the 50-volt range?

19 What is the half-scale adjustment tolerance for the 50-volt range?

20 What is the half-scale repeated adjustment tolerance for the 50-volt range?

21 What is the half-scale acceptance tolerance for the 10-volt range?

22 What is the full-scale acceptance tolerance for the 10-volt range?

23 What is the full-scale repeated acceptance tolerance for the 10-volt range?

24 What is the half-scale repeated acceptance tolerance for the 10-volt range?

25 What is the full-scale adjustment tolerance for the 10-volt range?

26 What is the half-scale adjustment tolerance for the 10-volt range?

27 What is the full-scale repeated adjustment tolerance for the 10-volt range?

28 What is the half-scale repeated adjustment tolerance for the 10-volt range?

29 What is the half-scale acceptance tolerance for the 2.5-volt range?

30 What is the full-scale repeated acceptance tolerance for the 2.5-volt range?

31 What is the half-scale adjustment tolerance for the 2.5-volt range?

32 What is the full-scale repeated adjustment tolerance for the 2.5-volt range?

System and Units
of Measurement 3

To avoid confusion in a study of measurements and calibration techniques, the reader must fix the definitions of two important terms in his mind. These terms are "units" and "standards."

1. A "unit" *is a value or magnitude.* A unit is fixed by definition and is independent of environmental conditions. Examples of units include a foot, a meter, a volt, an ohm.

2. A "standard" *is an object constructed in such a manner that it is a physical representation of a unit.* In general, standards are dependent upon surrounding conditions and are an accurate representation of a unit only under specific conditions. For example, the platinum-iridium bar which is our meter *standard* has a true *unit* length of 1 meter only at a definite temperature.

THE DIMENSIONAL REFERENCE SYSTEM

ABSOLUTE DIMENSIONS An accurate absolute system of dimensions may be defined as a system in which the various quantities are all expressed in terms of a small number of fundamental dimensions. There are many possible systems. Several systems have been set up and used by various scientific factions. Many others have been derived mathematically for purposes of investigation.

The system used today has, as its arbitrarily chosen fundamental dimensions, length, mass, time, and temperature. These basic quantities cannot be defined in terms of any other physical quantity. This is why they are called "fundamental," or "absolute" dimensions.

DERIVED QUANTITIES All quantities may be derived from the fundamental quantities of length, mass, time, and temperature. A surface has two dimensions of length so that its area may be derived as

$$\text{area} = L \times L = L^2$$

which is a length in the second degree. Volume becomes length in the third degree, L^3.

If length is divided by time, the result is velocity. Therefore, velocity is derived in terms of the absolute dimensions by the equation:

$$\text{velocity} = \frac{L}{T} = LT^{-1}$$

In the same manner,

$$\text{acceleration} = \frac{\text{velocity}}{\text{time}}$$

or, dimensionally,

$$\text{acceleration} = \frac{LT^{-1}}{T} = LT^{-2}$$

Again,

$$\text{force} = \text{mass} \times \text{acceleration}$$

Dimensionally,

$$\text{force} = MLT^{-2}$$

Using this general procedure of dimensional analysis, all physical quantities may be derived from the four absolute dimensions. This facilitates absolute measurements and the construction of absolute standards, since

19

it predetermines that a minimum number of such standards and measurements will be required.

Table 3-1 gives a comprehensive listing of mechanical and thermal quantities in terms of the absolute dimensions. Considering the large number of measurement units used throughout the world (feet, meters, pounds, grams, etc.), entanglement in inter unit conversions can often be unsnarled by referring to the fundamental expressions. These expressions must remain fixed throughout all systems of units.

Table 3-1 Mechanical Quantities in Terms of Absolute Dimensions

Quantity	Dimension	Quantity	Dimension
Mass*	M	Stress, pressure	$ML^{-1}T^{-2}$
Length*	L	Compressibility	$M^{-1}LT^{-2}$
Time*	T	Strain	Unity
Area	L^2	Linear momentum	MLT^{-1}
Volume	L^3	Angular momentum	ML^2T^{-1}
Angles	Unity	Density	ML^{-3}
Linear velocity	LT^{-1}	Work (energy)	ML^2T^{-2}
Linear acceleration	LT^{-2}	Power	ML^2T^{-2}
Angular velocity	T^{-1}	Frequency	T^{-1}
Angular acceleration	T^{-2}	Temperature*	θ
Force	MLT^{-2}	Heat	ML^2T^{-2}
Torque	ML^2T^{-2}	Thermal capacity	$L^2T^{-2}\theta^{-1}$
Pressure	$ML^{-1}T^{-2}$	Specific heat	Unity
Moment of inertia	ML^2	Thermal resistivity	$M^{-1}L^{-1}T^3\theta$

* Absolute quantities; all others are derived.

THE CGS AND MKS SYSTEMS OF UNITS

CENTIMETER-GRAM-SECOND SYSTEM The CGS system, which is one of the oldest systems of units (remember, a unit is a magnitude of measurement fixed by definition and independent of surrounding conditions), uses the centimeter, gram, and second as the absolute units of length, mass, and time. Temperature, the fourth absolute dimension, is treated separately in the discussion of thermal units.

With these fundamental units, the various

Table 3-2 Mechanical Units

Quantity	CGS unit	MKS unit	British unit
Mass*	gram	kilogram	pound
Length*	centimeter	meter	foot
Time*	second	second	second
Area	centimeter²	meter²	foot²
Volume	centimeter³	meter³	foot³
Velocity	cm/sec	meter/sec	foot/sec
Acceleration	cm/sec²	meter/sec²	foot/sec²
Force	dyne	newton	poundal
Work (energy)	erg	joule	foot-poundal
Power	erg/sec	watt	foot-pd/sec
Temperature	°K (Kelvin)	°K	°R (Rankine)
Frequency	cycles/sec	cycles/sec	cycles/sec

* Absolute quantities; all others are derived.

derived mechanical quantities can be assigned units. The units for area and volume, of course, are the simplest: square centimeter (cm^2) and cubic centimeter (cm^3).

From Table 3-1 the derived unit for velocity (LT^{-1}) becomes cm-sec^{-1} or centimeter per second; acceleration, centimeter per second per second (cm-sec^{-2}); and force, gram-centimeter per second per second.

When the fundamental-unit designation of a quantity becomes rather complex, as that of force, a new name (unit) is usually assigned. In the CGS system, the unit of force, gm-cm-sec^{-2} is renamed *dyne*. Similarly, the unit of work, gm-cm²-sec^{-2}, is called the *erg*.

A complete listing of mechanical quantities in the CGS system is given in Table 3-2, along with the units of two other commonly used systems of measurement.

METER-KILOGRAM-SECOND SYSTEM As experimentation and measurement progressed, it was found that the centimeter and gram were rather small units of measure as far as practical distances and masses were concerned. This resulted in the development of the MKS system, in which the meter, kilogram, and second were adopted as the absolute units of length, mass, and time.

The same method of deriving units for other quantities as used in the CGS system is employed in the MKS system. Consulting Table 3-1, velocity is measured in meters per second; acceleration, in meters per second per second; and force, in kilogram-meters per second per second. The unit of force is renamed *newton*.

The mechanical units of the MKS system are given in Table 3-2.

THE BRITISH SYSTEM OF UNITS The British system of units, commonly employed in the United States, uses the foot, pound, and second as the absolute units of length, mass, and time. Slightly different definitions for the foot exist in Great Britain and the United States; there are also two definitions for the foot employed in the United States. The units based on all three definitions, however, differ by only a few parts in a million.

As a result of the arbitrarily chosen fundamental units, velocity is given by feet per second, acceleration by feet per second per second, and force by pound-foot per second per second. The new name given this unit of force is the *poundal*.

DEVIATIONS FROM THE ABSOLUTE SYSTEMS

In some fields, it is more convenient to pick absolute dimensions other than mass, length, and time. In structural engineering, as one example, forces are more important than masses. Here, a length-force-time system employing absolute units of foot, pound, and second is used. Since the pound of force is fundamental in this system, the unit of mass is a derived quantity. A detailed discussion is beyond the scope of this manual, and the reader is referred to any college text on physics (mechanics) for further information.

All physical measurements can be expressed in terms of the absolute, or fundamental, units of the three systems discussed. Frequently, however, in the initial stages of a new field, measurements are made without direct reference to the fundamentals. The units candlepower, curie, roentgen, etc., are examples. Eventually, these units will be redefined in terms of absolute units.

THERMAL UNITS

Thermal measurements require a specification of temperature as well as mechanical dimensions. For this reason, temperature was adopted as the fourth absolute dimension, as previously stated.

Four temperature scales exist. The two in common use are the Centigrade scale ($°C$) and the Fahrenheit ($°F$) scale. The other two are "absolute" temperature scales. They are the Kelvin scale ($°K$), which is matched against the Centigrade scale, and the Rankine scale ($°R$), which is matched against the Fahrenheit scale. The basis and interrelation of these scales is discussed in Chapter 4, "Basic Standards and Measurements."

Since heat is a form of energy, any mechanical unit of energy (erg, joule, footpound) may be used to measure quantity of heat. Other units, established in early thermal investigations, however, still persist. The calorie and British Thermal Unit are the most common. They can be easily converted into the derived mechanical units. A complete table of inter unit conversion is given in Appendix B.

ELECTRICAL AND MAGNETIC UNITS

At least ten different systems of electrical and magnetic units are in common use. Each of these is based on a particular choice of the proportionality constants (ϵ and μ) used in a verified physical law.

Electrostatic systems (esu systems) begin with Coulomb's law. The proportionality constant (permittivity) is then arbitrarily chosen for convenience to form the basis of the various electrostatic systems.

Electromagnetic systems (emu systems) begin with the law of attraction between currents in parallel wires. Here, the value for the permeability constant is conveniently chosen to produce various emu systems.

The practical system of units used extensively by engineers and technicians (ohm, volt, ampere, henry, etc.) is far removed from the absolute dimensions and units of mass, length, time, and temperature. Each of these practical units, however, can be related back to the absolute source. Because of this, electrical and magnetic units are among the most precisely measured quantities of the present time.

LEGAL ELECTROMAGNETIC UNITS   In 1950 an international agreement established the rationalized meter-kilogram-second system as the legally accepted system of electromagnetic units. Of particular importance in choosing this system was the fact that its units coincide with the practical system of units in common engineering usage.

To develop this system, the absolute unit of current was defined, rather than arbitrarily choosing a value for permeability and permittivity. Thus, in electromagnetic measurements, the absolute ampere takes its place alongside the meter, kilogram, second, and degree as an absolute unit.

With current as an absolute quantity, the dielectric constant (permittivity) and permeability constant become derived quantities and have dimensions in terms of the absolute units.

The practical (MKS) electromagnetic units are listed in Table 3-3.

In order to show that these practical units *can* be traced back to the absolute dimensions as given in the table, consider the "volt." The volt is defined as the potential difference which exists when 1 watt of power is dissipated with a current of 1 amp.

$$\text{volt} = \frac{\text{watt}}{\text{ampere}}$$

The watt, in turn, is the consumption of one joule of energy in 1 sec.

$$\text{watt} = \frac{\text{joule}}{\text{sec}}$$

Using these two true relationships and the mechanical units derived previously,

$$\text{volt} = \frac{\text{watt}}{\text{ampere}} = \frac{\text{joule}}{\text{amp-sec}} = \frac{\text{newton-meter}}{\text{amp-sec}}$$

$$= \frac{\text{kg-meter}^2}{\text{amp-sec}^3} = \frac{ML^2}{IT^3} = ML^2 I^{-1} T^{-3}$$

The final expression checks with the absolute dimension of the volt as listed in Table 3-3. A similar analysis can be applied to any of the units.

Table 3-3 The Rationalized MKS (Practical) System of Electromagnetic Units and Dimensions

Quantity	Unit	Dimension
Current*	ampere	I
Emf and potential	volt	$ML^2I^{-1}T^{-3}$
Resistance	ohm	$ML^2I^{-2}T^{-3}$
Charge	coulomb	IT
Inductance	henry	$ML^2I^{-2}T^{-2}$
Capacitance	farad	$M^{-1}L^{-2}I^2T^4$
Inductive reactance	ohm	$ML^2I^{-2}T^{-3}$
Capacitive reactance	ohm	$ML^2\ I^{-2}\ T^{-3}$
Energy	joule	ML^2T^{-2}
Power	watt	$ML^2\ T^{-3}$
Mmf	ampere turn	I†
Magnetic flux	weber	$ML^2I^{-1}T^{-2}$
Pole strength	unit pole	$ML^2I^{-1}T^{-2}$
Frequency	cycle/sec	T^{-1}

* Absolute quantity; all others are derived.
† Based on current in one turn of a conductor.

LIGHT AND RADIATION UNITS

The units used in photometric measurement (measurement of light) and radiation physics are among the arbitrary units mentioned in the discussion, "Deviations from the Absolute Systems." Currently, they are not related to the absolute units of mass, length, time, temperature, and current. At some future date, this relationship will undoubtedly be established.

Any formal explanation and study of light and radiation is enveloped in the duality of particles and waves as established by classical and quantum physics. Such a discussion is beyond the scope of this manual. Any fundamental concepts which must be introduced will be explained by whatever approach is most appropriate, thereby avoiding the usual complexities.

Most artificial sources of light are hot bodies which radiate not only visible light but infrared radiation as well. High-temperature light sources approach the sun in the whiteness of their radiation, but none can compare to the $6000°C$ temperature of the sun's photosphere where sunlight is produced.

Nuclear physics, as the study of nuclear processes, began in 1919 when Rutherford first recognized the artificial transmutation of one element into another. Early in nuclear studies several unexplainable "radiations" were discovered—an alpha (α) ray, a beta (β) ray, and a gamma (γ) ray. Subsequent studies showed that the α and β rays were actually particles (positively charged helium nuclei and electrons, respectively). The γ ray was the only true electromagnetic radiation. Today 22 atomic, subatomic, and subnuclear particles are known, and many others are theorized. Table 3-4 gives a list of the more important particles. All the listed particles are stable except the neutron, which exists for about 15 minutes as an isolated entity. The life of the antiparticles is unknown.

Table 3-4 Important Particles and Radiations of Atomic Physics

Name	Charge	Name	Charge
Electron	$-e$*	Positron	$+e$
Proton, $_1H^1$	$+e$	α-particle, $_2He^4$	$+2e$
Antiproton	$-e$	Deuteron, $_1H^2$	$+e$
Neutron, $_0n^1$	0	γ-ray	0
Antineutron	0	Antineutrino	0

* e = unit electron charge.

In a discussion of nuclear structure, the term "nuclide" refers to any atomic structure capable of exhibiting more than a transient existence. This term covers all the particles of Table 3-4 (except the antiparticles), plus all elemental atomic nuclei. A short-hand notation for designating a nuclide is written in the form:

$$_Z(\text{chemical symbol})^A$$

where Z is the atomic number (number of protons) and A is the atomic mass number (sum of protons and neutrons in the nucleus). Examples of this notation are shown in the table: the neutron ($_0n^1$), showing no protons and 1 neutron; the proton ($_1H^1$), which is the normal hydrogen nucleus of 1 proton, no neutrons; the deuteron ($_1H^2$), which is heavy hydrogen with 1 proton and 1 neutron; and the α-particle, $_2He^4$, which is the helium nucleus with 2 protons and 2 neutrons. The difference between the subscript and superscript (A - Z) is the number of neutrons associated with the nuclide.

A common unit of wavelength in light and radiation studies is the *Angstrom,* which is a subdivision of the standard measure of length. One Angstrom unit (A) is equal to 10^{-10} meter.

Photometry is concerned with the region of visible light, which has wavelengths of 3900 to 7600A. Nuclear radiations are of much shorter wavelength, i.e., smaller Angstrom numbers.

A common unit of mass encountered in nuclear physics is the *atomic mass unit* (amu), which is defined as one-sixteenth the mass of one atom of the most abundant isotope of oxygen, $_8O^{16}$.

PHOTOMETRIC UNITS The flow of light from a source is called "radiant flux." Other photometric quantities are defined in terms of radiant flux. Radiant flux, however, is basically defined as the total radiant energy per unit time which is effective in producing the sensation of sight. Sensation of sight is a relative term depending on the individual human eye. For this reason, it is more convenient to start a system of photometric units with a measure of radiant intensity.

The unit of radiant intensity, the *candle,* was originally defined in terms of the flame produced by a specially constructed candle burning at a specific rate. In 1948, the National Bureau of Standards constructed a standard using incandescent platinum at a

UNIT
SOLID
ANGLE

A = r²

Fig. 3-1 The unit solid angle, or steradian.

temperature of 2046°K. The candle was redefined as the radiant intensity of $\frac{1}{60}$ sq cm
of this incandescent platinum standard.

The *lumen,* the unit of radiant flux, was
then defined as the flux passing through a
unit solid angle from a uniform point source
of 1 candle intensity. The unit solid angle,
a *steradian,* is an unusual concept; it is the
angle which encloses a surface area, A, on a
sphere equal to the square of its radius, as
shown in Fig. 3-1. For any sphere, the total
solid angle must be 4π steradians, since the
spherical surface area is $4\pi r^2$.

The third concept considered in photometry is a measure of the illumination of a
surface—the luminance or radiance. Stated
another way, luminance is the total radiant
intensity received, emitted, or reflected by a
unit surface area. The basic unit of luminance
is the *lambert,* which is equivalent to 1 lumen
per square centimeter. Other units include
the foot-candle (lumen per square foot) and
the lux (lumen per square meter).

RADIATION UNITS The term "radiation," as
encountered in studies of atomic and nuclear
physics, can easily be misleading since, in
general, it may imply both the emission of
particles and the emission of electromagnetic
waves (true radiation). For clarity, this manual uses the term "emission" and its deriva-

tives when referring to particles or nuclides.
The term "radiation" and its derivatives is
reserved for true electromagnetic phenomena.

The measurement of radiations and emissions from radioactive materials is based on
the fact that the passage of charged particles
and rays (products of nuclear disintegrations) through a gas produces ionization.
When ionization occurs, ion-pairs—a negative
ion and a positive ion—must be produced.
Specific ionization refers to the number of
ion-pairs produced per centimeter of particle
path. Higher-energy particles produce fewer
ion-pairs because of the rapid transit of the
particles through the gas.

Energy, in this realm, is measured in *electron volts.* The electron volt (ev) is the
energy of a charged particle carrying a unit
electron charge (1.6020×10^{-19} coulomb)
through a potential difference of 1 volt. It is
equivalent to 1.601864×10^{-12} erg. Although
the ev is used extensively in solid-state physics, it is a rather small unit. Larger units of
energy in common use are kiloelectron volts
(Kev) and million electron volts (Mev).

One of the earliest units of radioactivity
was the *curie.* This unit was redefined in 1953
by the International Commission on Radio-
logical Units as "the quantity of any radioactive nuclide in which the number of
disintegrations per second is 3.700×10^{10}."

A *rutherford* is a smaller unit, equal to
10^6 disintegrations per second.

After work in nuclear physics was stepped
up in pace, biologists began to show concern
over the effect of exposure to radiation on
human tissue. The first unit expressing this
exposure was the roentgen. This is the quantity of radiation which will produce one
electrostatic unit of electricity (2.08×10^9
ion-pairs) in 1 cubic centimeter of dry air
at 0°C and standard atmospheric pressure.

Radioactive particles also produce a damaging effect on human tissue. In order to
extend the exposure unit to emissions as well
as radiations, the *roentgen equivalent physical* (rep) is used. This is defined as the
quantity of emanation which produces an

energy gain of 83 ergs when absorbed by 1 gram of human tissue.

It was thought that the rep would produce the same effect as 1 roentgen of radiation (83-erg gain in energy). This was not true, however, and a third unit, the *roentgen equivalent man* (rem) came into being. This is defined as the quantity of emanation which will produce the same biological damage as 1 roentgen of radiation.

QUESTIONS

1 What absolute dimensions are used to derive the physical quantity of pressure?

2 What is the absolute unit of measurement for electromagnetic quantities?

3 What absolute dimensions are used to derive the physical quantity of magnetic flux?

4 Define the following terms:

(a) Angstrom
(b) Atomic-mass unit
(c) Candle
(d) Lumen
(e) Lambert
(f) Steradian

(g) Electron volt
(h) Curie
(i) Rutherford
(j) Roentgen
(k) Roentgen equivalent physical
(l) Roentgen equivalent man

Basic Standards
and Measurements 4

Our present-day measuring system has developed in such a manner as to insure maximum precision and accuracy. Standards have changed from time to time as better measurement methods have come into existence. International standards are occasionally checked against each other. This has enabled these standards to remain within ± 20 parts in a million with the international prototype standards maintained in Sevres, France.

Just as all physical quantities can be related back to the absolute dimensions of mass, length, and time, so can all measurements be related back to the absolute, or prototype, standards for these dimensions. To make direct measurements in terms of the absolute standards, however, would be extremely inconvenient and inaccurate. Hence, primary standards are constructed for the various derived physical quantities. These standards, in turn, are derived from the units fixed by the absolute standards and experimentally verified defining equations, and must be checked periodically. Illustrations of this procedure will be developed in the following sections.

Obviously, derived standards cannot have the inherent accuracy of prototype standards because of errors introduced by experimentally derived equations. Electrical quantities are the most accurate of the derived standards, and are frequently used in measuring other physical quantities, such as stresses, pressure, temperature, etc.

An insight into how well the measuring system works in actual practice is given by Table 4-1. This table, taken from a paper by A. G. McNish, NBS, shows the "probable error" in relating derived standards with prototype standards (column labeled "Accuracy") and in relating two identical standards for the quantity involved (column headed "Precision"). Derived standards can be compared with similar ones with far greater precision than they can be compared with absolute standards.

MASS, LENGTH, AND VOLUME

MASS The primary standard of mass for this country is the United States Prototype Kilogram 20. It is a platinum-iridium cylinder whose mass is known in terms of the International Prototype Kilogram at Sevres, France.

Other standards of mass are specified by NBS in terms of the prototype. These standards are divided into four groups according to use: (1) precision laboratory standards, (2) laboratory weights, (3) commercial standards, (4) trade weights. There are many subdivision classifications according to precision. The class S weights are metric laboratory working standards used in secondary standardizing labs for calibration. Tolerances start at 0.014 milligram for the smallest class S weights and decrease to 5 parts per million for the larger weights.

Class S-1 weights are similar in tolerance but are constructed in terms of nonmetric units. The avoirdupois pound is related to the metric prototype standard by the relationship, 1 lb = 0.45359 kg.

LENGTH The primary standard of length is determined in terms of the orange-red radiation of a krypton 86 lamp. The meter is defined as 1,650,763.73 wavelengths of this radiation. Originally the meter was intended to be one ten-millionth of the length of the north polar quadrant of the Paris meridian.

The ratio of the United States yard to the standard meter is exactly 3600/3937 by definition. The more common distance measurement, the foot, is then defined as ⅓ of the yard.

Working standards of the meter class should be accurate to 0.01 mm or better at a temperature of 20°C. The yard standard should be accurate to 0.0005 in. at 68°F. The graduation lines for these working standards are ground on a highly polished, nontarnishing surface. The H-shaped cross section is preferred, although a rectangular cross section with supports at definite positions is also used. The graduation lines are perpendicular to the longitudinal axis of the bar, and, to facilitate alignment, two parallel longitudinal lines are inscribed.

The most widely used precision standards of length in industry are precision gage blocks (Fig. 4-1), whose accuracy, range of sizes, and relatively low cost, have made pos-

sible the mass production of interchangeable industrial components. These blocks of metal (usually steel) have two opposite faces; plane, parallel, and a specified distance apart. Errors of construction seldom amount to more than 0.5 micron (0.00002 in.), and in most cases not more than 0.25 micron.

VOLUME Units of volume are not represented by absolute standards since they are derived units. The validity of primary standards constructed by NBS stems from their calibration against the linear absolute standards (mass and length).

Fig. 4-1 Group of gage blocks. This group was used in an extensive investigation to determine the stability of gage block materials. The foremost block is the most promising—Nitrided 410 stainless steel. (Courtesy, National Bureau of Standards.)

Table 4-1 Estimates of Accuracy and Precision in Measuring Physical Quantities

Physical quantity	Device	Magnitude	Uncertainty in parts per million	
			Accuracy	Precision
Length	Meter bar	1 meter	*	0.03
	Gage blocks	0.1 meter	0.1	0.01
	Geodetic tape	50 meters	0.3	0.10
Mass	Cylinder	1 kilogram	*	0.005
	Cylinder	1 gram	1	0.03
	Cylinder	20 kilograms	0.5	0.1
Resistance	Resistor	1 ohm	5	0.1
	Resistor	1000 ohms	7	1
	Resistor	0.001 ohm	7	1
Voltage	Standard cell	1 volt	7	0.1
Temperature	Triple-point cell	273.16°K	*	0.3
	Gas thermometer	90.18°K	100	20

* Accurate by definition.

The liter, which is the metric unit of volume, is defined as the volume occupied by a mass of 1 kg of pure distilled water at its maximum density (4°C) and at a pressure of 1 atmosphere (atm).

The United States gallon is 231 cu in. in volume, which corresponds to 8.345 lb of distilled water (1 gal = 3.78543 liters) at 4°C.

Secondary standards of volume are constructed and calibrated against the NBS primaries.

TIME AND FREQUENCY

Time and its reciprocal, frequency, can be measured with the greatest degree of accuracy of any of the physical quantities. However, the accurate comparison of time against a standard—and even the establishment of an absolute time standard—presents a basic problem. Meter bars may be laid side by side and their lengths then compared—even microscopically, if such a degree of accuracy is required. Two time intervals cannot be similarly compared.

The present time standard is based on astronomical observations of the planets and stars. Corrections for tidal slowing, orbital perturbations, planetary wobble, and other changing characteristics must be made. Precision comparisons involve checks made over a period of *years.*

Recent investigations by NBS have shown that extremely stable atomic resonance conditions (atomic frequencies) would serve as excellent standards for time and frequency. There is considerable difficulty in precisely relating these frequencies to the present unit of time. Since atomic standards are better standards than astronomical constants, however, the latter may soon be rejected as the absolute standard. Furthermore, atomic standards are more accessible than astronomical constants.

EPHEMERIS TIME The orbital motion of the earth about the sun provides the present time scale called Ephemeris Time (ET). In 1956, the International Committee on Weights and Measures defined the second as 1/31,556,925.9747 of the tropical year 1900. (The "tropical year" is the time between two successive passages of the center of the sun across the celestial equator in the same sense.) The year 1900 was chosen because accurate tables for astronomical variations were already available.

Other time scales are also used. The most common is mean solar time based on the rotation of the earth about its axis. Mean solar time was recently termed "Universal Time" (UT). Since the rotational speed of the earth varies, UT is not constant. Astronomically observed time, uncorrected for polar variation and annual rotational speed changes, is labeled UT0. UT1 is UT0 corrected for polar variations and UT2 is corrected for both polar and annual speed variations. All these time scales are related to ET by various factors.

UNITED STATES FREQUENCY STANDARD The United States Frequency Standard (USFS) provides a primary time scale through the standard frequency broadcasts of radio stations WWV (U.S.) and WWVH (Hawaii). All carrier and modulation frequencies at WWV are derived from a common 2.5 mc quartz oscillator, stable to 1 part in 10^9 (one billion). Frequency adjustments are made so that WWV transmissions have an error not exceeding 2 parts in 10^{10} from day to day.

The continuous radio-frequency transmissions of WWV and WWVH are given in Table 4-2.*

Table 4-2 NBS Continuous Transmission

Frequency (Mc)	Power (Kw)	
	WWV	WWVH
2.5	1	—
5	8	2
10	9	2
15	9	2
20	1	—
25	0.1	—

* From NBS Miscellaneous Publication 236, December, 1960.

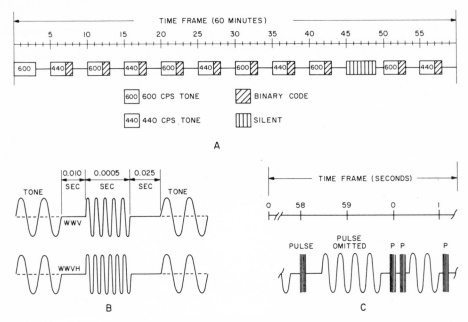

Fig. 4-2 Calibration and information program for USFS.

The various calibration and information services provided by NBS are amplitude-modulated on all r-f carrier frequencies. The basic WWV signal consists of two audio frequencies, one at 600 cps and the other at 440 cps. The 600-cps signal commences "on the hour" of each hour. This initial tone lasts for 3 min. The 600-cps tone is then rebroadcast at the beginning of each 10-min interval for a period of 2 min (see part A of Fig. 4-2). Starting at each odd 5-min interval, the 440-cps tone lasts for a period of 2 min as shown. There is one exception to this, occurring at 45 min past each hour, when WWV is silent for 4 min. The same accuracy stated previously applies to these audio tones.

At intervals of precisely 1 sec, seconds pulses are transmitted with an accuracy of ± 2 parts in $10^8 \pm 1$ μsec. The pulse duration is 0.005 sec. The pulse train is shown in part B of Fig. 4-2. Each WWV pulse consists of five cycles of a 1000-cps frequency, and each WWVH pulse contains six cycles of a 1200-cps frequency.

The 2-, 3-, and 5-minute intervals are marked by the beginning or ending of the periods when the audio frequencies are off. Intervals of 1 min between these distinguishing marks are indicated by omitting the pulse at the beginning of the last second of every minute and by starting each minute with two pulses spaced by 0.1 sec, as shown in Fig. 4-2C.

Since January 1, 1961, a special timing code which gives the day, hour, minute, and second (UT) in binary code form has been transmitted. This is a 36-bit, 100-pulse/sec code suitable for digital computer use. The code is intended to provide a timing basis for simultaneous scientific observations. Except at the beginning of each hour, the code is broadcast for 1-min intervals following both standard audio tones. The special timing code is not broadcast at WWVH, where all tone periods are of 3-min duration.

Other information is also transmitted, but it is of lesser importance in calibration and measurement discussions. This information includes Morse code and voice time-of-day signals, radio propagation forecasts, and geo-physical alerts.

The U.S. Naval Observatory minutely measures the time of rotation of the earth with respect to various heavenly bodies. Over a period of several days, the exact time is compared with the crystal clocks NBS uses to check the transmitted time signals. Corrections are made when necessary.

SECONDARY STANDARDS Highly stable harmonic generators with one or more divider stages (so that operation between 25 and 1000 kc is provided) are used as secondary frequency standards. Oscillator frequency is fixed by a temperature-controlled oven or compartment. Periodic calibration checks must be made against WWV or WWVH in order for accuracy to be maintained.

FORCE AND ENERGY

Force and energy are abstract quantities defined in terms of mass, length, and time. The force of impact between two objects, as well as the pressure (force distributed over an area) of a column of water, are apparent from the sense of touch. Energy in the form of heat radiation can be felt and it can be seen, in a relative sense, by observing the color of the radiating body. The *results* of work, a useful embodiment of energy, can also be seen. It is impossible, however, to visualize and construct objects which represent force, pressure, heat, and work similar to the standards for mass and length. For this reason, *standard reference methods* must be developed so that force and energy measurements can attain universal expression.

FORCE AND PRESSURE　The *weight* of an object is, in reality, a measure of force. This results from the definition of force:

$$F = ma$$

where m is the mass of the object under consideration and a is the acceleration the object

experiences. Weight is conveniently defined by

$$W = mg$$

where g is the acceleration an object experiences due to a local gravitational field (9.80665 meters/sec^2 at sea level and 45° latitude). Since the value of g can vary according to position relative to the earth's center, weight is also a variable. In contrast to this, the mass of an object *never* varies except during nuclear destruction and at velocities approaching the speed of light.

Force-measuring instruments are known as *dynamometers*. The measurement is accomplished by balancing the force against known weights. The value of the weights, in turn, is known in terms of the standard for mass and a value of g at some locality chosen by international agreement. By making measurements against known weights, it has been possible to develop, as a working standard, a device known as the *Morehouse proving ring* (shown in Fig. 4-3).

When a force is applied to the proving ring, the ring undergoes a deformation proportional to the magnitude of the force. The micrometer device shown in the figure is used to measure the diametral deformation. When the micrometer tip contacts the vibrating reed, a constant characteristic sound is produced. The position where this sound is produced provides a reproducible reference for the measurements. Proper proportioning of the radical thickness, diameter, and width of the proving ring allows the production of a portable working standard for all forces, large or small.

Pressure is the measure of a force directed perpendicular to a surface and uniformly distributed over the surface (newton/meter^2 in the MKS system). This is generally due to the weight of a fluid (gaseous or liquid) on a supporting surface. Such pressure is termed *static*, or *absolute*, and does not take atmospheric conditions into consideration.

Pressure-measuring devices, as a rule,

determine the difference between the fluid pressure desired and atmospheric pressure. This difference is called *gage pressure.* Absolute pressure is given by

$$P_{abs} = P_{gage} + P_{atm}$$

Standard atmospheric pressure is 101,300 newtons/meter², which is the weight of a column of air that will support a column of mercury 0.76 meter high at 45° latitude, 0°C temperature, and sea level.

Similar to measuring forces, the most direct method of measuring pressure is to balance it against known weights. A working standard which accomplishes this comparison is known as a *dead-weight tester.* The principle of operation is simple. The pressure to be measured is applied beneath a piston of known area causing it to move upward in a cylinder (Fig. 4-4). The piston is then caused to move back to its reference position by placing known weights on it. Corrections must be made for atmospheric pressure and buoyancy effects (covered in detail in Chapter 5). Many different arrangements are available for introducing the fluid whose pressure is being measured and for applying the force of the balancing weights.

ENERGY   *Energy is the capacity for doing work.* It can exist in several forms and can be changed from one form to another. *Potential energy* is the energy possessed by a body due to its position or shape. *Kinetic energy* is energy due to the motion of a body. *Heat is a form of energy.* It is the energy due to molecular motions. Work is a useful (or sometimes wasted) embodiment of energy. Quite frequently, work is measured by heat-developing instruments and ma-chines.

TEMPERATURE

Temperature is a relative measure of the heat possessed by an object, and units of

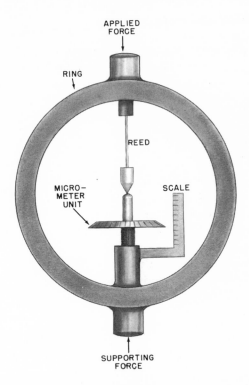

Fig. 4-3   Morehouse proving ring.

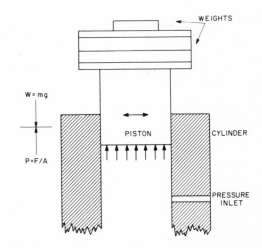

Fig. 4-4   Principle of dead-weight tester.

temperature are the fourth absolute dimensions of the measurement system.

The four commonly used temperature scales are shown in relation to one another in Fig. 4-5. Reference positions on the temperature scales are called *fixed points* because they are easily reproducible and, under standard conditions, will always produce the same effect. The relationship between the Centigrade and Fahrenheit scales is given by

$$\frac{C - 0°}{F - 32°} = \frac{100° - 0°}{212° - 32°}$$

The absolute Centigrade scale, or *Kelvin* scale, is based on the laws of thermodynamics and is independent of the properties of materials. Similarly, the *Rankine* scale, is an absolute thermodynamic scale based on the Fahrenheit scale. The relationships are given by

$$T°C = T°K - 273°$$
$$T°F = T°R - 460°$$

and the two absolute scales are related by

$$T°R = \frac{9}{5} T°K$$

Temperature standards consist of fixed points assigned specific numerical values by international agreement. These fixed points are listed in Table 4-3. The numerical values assigned are reproducible quantities at standard atmospheric pressure.

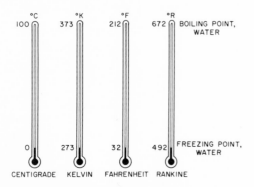

Fig. 4-5 Comparison of fundamental fixed points for temperature scales.

Table 4-3 Primary Fixed Points

Equilibrium point between	Numerical value
Solid and liquid gold	1063.0°C
Solid and liquid silver	960.8°C
Liquid and vaporized sulfur	444.6°C
Liquid and vaporized water	100.0°C
Ice and water	0.0°C
Liquid and gaseous oxygen	—182.97°C

The primary standard thermometer is a resistance thermometer of platinum wire constructed so that the wire is not subject to strain. The various numerical values between the fixed points are calculated by definite formulas based on the properties of platinum resistance wire. Above the gold point temperature, temperature is measured in terms of radiant energy.

ELECTRICAL STANDARDS

The ampere was chosen as the absolute unit for the foundation of the legal system (MKS) of electromagnetic units. The value of the absolute ampere can be very accurately established in terms of the force experienced on a current-carrying coil. The coil is carefully constructed in standard terms of length, and the force is carefully measured in standard terms of mass and time. Thus the value of the ampere is related to previously established prototype standards for the meter, kilogram, and second.

Since the foregoing process is time-consuming and cumbersome as far as providing a calibration standard is concerned, electrical standards must be derived in terms of the absolute ampere by a rather indirect process. This does not, however, decrease the preciseness of the *electrical* standards.

Before adoption of the MKS system on a worldwide basis, electrical standards were based on internationally defined apparatus representing the ohm, the volt, and the ampere. This system of three standards was not acceptable, but literature may still refer to the international ohm, international henry, etc. Hence, relationships between current absolute values and the obsolete international values are given throughout the following sections.

OHM'S LAW STANDARDS   There are many interactions between electrical and mechanical phenomena which can be utilized for determining electrical units in terms of mechanical units. There are also many interrelations between the various electrical quantities which enable them to be expressed in terms of each other.

The three most important electrical quantities are current, resistance, and potential difference. All other electrical quantities are easily expressed in terms of these three. Furthermore, these three quantities are related to each other very simply by Ohm's law:

$$E = IR$$

The specification of any two of the quantities in Ohm's law automatically sets the third. In the quest for physically realizable electrical standards, NBS scientists chose a devious route of experimentation and an application of Ohm's law.

The absolute value of current was measured, as previously stated, by using a current balance. This device makes it possible to weigh the mechanical force that is exerted between two current-carrying coils. The relation between the force and the current can be calculated from basic electromagnetic theory and reduces to formulas involving only the geometric shape of the coils.

Resistance was selected as the second independent quantity in Ohm's law. Here, again, devious, but accurate, methods were employed. A standard of self- and mutual inductance (both were used as a check against each other) was constructed. The value of the inductance was precisely calculated from the geometric dimensions of the coil. An experiment was then performed to determine the value of a resistor, in absolute ohms, in terms of the inductor react-

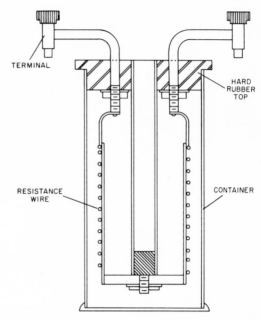

Fig. 4-6 National Bureau of Standards standard resistor.

ance at a known frequency. The final result of this lengthy process is called the "absolute measurement of resistance" and produced the primary group of standard resistors now maintained by NBS.

With values of resistance and current independently established, it was then possible to accurately calculate voltage values from Ohm's law.

From the absolute values measured by NBS, the following relationship was established with the old international units:

1 int amp = 0.999835 abs amp

1 int ohm = 1.000495 abs ohms

1 int volt = 1.000330 abs volts

The primary resistance standards are maintained in sealed containers to prevent changes in value due to moisture changes in the atmosphere. The general construction is shown in Fig. 4-6. The actual "resistors" range from metal strips (low resistance) to very fine wires (high resistance). These resistors are suited only for d-c measurements.

Suitable secondary and working standards were constructed after the primary standards were developed. Most standard resistors are made of an alloy called manganin. The standard values are given at 25°C, although there is little resistance change with temperature change, the value of the standard, R_t, can be calculated at any temperature, $t°$C, by the formula:

$$R_t = R_{25°C} + A(t - 25) + B(t - 25)^2$$

Coefficient A is usually less than 10×10^{-6}, and coefficient B lies between -3×10^{-7} and -6×10^{-7}. This means that 10° above or below 25°C, the resistance of the standard is less than the specified value by only 30 to 60 parts per million.

With alternating currents, particularly at high frequencies, the behavior of a resistance coil is affected by (1) winding inductance, (2) dielectric properties of the insulation, (3) distributed capacitance, (4) skin effect, (5) capacitance to surrounding objects.

Skin effect is usually not bothersome until very high frequencies are reached. A bifilar winding, or other system of coincident right-handed and left-handed turns, reduces inductance. For large resistances, coils are connected in series to reduce capacitive effects. For the small coils, several special winding techniques are employed so that

residual inductance and capacitance effects tend to neutralize each other. With such construction considerations, these standards may be employed up to frequencies of 3000 cps.

NBS is presently developing newer comparison resistors which will have the same value at the comparison frequency as when used with direct current.

There are many thermal and chemical sources of voltage and, consequently, many possible choices of voltage standards. The standard cell chosen by NBS for its long life and small temperature coefficient is the Weston Normal, or cadmium, cell.

The positive electrode of this cell is mercury, and the negative electrode is an amalgam of 10% cadmium. Over the mercury electrode is a paste of mercurous sulfate and cadmium sulfate crystals. The electrolyte is a solution of cadmium sulfate. These components are maintained in an H-shaped glass structure, as shown in Fig. 4-7.

Cadmium cells may either be saturated or unsaturated. If the cadmium sulfate solution is saturated, cadmium sulfate crystals are present at ordinary temperatures. These cells have a very constant emf, but they have a temperature coefficient slightly higher than that of the unsaturated cell. The emf produced by the Weston cell is set by NBS at 1.018300 absolute volts for 20°C. The emf at other temperatures is given by the equation:

$$E = E_{20°C} - 0.0000406(t - 20)$$
$$- 0.00000095(t - 20)^2$$
$$+ 0.00000001(t - 20)^3$$

More rugged portable working standards whose emfs range from 1.0188 to 1.0198 abs volts with the exact emf given on an accompanying tag are also available. These cells are designed for use at temperatures between 15 and 35°C. At these temperatures the emf may be calculated with reasonable precision by using only the first two terms of the equation given above.

Temperature inequality between the two legs of the standard cell may cause errors

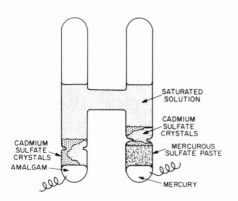

Fig. 4-7 Weston, or cadmium, standard cell.

of several hundred microvolts per °C of difference. To prevent this inequality, the cell is usually placed in a brass container insulated with mineral wool and lined with sheet copper.

A hysteresis error—a rapid change in emf with a gradual return to nearly the original value—occurs when an unsaturated cell is subjected to an over-all temperature change. The error may be determined by checking the cell immediately after the change in temperature. Several hundred hours may pass before the emf is normal again. Insulating against temperature changes reduces the hysteresis error, but the temperature of the container must be thermostatically controlled to eliminate the effect. Under normal lab conditions, if accuracies on the order of 0.03% are the rule, precautions against hysteresis effect need not be taken.

The resistance of the Weston working standard ranges from 500 to 800 ohms, and no more than 100 microamperes of current should be drawn from it.

As previously stated, a current standard, as such, cannot be preserved and maintained. In cases of extreme accuracy, standard resistors and standard cells are used to establish a definite current. Usually current measurements are less exacting, as will be shown in the section, "Basic Electrical Test Equipment, Measurements, and Calibration Techniques."

DERIVED STANDARDS The science of electromagnetism ties electric and magnetic quantities (current, inductance, magnetic flux, etc.) together with a set of exact mathematical equations. Similarly, the units for measuring these quantities (ampere, henry, weber, etc.) are related by exact definitions based on the equations.

Any group of fundamental units may be used to derive the other units. Voltage and resistance are the two units chosen since they can be accurately obtained from standard cells and resistors.

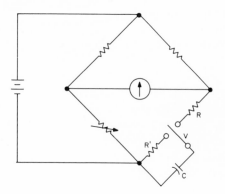

Fig. 4-8 Maxwell commutator bridge.

The unit of capacitance is derived from the ohm and the second, and capacitors which are constructed as standards are calibrated on this principle with a Maxwell commutator bridge (Fig. 4-8). The value of the capacitor (C) is measured in terms of the bridge-arm resistances and the frequency of vibration of the mechanical vibrator (V). The vibrator alternately charges the capacitor through R and discharges it through R^1. The vibrator is accurately controlled by USFS.

Standards of capacitance are constructed of interleaved square plates with air as a dielectric. The distance between the plates must be very accurately known. Parallel and series arrangements of the standard capacitors produce various values of capacitance.

Secondary air capacitors, as well as those with solid dielectric materials (mica, usually), are available as working standards.

Mica capacitors vary greatly in their properties, but once the characteristics of a specific standard are known, the capacitor always behaves the same as long as the same conditions are maintained. Good mica capacitors have the same capacitance for a-c measurements as that determined by the method of rapid charge and discharge with a d-c current—provided that the periods and time of discharge are the same. Mica standards are subject to changes on the order of two parts per hundred thousand for every 1 cm change in atmospheric pressure.

Paraffined-paper capacitors should not be used as standards.

In establishing primary inductance standards, it was more convenient to derive the henry from the ohm and the farad than from large geometrically constructed inductors used for absolute measurements (determination of the absolute ohm). NBS finally selected a Campbell standard of mutual inductance as the primary standard for both self- and mutual inductance.

Commercial standard inductors are available in various fixed values. The General Radio Company produces a set ranging from 100 μh to 10 henrys accurate to within nominal limits from $\pm 0.1\%$ to $\pm 0.25\%$ at 100 cps. This company also produces variable inductors which have a mutual inductance accuracy of $\pm 2.5\%$ ranging from 0 to 110 mh. When these inductors are used in series or parallel, a series accuracy of 1% and a parallel accuracy of 0.1% are claimed.

In using inductors it must be remembered that distributed capacitances exist between windings. Such considerations are specified with commercial equipment.

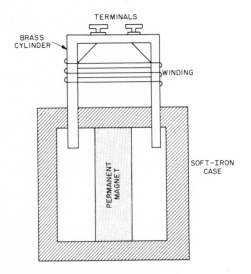

Fig. 4-9 Hibbert magnetic standard.

Electrical energy and power standards do not exist in the same sense as standards for voltage, resistance, capacitance, and inductance. Absolute measurements are made and instruments are calibrated by various methods, which are described in later sections of this manual.

MAGNETIC STANDARDS

The unit of magnetic flux, the weber, is derived from the henry and the ampere. The ampere is, in turn, derived from the volt and the ohm. The method used measures changes of flux in a standard mutual inductor when known changes of current are made. A ballistic galvanometer (construction and calibration of this device will be considered later) shows the changes in terms of an angular deflection. The deflections are then used to calculate magnetic flux in webers. When the angular measurements have been associated with flux, the ballistic galvanometer can be used to measure the flux produced by permanent magnets. These magnets are maintained, in turn, as magnetic standards.

It is often useful to have a standard flux source which does not depend on an external exciting current. The Hibbert magnetic standard is such a device. As shown in Fig. 4-9, a permanent magnet is enclosed in a soft iron container having a narrow circular air gap. A brass cylinder is arranged within the air gap. On this cylinder is wrapped an insulated winding of a conducting metal. At the release of a catch, the brass cylinder and winding assembly drops through the flux in the air gap. The consequent electrical current in the winding is a function of the flux. The rate at which the winding cuts the flux is constant since it depends on the local gravitational field.

The Hibbert device is a secondary standard and must be calibrated against the absolute mutual inductance already mentioned.

A portable secondary solenoid standard which does depend on external exciting current is shown diagramatically in Fig. 4-10. The flux at the center of such a solenoid can be accurately computed from the dimensions of the solenoid and the value of current in the winding:

$$\phi = \mu_0 NIA \text{ webers}$$

In this relationship, N is the number of turns per meter, I is the current in amperes, μ_0 is the permeability of free space $(4\pi \times 10^{-7})$, and A is the cross-sectional area of the solenoid in square meters.

The preceding calculation provides the value of flux at the center of the solenoid only. However, the flux is very nearly constant throughout the length of the device except near the ends. If the ratio of solenoid length to radius is 40, the flux near the ends will differ from that at the center by only 0.13%.

When the solenoid is used as a reference device, a secondary *exploring coil* must be placed around the solenoid. This is explained in Chapter 6.

LIGHT AND RADIATION STANDARDS

Light and radiation units of measurement are not directly related at present to the absolute units, because in many instances these unrelated units were derived from standard sources. This is in contrast to the construction of standards based on unit definitions previously encountered.

A multitude of standards are used in measuring radioactivity (disintegrations per second). This results from the need, in purity determinations, for comparing samples of *every* radioactive substance with an accepted primary standard for that substance. Another reason for the multiplicity of standards is the inherent differences in the chains of radioactive decay of different radioactive substances.

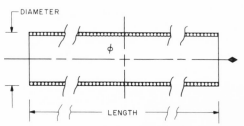

Fig. 4-10 Standard solenoid. The length must be many times the diameter for the calculated flux to be valid.

PHOTOMETRIC STANDARDS The present NBS primary standard for light, upon which the photometric units are based, utilizes an incandescent cavity in an ingot of platinum operated at 2046°K, the solidification temperature of platinum.

Working standards for candlepower commonly used are coiled-filament, clear-bulb incandescent lamps. In aligning these lamps on laboratory photometers, considerable care must be taken because of the coiled filament.

In 1959, NBS designed a frosted lamp working standard with its filament, filament supports, and mounting posts all in the same plane. With this construction there is little variation in candlepower regardless of lamp tilt or rotation. The decrease in radiant intensity in accordance with the inverse square of the distance from the light source (inverse square law) is accurate to within 1.0% up to 50 cm from the lamp. At 1 meter or greater the adherence to this law is within 0.5%.

Distance from the frosted lamp should be measured with reference to the filament plane. A small portion of the bulb is left clear so that this measurement may be made.

RADIATION STANDARDS Radium was the first standard of radioactivity. The international standard, which was prepared by Mme. Curie, consisted of 21.99 mg of pure radium chloride sealed in a thin-walled glass tube. This and later radium standards were based on mass—the activity of a given mass being measured in curies.

Other radium preparations are normally compared with the international standards

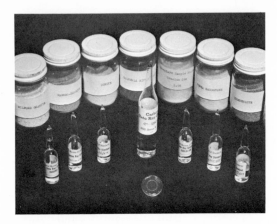

Fig. 4-11 Group of radioactive standards. The disk in the foreground is a radium D + E reference standard which is a deposited film. The solution ampules flanking the disk are secondary standards. In the background are a number of radium rock ore standards and one uranium ore standard. (Courtesy, National Bureau of Standards.)

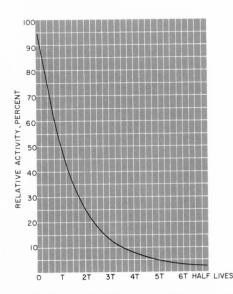

Fig. 4-12 Universal half-life curve. This curve may be used to compute the expected relative activity of any radioactive substance in terms of the substance's half life.

by comparing their gamma-ray effects. Such comparisons produce secondary standards.

Secondary standards are usually solutions of the active material enclosed in glass containers or ampules. A selection of these is shown in Fig. 4-11. Secondary standards are all of long radioactive life except for five short-lived nuclides: (1) sodium, $_{11}Na^{24}$; (2) phosphorus, $_{15}P^{32}$; (3) potassium, $_{19}K^{42}$; (4) iodine, $_{53}I^{131}$; and (5) gold, $_{79}Au^{198}$. All of these short-lived nuclides are man-made transmutations.

The disintegrations within atomic nuclei represent a loss of radioactivity. This must be remembered when making activity measurements. Radioactive samples disintegrate in an exponential manner, in accordance with the principle of half life. The half life of an element is the time required for the radioactivity of a given mass to decay to one-half its original value.

The principle of half life is shown diagrammatically in Fig. 4-12. Consider radium, $_{88}Ra^{226}$, for example, with a half life of 1612 years. Suppose that the initial activity is 8 $\times$ 10^{17} disintegrations per second. Consulting Fig. 4-12, in 403 years (one-quarter of the half life, or $1/4\ T$) the activity will be down to about 87% of the initial value, or 6.96 $\times$ 10^{17} d/sec. At the end of one half life ($T = 1612$ years) the activity will be 50% of the initial value, or 4 $\times$ 10^{17} d/sec. In a period of five half lives ($5T = 8060$ years) the activity will decrease to about 4%, or 3.2 $\times$ 10^{17} d/sec. Figure 4-12 provides a universal curve for determining activity-time relations.

From the preceding discussion, it might appear that the reduction in activity is of little consequence since it takes thousands of years for a noticeable decrease. But many radioactive samples, particularly those of the artificial elements, have half lives that are measured in days, hours, or even fractions of a second. For these substances the rate of decrease would be appreciable.

QUESTIONS

1 What is the primary standard of mass in the United States?

2 What is the primary standard of length?

3 What is Ephemeris time?

4 What services are offered by WWV and WWVH?

5 What relationship exists between WWV and the United States Naval Observatory?

6 Describe a Morehouse proving ring.

7 Briefly describe a dead-weight tester.

8 What is the emf of a Weston Normal cell at 20°C?

9 What precautions should be made when using a standard cell?

10 Describe the Hibbert magnetic standard.

PROBLEMS

1 If a centigrade thermometer registers a temperature of −40°C, what is the temperature in degrees Fahrenheit?

2 Referring to Table 4-3, calculate the temperature in degrees Kelvin for the equilibrium point between solid and liquid gold.

3 Referring to Table 4-3, calculate the temperature in degrees Fahrenheit for the equilibrium point between solid and liquid silver.

    (a) 1420.8°F   (c) 1697.44°F
    (b) 1761.44°F   (d) 1729.44°F

4 Referring to Table 4-2, calculate the temperature in degrees Rankine for the equilibrium point between liquid and vaporized sulphur.

    (a) 1105.28°R   (c) 717.6°R
    (b) 1292.28°R   (d) 1291.68°R

5 Referring to Table 4-3, calculate the temperature in degrees Kelvin for the equilibrium point between liquid and vaporized water.

    (a) 212°K   (c) 373°K
    (b) 560°K   (d) −173°K

6 Referring to Table 4-3, calculate the temperature in degrees Kelvin for the equilibrium point between liquid and gaseous oxygen.

    (a) 90.03°K   (c) −90.03°K
    (b) 455.97°K   (d) −455.97°K

Mechanical Test Equipment: Measurements and Calibration Techniques 5

PRECISION BALANCES

The mass of an object is best compared with mass standards by using an equal-arm balance. Such a balance is illustrated in Fig. 5-1. Since $L_1 = L_2$ and the balance arm is pivoted exactly at its center, equilibrium exists when the pointer is at zero. When the pans are empty, the pointer should naturally come to zero. If it does not, screw adjustments can usually be made somewhere in the supporting mechanism.

The statement that the two masses are equal with zero pointer indication is true only if the comparison takes place in a vacuum or if the two masses have the same density. Otherwise, the masses experience a buoyant effect due to the surrounding air similar to the buoyant forces experienced by objects in water.

With different densities the unknown mass is given by

$$M_2 = M_1 \left[1 + \left(\frac{\rho_a}{\rho_1} \right) \left(\frac{\rho_1 - \rho_2}{\rho_2 - \rho_a} \right) \right]$$

In this equation ρ represents density in kilograms/meter^3. The subscripts a, 1, and 2 refer to the densities of the air, the standard mass, and the test specimen, respectively.

It is possible that an unknown inequality may exist between L_1 and L_2 of the balance arm. The undesirable effects of this condition can be entirely eliminated by balancing the unknown mass in the right pan and then reversing the standard and unknown masses and balancing again. The geometric mean $(\sqrt{m_1 m_2})$ of the two mass values is independent of relative arm lengths.

DIMENSIONAL EQUIPMENT

MONOCHROMATIC LIGHT   Theoretically, monochromatic light is light of one color, i.e., light having one frequency or wavelength. Actually, no source of light radiation is strictly monochromatic. At best a very narrow band of frequencies is obtained. A series of prisms and baffle plates with narrow slits is often used to spread out the frequency spectrum and "mask" most of the undesired frequencies.

When the light beam is composed of one predominant frequency, it may be used to provide a finely divided measurement scale. The divisions of this scale can be on the order of one-millionth of an inch if the proper frequency is chosen.

The degree of measurement which can be made depends on the wavelength of the light beam, which is given by

$$\lambda = \frac{c}{f} \text{ meters}$$

where f is the frequency in cps and c is the speed of light (2.99776×10^8 meters/sec).

This light scale, used for measuring flatness, parallelism, and precise lengths, results from an optical phenomenon known as *interference*. Optical interference may occur when a beam of light is separated into two parts. The parts follow two different paths and are then brought back together into one beam. If the two paths are not of identical optical length, the two beams will not be in phase when they are brought together. Out-of-phase light beams falling on a reflective surface produce an interference pattern (Fig. 5-3A).

The dark lines represent destructive interference, and the bright spaces between lines correspond to constructive interference areas.

Maximum destructive interference occurs when the two beams are 180° out of phase (Fig. 5-3B). The fringes (dark lines) must then be spaced by a distance of one-half wavelength.

A good example of interference fringes can be seen by placing two flat pieces of glass together so that they are separated by a slightly tapered wedge of air. If the reflecting surface and lower piece of glass are truly flat, the interference lines will be parallel to the point of contact between the glass pieces as well as parallel to each other. The spaces between fringes will be equal (Fig. 5-3C). If flatness does not exist, a distorted image will be formed.

The fringe spacing for commercial monochromatic lights represents a distance of 11.6 microin.

OPTICAL FLATS Optical flats are carefully ground pieces of clear, hard glass polished until one surface is perfectly flat. They are used in flatness and parallelism checks of surfaces and are especially suited for use in calibrating gage blocks.

Working grade optical flats must, themselves, be calibrated about once every three months; since the calibration procedure is simple, however, it is usually a good idea to calibrate them before each use.

The equipment required for the calibration consists of a monochromatic light, suitable cleaning materials, and a master reference optical flat. The master reference flat must be previously calibrated by a higher standardizing laboratory.

After both flats are thoroughly cleaned, the working surface of the reference flat is placed against that of the flat in question. The "flatness" of the flat being calibrated can be read from the fringe pattern which results.

In reading fringe patterns, true flatness exists when the fringes are equidistant and parallel (Fig. 5-4A and B). Any deviation from a

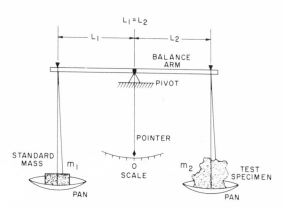

Fig. 5-1 Mass comparison by equal-arm balance.

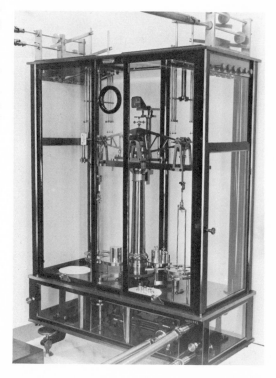

Fig. 5-2 Most accurate precision balance in the United States. This device is used to compare secondary mass standards with the national prototype kilogram. Remote control operation is used entirely to avoid the effects of heat given off by the human body. Recently, a photoelectric device was added to give continuous, automatic readings. A precision of 5 parts in one billion is obtainable. (Courtesy, National Bureau of Standards.)

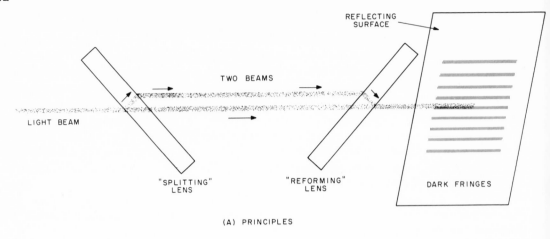

(A) PRINCIPLES

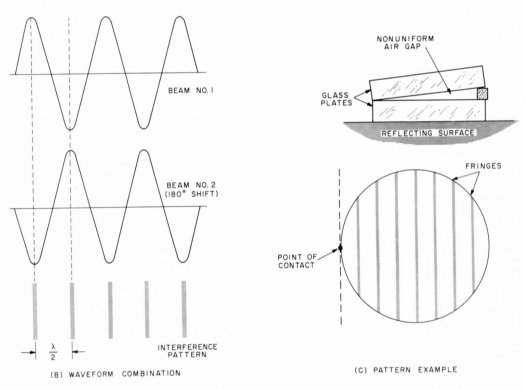

(B) WAVEFORM COMBINATION

(C) PATTERN EXAMPLE

Fig. 5-3 Optical interference.

true plane will show up as a curvature of the fringes. Figure 5-4C represents general concavity of a surface and Fig. 5-4D represents convexity.

In interpreting the fringe spacing as a length, it is important to establish a reference line on the flat. This may be done by stretching a piece of thread or holding a straightedge across the flat, as in Fig. 5-5. The deviation from the reference line can be read in terms of fractions of a fringe spacing. An experienced user should be able to interpret tenths of a spacing with no trouble. The fringe in Fig. 5-5 deviates by 1⅓ spacing. Since the fringes represent 11.6 microin., the flatness of the surface is off by 1⅓ × 11.6, or 15.48 microin. at this point.

The accepted tolerance for any given flat is specified by the manufacturer or will be determined by the use of the flat.

Optical flats may also be calibrated without a master reference flat. This is accomplished by using three working flats. The flats must be separately identifiable as "A," "B," and "C."

This procedure consists of placing two of the flats (A and B, for example) together under the monochromatic light. The deviation is read and interpreted as length. The deviation represents the sum of the deviations for flats A and B.

$$A + B = x \text{ in.}$$

Next, flats A and C are placed together (B and C may also be used). The deviation here represents $A + C = y$ in.

Subtracting the second reading from the first is the same as solving the two relations simultaneously and eliminating the deviation of flat A (or B):

$$\begin{array}{cc} A + B & x \\ -(A + C) & -y \\ \hline B - C & x - y \end{array}$$

If flat B is then placed on flat C, the deviation will represent $B + C = z$ in. If this reading is added to the difference of the two previous readings, the deviation of another flat is eliminated from the process:

$$\begin{array}{cc} B - C & x - y \\ +(B + C) & z \\ \hline 2B & x - y + z \end{array}$$

or,

$$B = \frac{x - y + z}{2}$$

Substituting the value of B into the equations representing the first and third deviations ($A + B = x$ and $B + C = z$) allows

the solution of A and C. The flatness deviation of all three flats is now known and can be checked against the acceptance tolerance.

In using this process, a "point of contact" must be temporarily marked on each optical flat. These points must be placed together when making all the required readings. Also, algebraic signs must be established for the direction of deviation. Concavity may be considered positive (+) and convexity negative (−). The converse may also be used. However, the system adopted must be used throughout the entire calibration process.

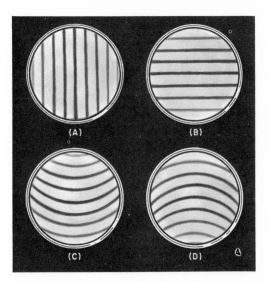

Fig. 5-4 Fringe patterns with optical flats.

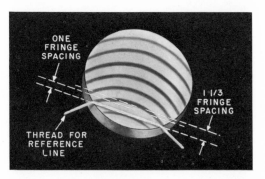

Fig. 5-5 Reading fringe spaces.

GAGE BLOCKS The frequency of calibration for *working* gage blocks depends on their usage. Since most gage blocks are very stable, a minimum period of one year between calibrations is often recommended. However, more frequent calibrations are advisable.

The working faces of gage blocks are "super-smooth" surfaces which adhere to one another on contact. This allows blocks of various sizes to be *wrung* together to produce odd-sized dimensions. For this reason the working surfaces must be flat and must be parallel to each other. Also, the actual size of the gage (distance between working faces) must agree with its nominal size within a very small tolerance.

With the foregoing conditions to be satisfied, calibration consists of checking the flatness, parallelism, and actual size of the block in question.

The procedure outlined holds equally well for grade-A blocks, or less, with exceptions as noted. The primary equipment involved consists of certified reference gage blocks, a calibrated optical flat of sufficient quality, a normalizing plate, and a calibrated comparator graduated in millionths of an inch.

Blocks less than 0.100 in. thickness are not checked for flatness since they are inherently subject to warp.

In length comparisons, the temperature of the unknown block and the reference block must be equal. To achieve this, the blocks are placed near each other on the normalizing plate for a period of one hour per inch of length. If an abnormal temperature difference exists between the two blocks, 8 to 12 hours is an advisable normalization period.

Since body heat can cause noticeable changes during the calibration procedure, the blocks should be handled with plastic-tipped

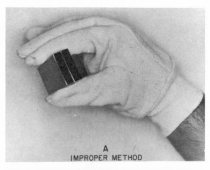

A
IMPROPER METHOD

B
PROPER METHOD

Fig. 5-6 Handling gage blocks. (Courtesy, National Bureau of Standards.)

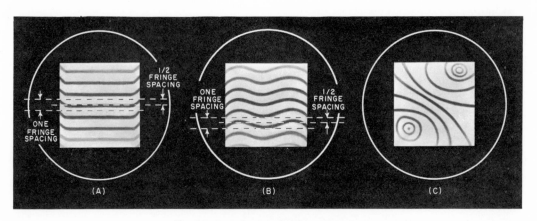

Fig. 5-7 Irregular interference patterns.

or heat-resistant forceps. Asbestos gloves may also be used with the proper method of grasping shown in Fig. 5-6B. Figure 5-6A shows an improper method of handling. One block is near the palm of the hand and will, therefore, absorb heat more readily.

Before detailed calibration, a visual inspection of the surface quality of the block should be made. This will show up any large scratches which may immediately disqualify the block.

In checking the block for flatness, place the optical flat on the working surface of the block and gently slide the flat until the interference patterns are seen. Then tip the flat slightly to insure contact at one point or in one area. The tipping can be adjusted until the fringes are easy to distinguish under the monochromatic light.

The degree of flatness can be read from the fringe spacing as previously outlined for calibrating the optical flat. Gage blocks, however, may show up very irregular patterns. Some of these are shown in Fig. 5-7. Figure 5-7A indicates that the edges of the block are raised one-half fringe spacing, or 5.8 microin. Convexity and concavity are both shown in Fig. 5-7B, indicating a valley 5.8 microin. down the center and a rounding of the block edges on the order of 5 microin. Two high points are shown in Fig. 5-7C since fringes will always curve around points of contact. There are eleven fringes between the high spots, indicating that a low point, or valley, 127.8 microin. deep exists.

For all blocks, flatness must be checked on both working surfaces and in both directions parallel to the block edges on each surface.

After temperature normalization check the length of the test block against the length of the reference block. The reference block should be placed on the comparator and the zero setting made. Remove the reference block and replace it to insure that the setting repeats itself. This setting is made on the calibration point marked with an "X" on the reference block.

With the zero setting made and checked,

A
MICRO–COMPARATOR

B
UNIVERSAL MEASURING MACHINES

Fig. 5-8 Length comparators: (A) Cleveland micro a-c electronic comparator, accurate to ±3 millionths of an inch. The box on the left contains NBS certified gage blocks. (B) Pratt and Whitney Universal Measuring Machine, accurate to ±10 millionths of an inch.

place the test block in the comparator. Deviation (+ or −) should be recorded. A sufficient number of readings should be made at each spot checked and an average used for the final deviation.

Occasionally, the reference block should be returned to the comparator to make sure that the zero setting has not been disturbed.

Parallelism can be checked by taking length readings at four different points on the gage block surface. These points are indicated by X's in Fig. 5-9.

MICROMETERS AND VERNIER CALIPERS The micrometer and vernier calipers shown in Fig. 5-10 are used to make measurements accurate to 0.001 in. The common micrometer has a maximum opening of only 1 in. Vernier calipers as large as 18 in. are available. The micrometer measures outside dimensions while the vernier caliper jaws may be

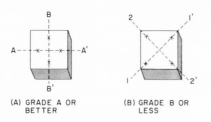

Fig. 5-9 Checking block parallelism. The crosses mark the points to be checked in order to establish the proper reference axes.

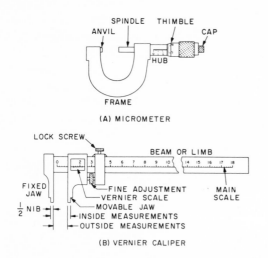

Fig. 5-10 Micrometer and vernier calipers.

machined to measure outside or inside, or both, dimensions.

The piece to be measured with the micrometer is placed between the anvil and the spindle and the spindle is moved down until it touches the object with only the slightest pressure. There should be no clamping action. *Clamping the micrometer into position will ruin it.*

Along the tapered edge of the thimble are 25 graduations. When the thimble is turned from one of these graduations to the next, the distance between the spindle and the anvil is changed by 0.001 in. This is because the screw on the spindle has 40 threads to an inch. Starting with the spindle against the anvil, it requires 40 turns of the thimble to move the spindle 1 in. Hence, one turn equals

1/40 or 0.025 in. Since there are 25 thimble graduations, each must equal 0.001 in.

On the hub is a line called the datum, or reference, line. This line is also graduated. Each graduation represents one turn of the thimble (0.025). Every fourth graduation is numbered and represents 0.100 in.

To read a micrometer, first read the number of thousandths indicated by the divisions on the datum line disregarding any fractional part of a division. Then read the number of thousandths indicated by the thimble and add the two together. The setting shown in Fig. 5-11 is read as 0.237 in.

The main scale of the vernier caliper is graduated on the beam, or limb, of the caliper. It is marked in inch divisions and each inch division subdivided and marked with graduations equal to 0.025 in. as with the hub scale on the micrometer. The vernier scale is divided into 25 intervals if the scale is to be read in thousandths. Other vernier divisions are also available. The value of each vernier division is given by $0.025/n$, where n is the number of vernier divisions.

The setting of the vernier scale, however, is interpreted in a manner different from the micrometer setting. There is one vernier graduation which is coincident, or more nearly coincident, with a main-scale graduation than are any of its neighbors. The ratio of the numerical value of this graduation to the number of vernier graduations is the fraction of 0.025 by which the vernier index passes its nearest main-scale division to the left of the index. An example reading is given in Fig. 5-12.

Micrometers and vernier calipers are checked directly against reference-quality gage blocks. Before calibration, the condition of the mating faces of the micrometer anvil and spindle must be checked. This is accomplished by inserting an optical parallel between anvil and spindle with a slight pressure to ensure contact. The optical parallel is a thin optical flat which, when used with a monochromatic light, produces interference patterns. *The surface of the anvil and spindle must be flat and parallel,* as indicated by straight, parallel fringe lines.

If the flat and parallel condition does not exist, the faces must be lapped by the use of *laps.* Laps are two small cast-iron disks, one thicker than the other, charged with grinding compound. The spindle is rotated 180 degrees with the laps lightly held between anvil and spindle surfaces. It is necessary to recheck flatness with the optical parallel occasionally. Before each check the surfaces of the anvil and spindle must be thoroughly cleaned.

With the micrometer spindle closed against the anvil, the index (zero mark) of the thimble scale should align itself with the datum line. If it does not, remove the thimble cap and make the necessary adjustments.

With the vernier caliper jaws closed, the OUTSIDE scale should have the index of the vernier coincident with the zero of the main scale. The INSIDE scale should give a reading equal to the nib width (Fig. 5-10B).

All classes of micrometers and calipers can be calibrated by choosing appropriate reference gage blocks to fully cover the scale of the instrument being tested.

FORCE MEASURING EQUIPMENT

Since pressure is defined as force per unit area, measurements of pressure and force are virtually the same thing. Measurements of pressure are accomplished by balancing the pressure against a known force. The known force is usually the force due to gravity acting upon mass standards, although some instruments use a spring-produced force.

TESTING MACHINES The parts of a dead-weight testing machine (see Chapter 4) must perform two essential functions—they must provide a means for applying the load to the test specimen, and they must measure the applied load. These two functions may be entirely separate, or they may be accomplished by the same mechanism.

A *screw-gear machine* may apply the load directly by a screw-gear mechanism or indi-

rectly by levers. *Hydraulic machines* are used for larger loadings. NBS has a hydraulic machine for compression tests of 10,000,000 lb. Screw-gear capacity, in general, does not exceed 400,000 lb.

The screw-gear machine has smaller capacity because the measuring function for these machines is accomplished by a balancing process. The balancing force is applied, counter to the loading force, through a series of lever arms pivoted on knife-edge fulcrums to reduce friction. These knife edges bear the entire load, and since the area of contact is small, they are subjected to large stresses.

The knife edges must be checked occasionally for dullness, chipping, clogging, and seating. The hold-down bolts on the bed plate should be checked at the beginning of each test to see that they are slightly loose.

The crosshead of most hydraulic machines can be moved up and down to handle various lengths of test specimens.

There are three methods commonly used to calibrate testing machines—the use of mass

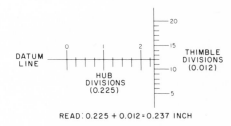

READ: 0.225 + 0.012 = 0.237 INCH

Fig. 5-11 Interpretation of micrometer scale.

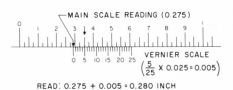

READ: 0.275 + 0.005 = 0.280 INCH

Fig. 5-12 Interpretation of vernier scale. The arrow indicates the point of coincidence between the vernier- and main-scale graduations.

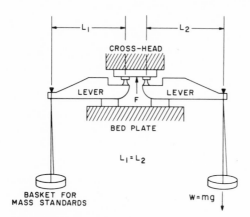

Fig. 5-13 Proving levers. Equal amounts of load must be placed in both baskets. The length of the lever arms is such that F = 10W.

standards applied directly, the use of levers and mass standards, and the use of elastic calibration devices.

The direct application of mass standards is the simplest method. They are placed directly on the bed plate. This method, however, is restricted in calibration range by the limited amount of available space. One thousand pounds is a common limit for this method.

The calibrating range may be extended to 10,000 lb by using a pair of levers, as shown in Fig. 5-13. These are called *proving levers* and are usually made with a 10:1 lever-ratio. Remember that the actual load due to the mass placed in the baskets is dependent upon the weight of the standards—the product of the mass and the local value of the gravitational constant.

Levers and mass standards are difficult to transport and are limited in range. Hence, the most practical method of calibrating testing machines is to use either a Morehouse proving ring or a strain-gage device. The proving ring is a standard certified by NBS, whereas the strain gage must be calibrated before it may be used to calibrate any other device.

MANOMETERS AND BAROMETERS The manometer is used to measure low pressures by balancing the pressure against the weight of

a liquid column. This provides an absolute method of pressure measurement by the relation:

$$P = h\rho \text{ lb/in.}^2$$

where h is the height of the liquid column in inches and ρ is the density in lb/in.^{3}

The manometer comes in two basic forms, as illustrated in Fig. 5-14. Essentially it is an open tube filled with liquid. The pressure to be measured is applied at one end of the tube. The height of the liquid column changes until the unknown pressure is balanced.

If the tube of the cistern manometer is closed at the top, a mercurial barometer is produced. Since the space between the top of the mercury column and the closed top of the tube is filled with mercury vapor, the value of the applied force (barometers are usually used to measure atmospheric pressure only) is

$$P_{at} = ph + P_v$$

In this equation, P_v is the saturated vapor pressure of mercury. For most purposes, this term can be neglected.

The calibration of a manometer includes a *zero check*. With the U-tube device, when both openings are vented to the atmosphere, the measurement column should be at zero. However, the specific gravity of mercury (normally 13.6) changes as the gravitational constant changes. Appendix B-4 provides the necessary information for making corrections. The value of local gravity is found by subtracting the *elevation correction factor* from the value of g at the latitude of test. The correction factor for the mercury column is then given by:

$$C = \frac{\text{Local } g - 9.80665}{9.80665}$$

The value obtained for the correction factor may indicate that the column is either above or below the true-reading value.

The calibration procedure should be conducted at 68°F (20°C).

Deviations of the column from the desired corrected height can be eliminated by adding or removing small quantities of triple-distilled mercury. This should be done with a medicine dropper.

The scale graduations can be checked with a calibrated height vernier gage or other suitable length-measuring device. They may also be checked, in terms of pressure, against a calibrated barometer.

Mercurial barometers are calibrated in a manner similar to manometers. If a check of the scale graduations by length-comparison devices is not considered sufficient, however, a standard barometer certified by an appropriate laboratory must be used.

After corrections for the local gravity effect are made, the mercury level in the barometer and the cistern should be effectively equal when the tube top and cistern are opened to the atmosphere. This provides a zero-adjustment check as before.

If the barometer is to be checked against a standard, the equipment should be arranged as shown in Fig. 5-15.

PRESSURE GAGES

Pressure gages employ various elastic movements to produce a pointer deflection proportional to the applied pressure. Two common types are the Bourdon and bellows movements, shown in Fig. 5-16.

The elastic tube of the Bourdon movement is of an oval cross section bent into a circle and sealed at one end. Pressure changes produce a change in the cross section which, in turn, produces movement away from the over-all circular arc. This deformation is transmitted to the pointer through a mechanical linkage, sector, and pinion mechanism.

The bellows movement is sensitive to much lower pressures than the Bourdon. A spring inside the bellows tends to return it to its normal position.

The bellows may be replaced by an elastic diaphragm to form a third movement. The diaphragm separates the airtight case into

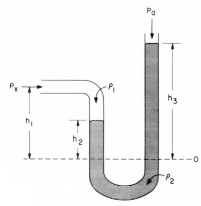

$$P_x = P_a + P_2 (h_3 - h_2) - P_1 (h_1 - h_2)$$

(A) U-TUBE MANOMETER

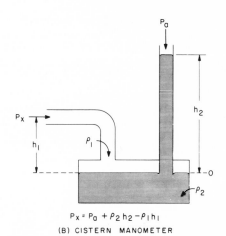

$$P_x = P_a + P_2 h_2 - P_1 h_1$$

(B) CISTERN MANOMETER

Fig. 5-14 Manometers. The equations given for the instruments are balance equations. The heights are measured relative to the tops of the mercury meniscus.

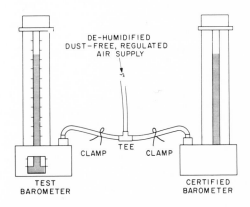

Fig. 5-15 Pressure comparison with barometers.

two compartments. The air is evacuated from the upper compartment and the unknown pressure applied to the lower compartment. Such an arrangement is used in *altimeters*.

Pressure gages are calibrated by using a dead-weight gage tester or by comparison with a certified manometer or barometer. The calibration curve in Fig. 5-17 will be used to explain the correction of errors.[*] The curves are plots of pressure versus gage error. Curve A is a plot of the original calibration test data without corrective action taken.

In order to overcome the nonlinearity of curve A, the sector and connecting link (Fig. 5-16) axes must be made perpendicular. If this correction is made, a new test run may yield a curve similar to curve B with a con-

[*] R. J. Sweeny, *Measurement Techniques in Mechanical Engineering* (New York: John Wiley & Sons, Inc., 1953).

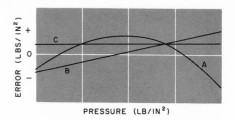

Fig. 5-17 Calibration curves for pressure gages.

stant positive or negative slope. This slope represents a constant multiplying error which may be eliminated by shifting the point where the link and sector are attached while *maintaining their axes perpendicular*. The length of the link is adjustable so that the proper working tension can be maintained.

After the constant multiplying error has been compensated for, the test is re-run. This may produce a new curve, such as curve C, which indicates a constant scale error. The pointer is shifted on the shaft to correct this error.

Altimeters are calibrated in a glass-windowed, air-tight test chamber with a connection for a calibrated manometer or barometer. The air is pumped out of the chamber, and the barometer (or manometer) pressure is recorded along with altimeter readings at various intervals. The altimeter readings may then be converted to pressure values and these values compared with the recorded manometer or barometer pressure readings.[†]

TORQUE INDICATORS AND TESTERS   The effect of a force upon rotational motion is dependent upon the perpendicular distance from the axis of rotation to the point through which the force acts. This distance is the *moment arm* of the force. The product of the force and its moment arm is the *torque* produced:

$$\text{torque} = \text{force} \times \text{moment arm}$$

[†] The pressure equivalent of any altitude from − 1000 to 80,000 ft. can be found in N.A.C.A. Technical Note 3182, available from Superintendent of Documents, Washington 25, D.C.

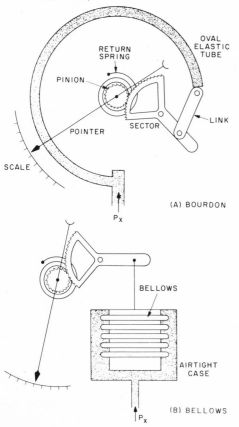

Fig. 5-16 Pressure gage movements.

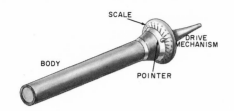

Fig. 5-18 Torque indicator.

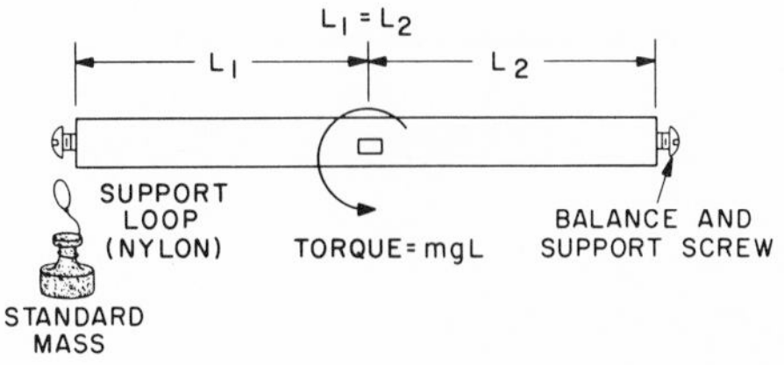

Fig. 5-19 Calibration torque arm.

Since this is a force times distance, the units are usually in inch-ounces or foot-pounds.

A simple torque indicator is illustrated in Fig. 5-18. The range of the instrument varies. Calibration is accomplished by firmly clamping the indicator in a V-block and applying calculated torque values. An adapter is fitted over the indicator drive mechanism, and a lever similar to that in Fig. 5-19 is placed on the adapter.

A vernier height gage is used to check the middle and end heights of the lever. If the three are not equal, adjustments of the mass-supporting screws may be made or small weights (usually washers) may be added to one of the ends until equality is achieved. *After equality, the balance screws must not be moved in any way.*

After the dial pointer of the indicator is set to zero, mass standards may be applied to one end of the lever-bar. The force, remember, is the product of the mass and the local value of the gravitational constant. The mass standard is then moved to the opposite end of the lever-bar.

With the tremendous stresses that present-day aircraft, rockets, and missiles must undergo, it has become more and more necessary to see that every nut, bolt, and screw has been tightened by the specified amount. This is accomplished by various types of *torque wrenches,* which are, as a rule, spring-loaded wrenches with an indicator to show the torque applied by the operator's tightening motion.

Torque wrenches must be calibrated by devices called *torque wrench testers* which

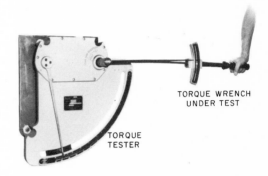

Fig. 5-20 Torque wrench tester, Model 71. (Courtesy, B. K. Sweeney Manufacturing Co.)

must, themselves, be calibrated by mass standards. A torque wrench tester, such as that illustrated in Fig. 5-20, is equipped with leveling pads to facilitate installation on a wall, beam, or bench. The primary moving part is a dead-weight pendulum actuated by a gear and pinion movement. *No springs are used.* Torque applied to the input transmits movement to the pendulum, which moves an indicator. The weight is trigonometric and is based on the angle through which the pendulum is moved. Accuracy is within 2%.

When a torque wrench is to be calibrated, it is mounted on the tester and pulled slowly and smoothly to the desired torque reading. The torque wrench reading is then compared to that of the tester.

Special calibrating attachments are available to check the torque tester against mass standards. One such device (companion to the tester of Fig. 5-20) is shown in Fig. 5-21.

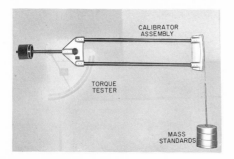

Fig. 5-21 Torque tester calibration assembly. The device, Model 73630, is shown mounted on the Model 71 Torque Tester. (Courtesy, B. K. Sweeney Manufacturing Co.)

BALL TYPE

DIAMOND CONE OR BRALE

Fig. 5-23 Rockwell hardness penetrators.

Fig. 5-22 Typical Rockwell hardness tester. (Courtesy, Wilson Mechanical Instrument Division, American Chain and Cable Co., Inc.)

The torque tester and calibrator assembly must be horizontal.

The mass standards are placed on the weight carrier of the calibrator assembly. As explained previously, the torque-producing force is actually the weight of the mass standards and is therefore dependent on the local value of gravitational constant (see Appendix B-4). Various masses are applied and allowed to settle before readings are taken.

Inaccuracies in the scale reading of the torque tester may be due to incorrect pointer friction. This friction is controlled by a set screw on top of the pointer. For the Sweeney instruments illustrated, clockwise turning of the screw increases friction; counterclockwise turning decreases friction.

HARDNESS TESTERS The hardness of a material is usually judged by the material's resistance to penetration. It is a relative term, and hardness numbers are not directly applicable in design calculations as are values of tensile strength, shear strength, etc. Choice of materials according to hardness numbers is made strictly on past experience.

There are several categories of hardness: (1) indentation hardness, (2) impact, or rebound, hardness, (3) scratch hardness, (4) abrasion, or wear, hardness, (5) machinability, or cutting and drilling resistance.

The Rockwell hardness tester (Fig. 5-22) is one of the most commonly used testers for static indentation tests. The *penetrator* used for the tests is either a steel ball or a conical-shaped diamond with rounded point, as shown in Fig. 5-23. The actual hardness value indicated on the dial is an arbitrary number based on depth of penetration. These numbers are meaningless references unless preceded by the letter prefix which indicates the type penetrator used as well as the loading value. Larger numbers indicate less penetration.

An initial minor load of 10 kg is used in all tests to achieve a "set" for the penetrator. A major test load of 60, 100, or 150 kg is used for actual tests. A complete specification of tests is given in Table 5-1.

Table 5-1   Rockwell Hardness Tests and Prefixes

Prefix letter	Penetrator (ball diameter in inches)	Test load (kilograms)
A	Brale	60
B	Ball (1/16)	100
C	Brale	150
D	Brale	100
E	Ball (1/8)	100
F	Ball (1/16)	60
G	Ball (1/16)	150
H	Ball (1/8)	60
K	Ball (1/8)	150
L	Ball (1/4)	60
M	Ball (1/4)	100
P	Ball (1/4)	150
R	Ball (1/2)	60
S	Ball (1/2)	100
V	Ball (1/2)	150

Both upper and lower surfaces of the test specimen should be flat and free of oxides, pits, and foreign matter. A single solid piece of the desired thickness should be used. The concave side of curved specimens should face the penetrator. The major test load should be applied over a period of several seconds. The tester should be cushioned and mounted to prevent the influence of external vibration.

Before the use or calibration of the tester, the penetrator should be checked with a magnifying glass. Flatness, burrs, scratches, or breaks demand that the penetrator be repaired or replaced. Surface irregularities can be removed with an Arkansas stone. The same inspection applies to the anvil.

The oil dashpot on the tester should cause operation to proceed from zero to full load in from 4–5 sec. A valve at the top of the dashpot permits adjustment.

The tester handwheel is raised slightly past zero until a positive resistance is encountered. At this point the small pointer should be at a 15° angle to the left of vertical and the large

pointer at C 30. If the handwheel is rotated back to zero (large pointer), the small pointer should be over the dot on the scale. Adjustment of the indicator is made by turning the set screw behind and above the indicator.

Special test blocks of specific hardnesses are used for the calibration of the Rockwell tester. The check should be made on an unused portion of the calibration block. Several tests should be made, and an average reading should be taken and compared with the hardness number indicated on the block.

A 90-day calibration interval is advisable, although a few "spot checks" should be made with the calibration blocks before use.

Only the thread and underside of the handwheel elevating nut should be oiled. Do not oil any other part of the tester.

HEAT AND TEMPERATURE MEASURING EQUIPMENT

Heat is the world's primary source of power. The control of heat flow is a major activity in industrial processes, as well as in the measurement and calibration of heat-sensitive devices.

Since temperature is a measure of the relative heat of different bodies, it determines the direction in which heat transfer will take place. Heat always "flows" from a body of higher temperature *toward* a body of lower temperature. Heat flow takes place by three different methods—radiation, convection, and conduction.

Radiant heat is an electromagnetic radiation higher in frequency than radio waves and extending through the infrared region of the electromagnetic spectrum. Because of its nature, heat may be radiated in a vacuum, as well as through conductive mediums.

Heat radiation may be absorbed, reflected, or transmitted by objects it strikes. Most solids and liquids are opaque to invisible (nonluminous) heat radiation and either absorb or reflect it. Polished metals are excellent reflectors. Most gases are transparent to heat radiation.

The heat radiated from one body at temperature T to a second body at temperature T_o (T_o less than T) is given by

$$q = \sigma \epsilon FA(T^4 - T_0^4)$$

The temperature must be specified by the appropriate absolute scale (°K or °R). The factor σ is *Boltzmann's radiation constant*, the value of which depends on the system of units used:

$$5.673 \times 10^{-12} \text{ watt/cm}^2 \text{ (°K)}^4$$
$$1.73 \times 10^{-9} \text{ Btu/ft}^2 \text{ (°R)}^4$$

The *emissivity factor*, ϵ, depends on the relative emission properties of the radiating body as compared to an ideal *black body* radiator. These quantities are listed in Appendix C-4. The factor F is called the *radial emittance factor* and depends upon the geometric relation between the two bodies. Values of F are also listed in Appendix C-4. The emitting area A must be in appropriate units. The units of q will, of course, depend upon other units used in the computation. Conversion factors, however, may be used to obtain q in watts, joules, Btu, ergs, or any other energy unit.

Heat transfer by conduction through solid objects is found by

$$q = \frac{KA(T - T_o)}{L}$$

Here T and T_o are the two surface temperatures of the conductor, A is the total conduction area, and L is the length of the conduction path. The factor K is the *conductivity* (see Appendix C-3) of the material in question. As with radiation calculations, consistent units must be used throughout, and these depend primarily on the units chosen for K.

Convection is the process by which heat is transferred through a fluid. *Free convection* takes place in a static fluid, and *forced convection* in a moving fluid. Here, fluid may be either a liquid or a gas. The heat due to convection is given by

$$q = hA(T - T_o)$$

where h is the *surface coefficient*, A is the mean area of the heat path, and T and T_o are the temperature of the surface of the wall bounding the fluid and the fluid itself. T must be the higher of the two. Appropriate units must be used. Many variables enter into the value of h, and hundreds of pages of experimental determinations have been compiled.

Any of the three types of heat transfer, or all three simultaneously, may exist in any particular situation. They must usually be treated separately. For series heat-flow paths, heat resistivities (reciprocal of conductivity) are additive. For parallel heat-flow paths, the conductivities are additive.

LIQUID-IN-GLASS THERMOMETERS   Nearly all substances expand when their temperature is increased. The liquid-in-glass thermometer makes use of the volumetric expansion of a liquid contained in a thick-walled glass tube with a capillary bore (stem). The bulk of the liquid supply is kept stored in a glass bulb at the base of the stem.

The liquid used in these thermometers is chosen on the basis of the temperature range to be measured by the device. The freezing point of the liquid must be below the lower limit of measurement, and the liquid boiling point must be above the upper limit. Common liquids include mercury, water, oil, alcohol, and toluene. The colorless liquids must have a dye additive included.

Unless otherwise specified, glass-stem thermometers are graduated for *complete immersion of the bulb and stem during the taking and reading of a temperature measurement*.

Since thermometers should be read without removal from the immediate measurement area, it is often necessary to leave a portion of the stem protruding in such a manner that it will be at a different temperature than the bulb. This also occurs when a *thermometer well*—a protective metal covering—must be used in conjunction with the glass bulb and stem. Under such a *partial immersion* condition, a correction must be made for stem exposure:

$$t_e = Kn(T - T_o) \text{ degrees}$$

In this equation, n represents the total number of degrees exposed, T is the temperature measured by the partially immersed thermometer, and T_o is the surface temperature of the exposed stem. The latter may be measured by placing the bulb of a *second thermometer* in contact with the emergent stem and binding the two together with asbestos tape or thread. The temperature error, t_e, will carry the proper algebraic sign since it must be added if T is greater than T_o and subtracted if the temperature relation is reversed.

The value of K is dependent upon the coefficient of expansion for glass and the thermometer liquid; therefore, it is a variable function of temperature. Values of K are given in Appendix B-6. *For computations using the Fahrenheit scale, the correction factor is 5/9 of the tabulated value.*

In thermometers for normal temperature ranges, the capillary bore is evacuated above the liquid fill. In thermometers for high temperatures, however, the capillary bore is pressurized with nitrogen or some other suitable gas to prevent evaporation of the liquid.

PRESSURE THERMOMETERS   The pressure produced by any fluid in a completely enclosed container is a function of the fluid temperature. An application of this principle appears in *pressure thermometers.* The fluid may be either a liquid, a gas, or a vapor. The indicator is usually a Bourdon-type pressure gage.

The general design of a pressure thermometer is shown in Fig. 5-24. The indicating device is located some distance from the bulb where actual measurements are being taken and where the bulk of the fluid is stored. The indicator and bulb are joined by a coiled capillary tube which also forms the elastic tube (see Fig. 5-16) of the Bourdon movement.

Because of the large size of the bulb, pressure thermometers have a considerable

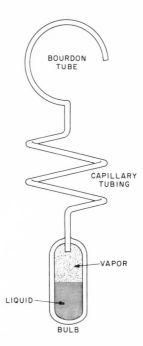

Fig. 5-24 Vapor-pressure thermometer.

time lag between application of temperature and final reading of the gage.

The error due to the difference in temperature between the connecting capillary tube and the bulb can be calculated by using the equation:

$$t_e = t_c \frac{V_T}{V_B} \text{ degrees}$$

where t_c is the temperature of the connecting tube and V_T/V_B is the ratio of the volume of the connecting tube to the volume of the bulb.

In choosing a fluid for a vapor-pressure thermometer, the lower limit of measurement is the boiling point of the fluid, and the upper limit is the *critical temperature*—the temperature at which the vapor-liquid equilibrium no longer exists and the fluid goes into its gaseous state.

The bulb of a vapor-pressure thermometer must be large enough to contain all of the liquid used (more than enough to fill the Bourdon elastic tube and the connecting

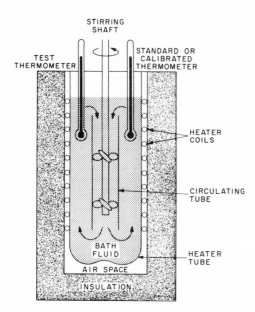

Fig. 5-25 Comparator bath for thermometer calibration.

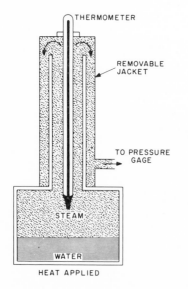

Fig. 5-26 Steam bath for thermometer calibration.

tubing). This insures that the liquid-vapor interchange will occur *inside the bulb.*

CALIBRATION TECHNIQUES As already discussed in this section and in Chapter 4, temp-

erature is measured only by its effect on the physical properties of materials. The three properties used have been (1) change of state, (2) vapor pressure, (3) expansion. The first two provide the necessary means for calibration references. This necessitates a comparison of the test instrument with a standard or previously calibrated instrument or a direct check of test instrument readings against *known boiling and melting points.* The latter reference temperatures are the fixed points listed in Table 4-3. Intermediate points may be found in Appendix C-5.

A test thermometer is compared with a calibrated or certified thermometer by use of a *comparator bath* similar to the one shown in Fig. 5-25. The bath liquid is water, oil, molten metals, or molten salts, depending upon the temperatures involved. Heating is provided by an electric coil. Cooling is usually accomplished by placing dry ice in the bath.

Fixed-point baths are used for the direct comparison of the test instrument reading and a known melting or boiling point. A convenient method of reproducing the ice point is to place clear ice shavings in an upright Thermos bottle or Dewar flask. Enough distilled water should be added to form a slush but *not enough to float the ice.* From time to time excess water should be siphoned off.

A steam bath (boiling point of water) is shown in Fig. 5-26. The bath consists of a double-walled steam jacket with the thermometer suspended so that it is surrounded by freely circulating steam. Steam pressure must be determined as shown by the barometer connection.

The metal-freezing points listed in Table 4-3 are obtained by heating the metal *only a few degrees above its melting point* in a carbon crucible. Any refractory material which will not contaminate the metal may be used in the place of carbon. A furnace arrangement is used to heat the crucible and metal uniformly. The metal should be allowed to cool very slowly.

QUESTIONS

1 How do incandescent and monochromatic light differ?

2 Could incandescent light be used with optical flats?

3 In Fig. 5-1, the length of the two balance arms is indicated as being equal (L1 = L2). Is it possible to make a precision mass comparison if L1 is not equal to L2?

4 What phase relationship must exist between two light beams for destructive interference?

5 What considerations must be made in handling gage blocks?

6 Describe a Bourdon pressure gage.

7 Explain the statement: "Temperature is measured indirectly through a process of energy conversion."

8 What kind of standards are used in the calibration of dead-weight and torque-testing machines?

PROBLEMS

1 What is the value of local gravity for a manometer calibration laboratory located at 30° North latitude and at sea level?

2 What is the value of local gravity for a manometer calibration laboratory located at 60° North latitude and 8000 ft above sea level?

3 What is the elevation correction factor to use in the calibration of a manometer when the calibration laboratory is located 55° North latitude and 5000 ft above sea level?

4 If a standard mass of 50 oz is applied to one end of an 18-in. level bar, such as shown in Fig. 5-19, how much torque is applied?

5 What is the emissivity factor of a 4 × 6-ft plate glass window?

6 What is the emissivity factor of a polished aluminium block?

7 What is the thermal conductivity factor (K) of copper?

8 What is the thermal conductivity factor (K) of window glass?

9 What is the thermal conductivity factor (K) of mineral wool?

EXERCISE 1   Calibration of Optical Flats

MATERIAL REQUIRED

1 Optical flat set

2 Monochromatic light source

3 Alcohol

4 Lintfree cloth

5 Grease pencil

6 Thread

7 Desk lamp

PROCEDURE

1 Select three optical flats from the set and place them aside in areas marked A, B, and C.

2 Turn on the monochromatic light source and adjust it so the working area is well illuminated by it.

3 Place flat A in the working area. With the grease pencil, mark a spot on the edge of the flat as shown in Fig. 5-27.

4 Make an identical mark on flat B and place flat B on flat A, with the marks coinciding.

5 Apply a slight pressure at the marked point until interference lines appear.

6 If the lines are straight and equally spaced, true flatness exists in both flats.

7 If the lines are not straight, stretch the thread across the flats connecting both ends of one line. See Fig. 5-28.

8 Using the thread as a reference line, measure the spacing from the thread to the mid-point of the next fringe line, in terms of fringe lines.

9 Multiply the quantity obtained in Step 8 by 11.6 μin. and label this value at X.

10 To determine the sign of X apply the following rule: If the ends of the lines curve away from the point of contact, the surface is concave and the sign is positive ($+$). If the ends of the lines curve toward the point of contact, the surface is convex and the sign is negative ($-$).

11 Remove flat B and place flat C on flat A, making the point of coincidence with the grease pencil.

12 Apply slight pressure at this point to show the interference lines.

13 Again use the thread for a reference and measure the fringe spacing. Multiply by 11.6 μin., determine the sign and label this value as y.

14 Repeat the procedure for flats B and C, labeling the result as 2.

15 Using the values for X, Y, and Z the deviation of the three flats may now be found by use of the formulas:

$$B = \frac{X - Y + Z}{2}, \quad A = X - B, C = Z - B$$

16 The signs of the results in Step 15 indicate whether the deviation is concave or convex.

FRINGE LINES

THREAD

GREASE MARK

Fig. 5-27   Fig. 5-28

17 By grouping all the flats of the set into groups of three, it is possible to find the one with the least deviation from flatness. This can be marked as the group standard.

18 The amount of deviation for each flat can be marked on the individual flat's case.

19 To show the necessity for a monochromatic light in the use of optical flats, replace the monochromatic light with an ordinary white light desk lamp.

20 Place a pair of optical flats under the lamp and apply pressure at one point to produce interference lines. A rainbow pattern should be observed. In order to use this pattern to measure flatness, only the bands of a particular color may be used. The obvious difficulty offered by this is at once apparent.

EXERCISE 2 Calibration of Gage Blocks*

MATERIAL REQUIRED

1 Certified reference (master) gage blocks

2 Optical flat

3 Monochromatic-light source

4 Deburring stone

5 Normalizing plate

6 Shallow pan

7 Camel hair brush

8 Cleaning solvent: trichloroethylene

9 Grain alcohol

10 Plastic-tipped forceps

11 Asbestos gloves

12 Cleveland micro a-c electronic micro comparator

13 Lintfree cloth or paper towels

14 Gage block set to be calibrated

PROCEDURE

1 Inspect the gage blocks to be calibrated for rough surfaces, nicks, or scratches.

2 If the blocks are free of roughness, wash them in the solvent. Wipe dry with the lintfree towel.

3 Carefully wring an optical flat over a gage block, and place under the monochromatic light.

4 If no fringe lines, or only very narrow ones, appear, brush the gage block with the camel hair brush.

5 If after brushing, broad fringe lines do not appear, rub the gage block firmly across a deburring stone until a tendency to stick or drag is sensed. Reclean as in Step 2, and again wring to the optical flat.

6 When the fringe lines are obtained, tilt the optical flat slightly against one edge of the gage block. This will cause the lines to appear parallel to the point of contact.

7 If the lines appear straight and evenly spaced, the gage block is flat in that direction.

8 If the lines appear curved (concave or convex) use a thread reference line to measure the deviation from flatness. Check to see whether the value is within the limits specified by the manufacturer.

* Based on calibration procedures as recommended by the Cleveland Instrument Company. (Courtesy of Cleveland Instrument Company.)

9 Apply contact pressure on an edge at right angles to that of Steps 6, 7, and 8. Measure the amount of deviation from flatness, parallel to this edge and compare with manufacturer's specifications.

10 Invert the gage block and check for flatness in both directions of the other side.

11 When the flatness of each block has been certified (excluding those of 0.100 in. or less) set the blocks next to the certified reference blocks on the normalizing plate. Allow a normalizing period of 1 hr per inch for each block.

12 Place the micro comparator close to the normalizing plate to lessen the handling of the blocks.

13 When moving blocks from the plate to the comparator, wear asbestos gloves and use the forceps.

14 Plug the amplifier power cable into an a-c outlet that provides the voltage and frequency specified on the side of the amplifier case.

15 Turn the RANGE SELECTOR switch to the LOW position, and allow 1 min for warmup.

16 Plug the gage head cable into the amplifier.

17 Place the two-rail anvil in the anvil holder with the lines parallel to the front of the stand.

18 Adjust the anvil so that the gage pin is several thousandths of an inch inside the rear rail. (See Fig. 5-29.)

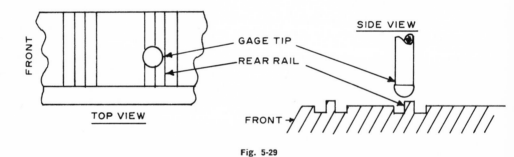

Fig. 5-29

19 Place a master gage block on the anvil.

20 Loosen the height adjustment lock and lower the gage head to the work surface by the height adjustment knob until the gage tip contacts the work as indicated by the meter hand coming on scale. Lock into position with the height adjustment lock knob.

CAUTION   To avoid "Brinnelling" of gage blocks, lower the gage head gently.

21 Turn the FINE POSITION ADJUSTMENT knob on the gage head to bring the meter hand to approximately the zero scale position. This knob provides a total adjustment range of about 0.050 in.

22 Set the range switch on the amplifier to the HIGH position.

23 Using the CENTERING knob on the amplifier, adjust the meter hand to zero.

24 Refer to the certification shunt for the master gage block.

25 Adjust the CENTERING knob on the amplifier until the meter indicates the amount of deviation as certified.

26 Remove the master block and insert the uncalibrated block.

27 Record the meter reading.

28 Repeat Steps 19 through 27 two more times.

29 Determine the average of the three readings.

30 Record this value on the calibration sheet for the uncalibrated gage blocks.

31 Repeat the calibration procedure for all the uncalibrated gage blocks.

EXERCISE 3 Calibrating the Micrometer

MATERIAL REQUIRED

1 Gage block set

2 Optical parallel

3 Laps

4 Micrometer

5 Monochromatic light

PROCEDURE

1 Insert the optical parallel between the spindle and anvil of the micrometer. Adjust the spindle only as much as needed to supply enough pressure to insure contact.

2 While holding under the monochromatic light, check the anvil and spindle for flatness, as indicated by straight, parallel fringe lines.

3 If either or both, the spindle or the anvil are not flat, insert laps between them and turn the spindle one full turn, increasing pressure on the laps. Remove the laps and clean the anvil and spindle.

4 Again check for flatness. If either is still not flat, repeat Step 3 until both are flat.

5 Close the spindle against the anvil but do not tighten it.

6 Check for a zero scale indication as in Fig. 5-30.

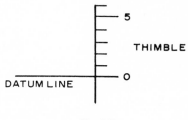

Fig. 5-30

7 If the zero does not align, remove the screw at the end of the thimble cap and set the micrometer to zero. Reset the screw in the cap.

8 Check the accuracy of the micrometer at the following points, using gage blocks, single or in wrung combination.

(a) 0.018 in.

(b) 0.076 in.

(c) 0.253 in.

(d) 0.587 in.

(e) 0.987 in.

Basic Electrical and Magnetic Test Equipment: Measurements and Calibration Techniques

6

Electromagnetic standards at all levels of use were discussed in Chapter 4. It was previously stated that these standards are employed on a world wide basis to insure that all units of measure are accurately referenced.

To maintain standards, however, is not enough in itself. It is necessary to have instruments which can "read" the dimensional units of the standard (volts, ohms, henrys, etc.) regardless of their nature.

Obviously, no instrument can "show" the value of a measurement without an indicating device of some sort. Furthermore, for an indication to be of value, all quantities must remain constant throughout the measurement process except that particular quantity being observed. To satisfy this condition, various precautions must be taken in the performance of a measurement or calibration procedure, as well as in the design of the instruments themselves.

This chapter is concerned with the procedures, devices, and indicators essential to the electrical measurements program, as well as the techniques for maintaining this equipment accurately referenced against the electromagnetic standards.

BASIC METERS

The basic indicating device in all current and voltage instruments is a galvanometer of one form or another. In general, this device uses the magnetic field of a current to produce a deflection proportional to the current.

TANGENT GALVANOMETER The tangent galvanometer is an *absolute instrument*. The primary structure is a circular coil of insulated wire of large radius as compared to the coil cross section (Fig. 6-1). A quartz fiber or small glass rod forms the vertical axis within the coil. A pointer is attached perpendicular to the suspension and moves over a scale graduated in degrees.

In use, the coil is placed vertically within a local magnetic field (usually the earth's magnetic field). When a current passes through the coil, the coil produces a magnetic field perpendicular to the local field, as shown in the figure. The pointer experiences a torque and moves to align itself with the resultant of the two fields.

The value of the current is calculated from the angular deflection:

$$I = \frac{10 \, Hr}{2 \, \pi \, n} \tan \theta \text{ amp}$$

where H is the horizontal component of the local magnetic field intensity (ampere turns/meter), r is the radius of the coil (meters), and n is the number of turns in the coil.

This instrument is suited to the absolute measurement of a steady single-valued current.

BALLISTIC GALVANOMETER The ballistic galvanometer shown in Fig. 6-2 is an extremely sensitive device particularly suited to the measurement of current impulses. A small coil is suspended within a local magnetic field provided by a permanent magnet. The suspension is a quartz fiber or small glass rod. The indicating device is a mirror, also suspended by the quartz fiber.

In use, the cover is placed over the instrument with the aperture directly in front of the mirror. A thin beam of light is focused on the mirror and is, in turn, reflected onto a circular scale, as shown by the solid line in Fig. 6-3. The center of the circular scale must be the axis of rotation of the mirror. When a current flows through the movable coil, the mirror is deflected slightly, and this deflection is greatly magnified by the reflection of the light beam (dotted line in the figure). A telescope is often employed in reading the circular scale.

The deflection may be magnified or reduced by moving the scale farther from, or closer to, the mirror. *However, the center of curvature for the scale must always be the axis of the mirror.*

The motion of the mirror is oscillatory. Thus, when a current impulse is measured, the initial maximum deflection, or *throw*, of the instrument is the desired reading. The quantity of electrical discharge through the coil is given by

$$Q = K\theta$$

where K is a constant determined by the particular instrument in use.

The ballistic galvanometer is not an absolute instrument and must, consequently, be calibrated before use. This is accomplished by passing a known charge through the instrument. This definite quantity of electricity is obtained by impressing a known voltage in a mutual inductor. The secondary winding of the inductor is placed in a series with the galvanometer, and the primary is in series with the voltage source. A typical arrangement appears in Fig. 6-4. A short tap of the key or sudden reversal of a double-throw switch causes the current impulse. The charge at the galvanometer is

$$Q = \frac{2MI}{R}$$

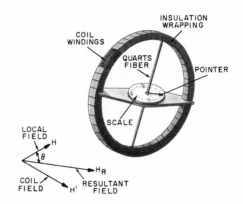

Fig. 6-1 Tangent galvanometer.

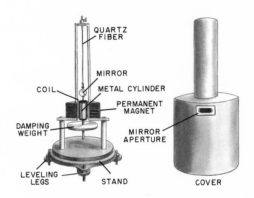

Fig. 6-2 Ballistic galvanometer.

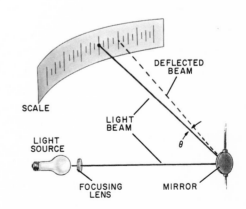

Fig. 6-3 Typical arrangement for reading the ballistic galvanometer.

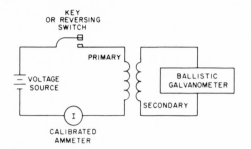

Fig. 6-4 Calibrating the ballistic galvanometer.

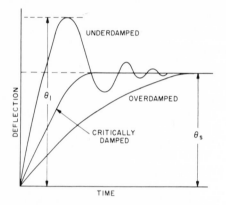

Fig. 6-5 Motion of galvanometer movement.

where M is the mutual inductance, I the current in the primary, and R the resistance of the secondary circuit. Since Q is also equal to $K\theta$,

$$K = \frac{2MI}{R\theta}$$

Ballistic galvanometers may also be used for accurately determining the flux of a magnetic field. In this application, some form of exploring coil structure must be used to "cut" the lines of flux and produce a proportional current impulse.

DAMPING   The deflection of a galvanometer may be oscillatory or nonoscillatory. The steady value is reached most quickly if the conditions are such that the motion is just becoming nonoscillatory. The instrument is

then said to be *critically damped*. The type of motion which is desired, however, depends upon the application involved.

The three types of motion associated with galvanometer movements are illustrated in Fig. 6-5. With underdamping the motion is oscillatory, having θ_1 as the first elongation, or throw, of the galvanometer, and θ_s is the steady deflection. For current impulses of very short duration, this motion is desirable. Here, θ_1 is the reading to be taken. Overdamped motion is a type of sluggish response and is usually undesirable. The motion of the critically damped meter is desirable in most applications because the instrument quickly reaches the steady value to be read and holds this value as long as it is present.

The type of motion is determined primarily by the resistance of the moving coil and its associated circuitry. The critical resistance for a particular instrument is given by the manufacturer. Thus, adjustments can be made in the external circuitry so that the critical resistance will exist if critical damping is desired.

SENSITIVITY

The current sensitivity of the ballistic galvanometer is given by

$$S_I = \frac{d}{r\ I_G}\ \text{mm/microampere}$$

where d is the scale deflection in millimeters, r is the radius of curvature of the scale in meters, and I_G is the current in microamperes. The unit of sensitivity is based on the deflection which would be obtained on a standard scale located *1 meter* from the mirror.

Voltage sensitivity is the deflection per unit voltage, or the current sensitivity divided by the critical resistance of the galvanometer circuit.

The mechanical sensitivity of the tangent and the ballistic galvanometer is such that wind, convection currents, and mechanical vibrations can entirely disrupt the validity of measurements. Hence, these instruments are usually found permanently installed in a calibration laboratory when used for minute measurements.

A Julius suspension, developed by Bell Telephone Laboratories, composed of triangular metal frames interconnected by springs, is used to reduce mechanical vibration. The galvonometer is clamped in a platform suspended by this arrangement.

D'ARSONVAL GALVANOMETER Most instruments that utilize direct current as a means of measuring electrical quantities use a moving-coil, or d'Arsonval, galvanometer as an indicating device. The original model was very similar to the ballistic galvanometer in structure. The present basic instrument is called the Weston movement—a rugged modification of the original.

Figure 6-6 shows the essential elements of the Weston galvanometer movement. A magnetic field is provided by the permanent magnet. Note that the moving coil itself is centered around a soft iron cylinder. The two are entirely encircled by the pole pieces of the permanent magnet. This provision produces a uniform magnetic field in the air gap at right angles to the coil regardless of the coil's angular position. Such a *radial* field makes a linear scale possible.

With no current flow, the pointer attached to the coil indicates zero on the calibrated scale. When current does flow, the field surrounding the coil interacts with the field of the magnet to produce a torque which rotates the coil. This turning action is opposed by the restraining spring. Eventually the current-produced torque and the restraining force balance, and the pointer indicates the value to be measured.

The uniformity of the radial field insures that the displacement of the coil is proportional to the torque, which in turn varies directly with the current. Thus a linear scale is obtained if the meter is calibrated for current or any quantity linearly related to current. If the meter is used as a null indicator, the zero graduation is in the center of the scale, and deflection to either side of zero may occur depending on current direction.

Critical damping is commonly employed in Weston movements.

Calibration of the Weston movement depends upon the type of instrument in which it is employed (ammeters, voltmeters, ohmmeters, impedance and frequency bridges, wave meters, etc.). For this reason, the calibration procedure is given in this manual in conjunction with the description of each applicable instrument.

A cheaper, less sensitive instrument employs a moving-iron plunger, as shown in Fig. 6-7, rather than the moving-coil arrangement. The pointer is attached to the plunger which moves until the magnetic torque is balanced by the restraining spring.

POTENTIOMETERS

Potentiometers are comparison devices. Essentially they are used to compare an unknown potential with a known or standard potential, although they may also be used in

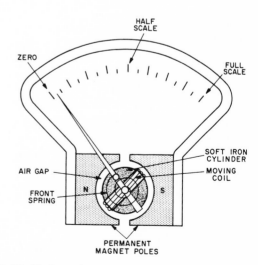

Fig. 6-6 Weston galvanometer movement.

current, resistance, impedance, and other comparisons. The principal advantage of a potentiometer is its ability to measure a small voltage without drawing power from the circuit being measured.

SLIDE-WIRE TYPE   The slide-wire potentiometer is the simplest form of potentiometer. Consideration of this device will provide a clear-cut understanding of the basic principle of operation of all potentiometers. The circuit for the slide-wire device is given in Fig. 6-8. The slide wire may be almost any wire of

known resistivity provided that its resistance at any point is determined by

$$R = \rho \ \frac{L}{A} \ \text{ohms}$$

where L is the length in centimeters, A is the cross-sectional area of the wire (cm^2), and ρ is the resistivity in ohms/cm.

The scale may be an ordinary meter stick graduated in millimeters, or it may be graduated directly in ohms by use of the equation preceding. It may also be graduated directly in volts since the slide wire should be uniform and the voltage along it, from Ohm's law, must also be uniform.

A known voltage must be impressed from A to B along the wire. To keep the current flow at a minimum, this voltage is usually set at 2 volts. This is accomplished by adjusting the calibration rheostat until the required value of current ($I = 2R_{AB}$) is read on the ammeter.

The polarity of the unknown voltage should be as marked in the figure. This arrangement predetermines that point A will represent zero. A differential current circulates in the right-hand loop when the key is closed. The galvanometer needle deflects from zero to show this. When the sliding contact is so placed that the potential along the slide wire is the same as the unknown

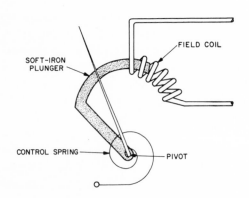

Fig. 6-7   Less-sensitive galvanometer movement.

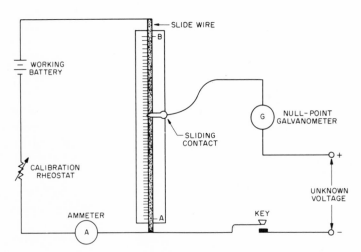

Fig. 6-8   Slide-wire potentiometer.

voltage, the circulating current ceases. This is shown by a zero reading on the galvanometer.

The key should not be depressed for long periods of time. If it is, heating effects will upset the resistivity and geometry of the slide wire.

The accurate application of this simple device presupposes that the slide wire and ammeter have been accurately calibrated. Resistance and ammeter calibration procedures are given in the next chapter. A standard cell may be connected across the unknown terminals to provide calibration of the potentiometer as a whole.

COMMERCIAL TYPES Commercial potentiometers are provided with many refinements in order to increase the accuracy and usefulness of the instruments. Protective devices, range multipliers, dial-type resistors (slide wires wound on circular forms), and built-in voltage standards are but a few of these improvements.

Laboratory potentiometers for general-purpose use read from 0 to 2 volts or from 0 to 1.5 volts in increments as small as 10 microvolts. Provisions are made for lower voltage ranges, although thermal effects often make it impossible to determine low values. Voltage dividers must be used when measuring higher voltages.

K-3 POTENTIOMETER The Leeds and Northrup Type K-3 Universal Potentiometer shown in Fig. 6-9 is one of the more advanced commercially available instruments. The K-3 is specifically designed to provide rapid readings with minimum interpolation error, measurements unaffected by thermal phenomena, and operation under difficult surrounding conditions without static or leakage disturbance.

The basic range of the instrument is from 0 to 1.61100 volts with two auxiliary ranges (one-tenth and one-hundredth of the basic range) provided. Standardization may be ac-

complished in any of the ranges with limits as follows:

high range: $\pm 0.01\% + 20 \, \mu v$
medium range: $\pm 0.015\% + 2 \, \mu v$
low range: $\pm 0.015\% + 0.5 \, \mu v$

Critical damping is obtained for a variety of null-indicating galvanometers by providing binding post connections for a critical damping resistance of 100, 400, 2000, or 10,000 ohms. Electronic null indicators may also be used.

In addition, the K-3 has the following features: a reversing switch for selecting either positive or negative unknown potentials without reversing the external leads; auxiliary terminals and switches for measuring different but related emf's; "guarding" to insure accurate operation in an atmosphere of as high as 90% relative humidity; and electrostatic shielding.

Working cells should be connected to the BA binding posts (7). Connect the standard cell to the SC binding posts (4), and set the SC dial (8) to the voltage indicated on the tag furnished with the cell. When this setting is made, the potentiometer readings will be in terms of the unit system (absolute, international, cgs, etc.) indicated on the cell tag. *Once set, the SC dial must not be disturbed.*

Connect the galvanometer between the 0 binding post and one of the other four galvanometer posts provided (5), selecting the post marked with a damping resistance value corresponding approximately to the external critical damping resistance specified for the galvanometer used. *Remove the link between posts 400 and 2000 when using posts 2000 and 10,000.* The 0 post is internally connected to + EMF if the REV key is not depressed.

If an electronic null detector is used, connect the side of the detector which is most highly insulated from its chassis to the 0 post on the potentiometer, and *do not use the REV key.*

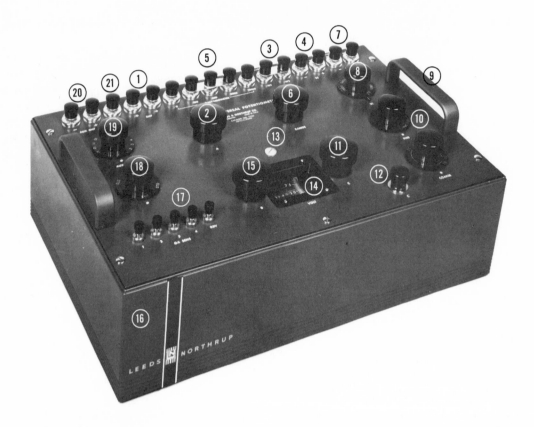

1.	EMF terminals	11.	Slide wire (C)
2.	15-position main dial switch (A)	12.	Slow motion drive for (C) (C')
3.	Galvanometer auxiliary terminals	13.	Potentiometer zero adjustment
4.	Standard cell terminals	14.	Central reading window
5.	Galvanometer damping terminals	15.	10-position decade switch (B)
6.	3-position range switch	16.	Extruded aluminum case
7.	Battery terminals	17.	Galvanometer sensitivity and reverse tap keys
8.	Standard cell dial	18.	EMF, standard cell switch
9.	Handle	19.	Auxiliary potentiometer switch
10.	Coarse and fine potentiometer current controls	20.	Auxiliary EMF terminals
		21.	Ground

Fig. 6-9 K-3 Potentiometer. (Courtesy, Leeds and Northrup.)

Connect the unknown emf (divided to a value less than 1.6 volts if necessary) between the binding posts marked EMF (1), observing polarity as marked when the polarity of the unknown potential is known.

Before the instrument is used, the current in the potentiometer must be standardized. After setting the SC dial to the cell voltage, turn the selector dial to either of its STD positions. While tapping GA SENS key 1,

adjust the COARSE dial, tapping key 1 after each step until a reversal of null current is indicated. Rotate the FINE dial to a slight overshoot of the null point; then turn the dial back to obtain a final, precise balance. Tap GA SENS key 1 after each small adjustment until only a very small deflection of the null indicator results. Then tap keys 2 to 4 in numerical succession, adjusting the FINE dial until there is no deflection when key 4 is tapped. Turn the selector dial back to EMF as soon as the standardizing adjustment has been completed.

During a series of measurements, it is advisable to check the potentiometer current occasionally and adjust it when necessary by repeating the foregoing procedure. *Do not disturb the settings of the FINE and COARSE dials until the next standardization.*

If the approximate magnitude of the emf to be measured is known, one of the three ranges can be selected accordingly by means of the RANGE knob. The range is indicated by the position of the decimal point in the digital reading. If the polarity of the emf is known to be reversed, set the selector dial to REV EMF. If the polarity and approximate value of emf are unknown, rotate the RANGE knob clockwise to the highest range and set the selector dial to EMF. Then proceed to obtain balance.

To obtain a preliminary balance, first rotate knobs A, B, and C to 1.5 $\times$ 99. Then turn knob A counterclockwise over its range of 15 steps, tapping GA SENS key 1 after each step, until the deflection of the null indicator reverses. *Then rotate knob A back one step*, and repeat the same procedure using knobs B and C in succession. When a reversal of deflection is obtained with knob B, turn this knob back one step and proceed to obtain final balance with knobs C and C′.

If a reversal of null deflection has not occurred when all knobs have been rotated over their full ranges, set the selector dial to REV EMF. Then repeat the foregoing procedure in reverse, rotating knobs C, B, and A, in succession, clockwise over their ranges. *This time however, when the first reversal of deflection occurs, rotate the particular knob being used back one step, and obtain final precise balance with knob C′.*

In some cases, when the highest range is used, it will be evident that a more accurate measurement can be made on a lower range. Adjust the knobs accordingly until the emf is indicated to the most significant figures

possible, and then obtain final balance with knobs C and C′.

When making final balance adjustments, first adjust knob C to an approximate balance point; then adjust knob C′ to obtain a final precise balance. Tap GA SENS key 1 after each small adjustment until only a very small deflection of the null indicator results. Then tap keys 2 to 4 in numerical succession, at the same time adjusting knob C′ until there is no deflection of the null indicator when key 4 is tapped.

Lock down tap key 4 by turning it slightly and tap the REV key. Adjust knob C′ until there is no deflection when the REV key is tapped. This use of the galvanometer reverse key, in effect, doubles the sensitivity of the null detector.

The measured emf value can be read quickly and easily from the single row of digits appearing in the window. The decimal point is properly positioned by the movement of the RANGE selector. The first two of the last three digits are read directly, and the third is interpolated from the scale divisions. Fig. 6-10A gives an example of a typical setting and the corresponding reading.

If the fourth digit in the window is replaced by an "X" as in Fig. 6-10B, consider the "X" as zero and numerically increase the preceding digit by "one." A direct reading for this value may be obtained, if desired, by rotating dials A and B one step clockwise unless the knobs are at the end of their particular range.

The C and C′ dials can be rotated with an overtravel of 10%, in which case the overlap scale markings (0 to 10) appear on a white background to distinguish them from the remainder of the scale values. To read such a setting, use the scale reading in the usual manner, and numerically increase the digit associated with dial B by "one." This is illustrated in Fig. 6-10C.

When using the K-3 to measure voltages higher than 1.6 volts (or related currents), voltage dividers, volt boxes, and current shunts must be used. These devices are discussed in the following sections.

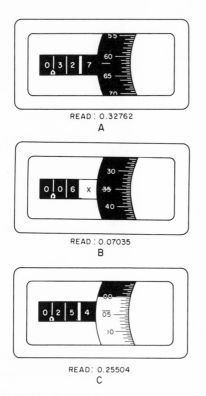

READ: 0.32762

A

READ: 0.07035

B

READ: 0.25504

C

Fig. 6-10 Reading the K-3 scale settings. The first three digits and the decimal point are associated with the RANGE and A dials. The fourth digit is associated with the B dial, and the last two digits with the C and C' dials. The white "over-ride" scale is shown in part C. (Courtesy, Leeds and Northrup.)

VOLTAGE DIVIDERS

Since the maximum voltage which can be handled by a precision potentiometer is from 1.5 to 2.0 volts, auxiliary devices must be used in order to compare higher voltages. Such an arrangement is a voltage divider—a resistor network which can be connected across the output terminals of a voltage source.

In operation, a voltage divider works in a manner similar to that of a slide-wire potentiometer—a definite voltage drop occurs across a uniform resistance. By "tapping" the resistance at various points, definite ratios of the total voltage can be obtained. Large resistances should be used in order to keep the current in the divider as low as possible.

In Fig. 6-11, a total of 40,000 ohms exists between terminal 0 and C. The potentiometer is placed across 400 ohms. Thus, the potentiometer will read 400/40000, or 0.01, times the voltage impressed at the terminals ($0.01 \times 200 = 2$ volts). Two other taps are provided so that a source of 100 volts and 50 volts may be used. The taps are arranged so that the ratio of 0.01 is maintained. Two other taps are provided so that a source of 100 volts and 50 volts may be used. The taps are arranged so that the ratio of 0.01 is maintained. Any voltage from 0 to 50 volts can be placed across terminals 0 and A, from 0 to 100 volts across terminals 0 and B, and

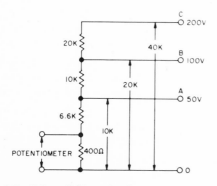

Fig. 6-11 Voltage-divider network.

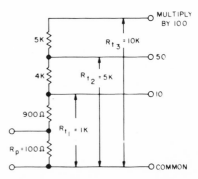

Fig. 6-12 Volt box arrangement.

from 0 to 200 volts across terminals 0 and C. Multiplying the potentiometer reading by 100 will always give the value of the unknown voltage.

An alternate divider network provides taps for various multiplication factors rather than various voltage ranges. This type is commonly employed in commercial devices called "volt boxes." The arrangement is shown in Fig. 6-12. The multiplication factor is given by R_{t_n}/R_p. The rating of the resistors and insulation used determines the maximum voltage which may be impressed on the box.

The resistors used in the construction of voltage dividers and volt boxes must be calibrated occasionally to insure their accuracy. A check of the instrument in its "cold" state and a check after it has had a voltage impressed upon it for a considerable time will show any variations due to temperature.

The fixed resistors may also be replaced by precision variable resistors.

VOLTAGE STANDARDIZER

The voltage standardizer is a voltage divider especially constructed to draw less than 100 microamp and provide a constant test voltage. A standard cell is placed across the terminals usually used for the potentiometer connections. Various multiples of the standard voltage then exist across the normal line terminals of the divider network.

CURRENT SHUNTS

Tangent and ballistic galvanometers, as well as the basic Weston movement, are limited as to the range of current values they can measure. However, just as the uniform potential drop along a series network of precision resistors can be tapped to provide voltage division, so can the Ohm's law shunting of current in a parallel network of resistors be utilized for current division.

Such a precision arrangement is called a "current *shunt*." Fig. 6-13 illustrates the prin-

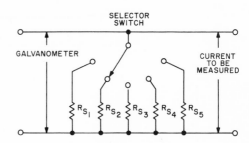

Fig. 6-13 Individual current shunts.

ciple involved. The current being measured will distribute itself between the galvanometer branch and the branch containing the individual shunt selected by the switch. From Ohm's law, the division will be such that the definite fraction of the total current given by

$$I_G = \left[\frac{R_{S_n}}{R_G + R_{S_n}} \right] I$$

will be measured by the galvanometer. The quantity in the brackets represents the *division factor* for the shunt.

In operation, the current reading of the galvanometer is multiplied by the reciprocal of this factor:

$$\frac{R_G + R_{S_n}}{R_{S_n}}$$

to obtain the value of the current being measured. Note that this multiplication factor is dependent on R_G—the resistance of the galvanometer and its associated leads. Thus, the multiplication factor for the individual shunts will change as different galvanometers are used. Since R_G and R_{S_n} are in parallel, the damping resistance will also change as different ranges are selected.

The universal shunt illustrated in Fig. 6-14 overcomes these disadvantages. To make the multiplying factor independent of R_G, a high shunt resistance, R_S, is placed in parallel with the galvanometer. The current being measured is fed into the parallel arrangement through a portion of this total resistance

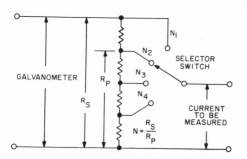

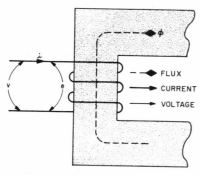

Fig. 6-14 Universal shunt. A large shunt resistance, R_s, stays in parallel with the galvanometer at all times, producing constant damping. The multiplying factor N is independent of R_G.

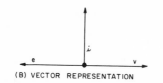

(A) DIAGRAMATIC REPRESENTATION

(B) VECTOR REPRESENTATION

Fig. 6-15 Basic transformer action.

as determined by setting of the selector switch. The value of the current being measured is given by

$$I = \frac{(R_G + R_S)\,N}{R_S}\,I_G$$

where I_G is the galvanometer reading. The multiplying factor is the quantity:

$$\left[\frac{R_G + R_S}{R_S}\right] N$$

The factor N is a *relative multiplying factor* which is dependent upon the position of the selector switch only. The ratio I_G/I remains the same regardless of the values of R_G and

R_S. Thus the relative multiplying factor can be marked on the shunt box and will remain fixed with any galvanometer connection. The factor surrounded by brackets in the preceding equation represents the effective damping resistance presented to the galvanometer. This factor will remain constant for a given galvanometer regardless of the value of N.

INSTRUMENT TRANSFORMERS

Transformers must be used in measuring high-voltage alternating quantities. They are also applicable as phase-shifting and impedance-matching devices in power measurements.

In operation, the ability of a transformer to transfer energy from its primary winding to its secondary winding through the magnetic flux linkages depends on a high mutual inductance between windings. This is provided by using a core of iron or steel or a special magnetic alloy.

Basic transformer action requires that a changing voltage be applied to the terminals of one winding, to produce a changing current flow through the winding. The voltage induced in the winding is called the "back emf" or "counter-emf" of the applied voltage. This back emf is equal to the negative (indicating a 180° phase reversal) of the applied emf and is related to the changing current by

$$-e = v = L\,\frac{di}{dt}\ \text{volts}$$

where L is the self-inductance of the winding in henrys.

The relationship above is shown diagrammatically and vectorially by Fig. 6-15. Applying the right-hand rule* to the winding in this figure reveals that flux will flow in the

---

* Right-hand rule: by grasping an inductor in the right hand with the fingers curled around the inductor in the direction of current flow, the extended thumb points in the direction of flux movement. The flux, of course, flows from the so-called north pole to the south pole.

direction shown. The current i lags the applied voltage by 90°.

Faraday's law gives a second relationship for defining the induced emf:

$$e = -N \frac{d\phi}{dt} \text{ volts}$$

where N is the number of turns in the winding and ϕ is the flux in webers. If the flux is sinusoidal, $\phi = \phi_{max} \sin \omega t$ and from Faraday's law:

$$e = -N\phi_{max} \omega \cos \omega t$$

which shows a 90° relationship between the flux and the applied voltage. Since the flux is produced by the ampere turns of the winding, it is in phase with the current—leading the induced emf by 90° and lagging the applied emf by 90°.

The equation just given is an expression for the instantaneous induced voltage. Since it is sinusoidal, it may be converted to the effective (r-m-s) value by multiplying by $\sqrt{2}$ and dropping the cos ωt ($\omega = 2\pi f$) factor:

$$E = \frac{2\pi f N \phi_{max}}{\sqrt{2}} = 4.44 \ f N \phi_{max}$$

This equation shows that transformer action is frequency dependent—a fact which must be considered when using transformers for precision measurements. The equation is known as the *transformer equation* and may be generalized for any a-c waveshape by writing it in the form:

$$E = 4KfN\phi_{max}$$

Where K is a constant known as the *form factor* of the voltage waveshape:

$$K = \text{form factor} = \frac{\text{r-m-s value}}{\text{average value}}$$

For the sine wave, $K = 1.11$.

The foregoing theoretical development assumes that the transformer is a "perfect" piece of equipment, with all the flux confined within the core material and no power taken from the exciting current. The assumption may approach reality but usually is not

completely true. Some flux "leaks out" of the winding as illustrated in Fig. 6-16A. Both windings also have a certain amount of d-c resistance, which causes a power loss when the exciting current flows. Other power losses occur because of hysteresis effects and eddy currents in the core material.

It is desirable to develop an equivalent electrical network for the transformer winding which would allow perfect energy transfer from primary to secondary and represent flux and power losses by external resistors and inductors. The first step in doing this is shown in Fig. 6-16B. The series resistance (R) and the reactance $(X = 2\pi fL)$ represent the d-c winding resistance and the leakage reactance, respectively.

Fig. 6-16C gives the complete transformer equivalent circuit. The parallel network shown in the primary represents all the actions which occur in the "imperfect" transformer cone, leaving a perfect transformer as shown. R_o is a resistance of such value that its power loss represents the power losses of the core due to hysteresis and eddy-current effects. The reactance, $X_o = 2\pi fL_o$, represents the working reactance of the transformer which stores energy and accounts for the energy transfer from primary to secondary. The windings $(N_1:N_2)$ are shown as perfect inductors capable of unimpeded energy transfer. The two currents flowing in the parallel arrangement are the current which must produce the d-c power loss (I_p) and the excitation current (I_{ex}). V_1 and V_2 are the input and output voltages respectively, and E_1 and E_2 are the voltages induced in the perfect windings.

For ideal windings, the ampere turns (magnetizing force) of the primary must equal the ampere turns of the secondary:

$$N_1 I_1 = N_2 I_2$$

This can be further extended to induced voltages by application of Faraday's law to yield

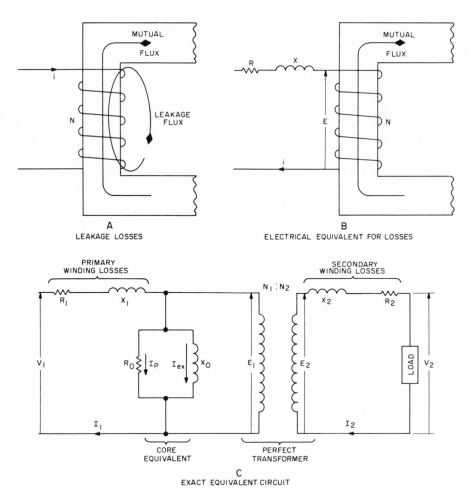

Fig. 6-16 Development of the equivalent transformer.

$$\frac{E_1}{E_2} = \frac{N_1}{N_2}$$

In analyzing circuits containing transformers, it is more convenient to "reflect" the secondary parameters into the primary circuit. This reflection is based on the foregoing equation for voltage, current, and turns ratio (N_1/N_2) and also on the fact that the power in the primary and secondary windings must be the same. The completed equivalent circuit is shown in Fig. 6-17A. The conversion factors for reflecting secondary parameters into the primary circuit

are given in Table 6-1. Figure 6-17B shows the vector relationships. In constructing the phasor diagram, the output voltage, or voltage across the load (aV_2), is taken as a reference. The secondary current $(-I_2/a)$ is constructed at its angle β with respect to the reference. The voltage drop across R_2 is in phase with $-I_2/a$. The drop across X_2 leads this drop by 90°. The vector sum of the three phasors $(aV_2,\ V_{R_2},\ \text{and}\ V_{X_2})$ represents aE_2, which is also $-E_1$. This induced voltage leads aV_2 by ρ. The flux and, therefore, the excitation current (I_{ex}) lag $-E_1$ by 90°. The current I_p is in phase

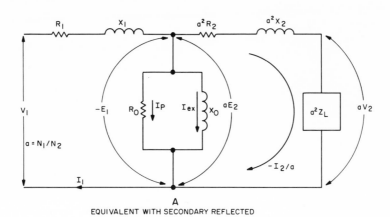

A
EQUIVALENT WITH SECONDARY REFLECTED

B
VECTOR RELATIONSHIPS

Fig. 6-17 Transformer analysis.

with $-E_1$. The vector sum of these two currents and $-I_2/a$ yields I_1, which lags aV_2 by $\triangle$. The drop across R_1 is in phase with I_1, whereas the drop across X_1 leads I_1 by 90°. The vector sum of $-E_1$, V_{R1}, and V_{x1} gives the applied voltage V_1. In this case V_1 leads V_2 by γ. Leading and lagging angles, however, vary with the load.

From this analysis, it can be seen that V_1 and V_2 are not 180° out of phase, as would be expected with a transformer having secondary and primary windings wound in opposite directions. With windings in the same direction, the ideal transformer would

Table 6-1 Reflection of Secondary Parameters Into Primary

Quantity	Multiply by
R_2	a^2
X_2	a^2
Z_L	a^2
Any voltage	a*
Any current	$\dfrac{1}{a}$

$$*a = \frac{N_1}{N_2}$$

have no phase reversal between V_1 and V_2 ($E_2 = E_1$ instead of $E_2 = -E_1$). That this is not exactly true can also be shown with the equivalent circuit.

A
1200 VOLTS, 100 : 5 AMPS

B
600 VOLTS, 200 : 5 AMPS

C
600 VOLTS, 3000 : 5 AMPS

D
15 - KILOVOLT MODEL

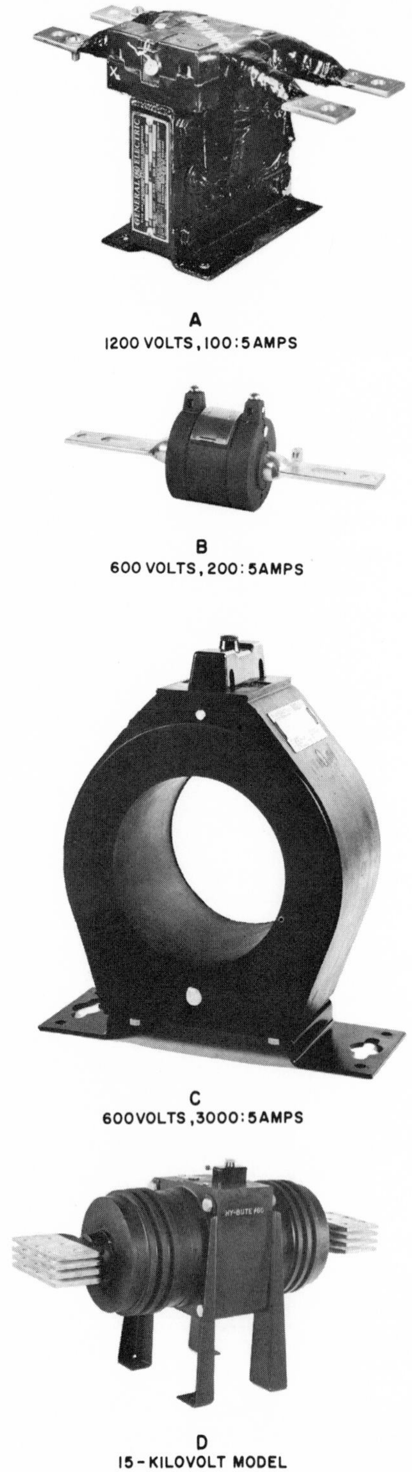

Fig. 6-18 Typical current transformers. (Courtesy, General Electric.)

The phasor diagram is not drawn to scale. The magnitudes of voltages and currents are dependent on circuit conditions. The load is shown to be the primary factor upon which the analysis is based. For this reason, all analyses and all determinations of values for dependent parameters must be made with the load to be used in actual practice.

Transformer cores sometimes maintain a residual magnetism after continuous use. Demagnetization may be accomplished by placing a very large (several megohms) variable resistance across the secondary. While full current is being passed through the primary, gradually decrease the secondary resistance to zero in as uniform a manner as possible. This decreases the magnetization from a very high value to its normal value slowly enough so as to not disrupt the magnetic properties of the core.

CURRENT TRANSFORMERS   Several current transformers are shown in Fig. 6-18. The design configuration is dependent on ap-

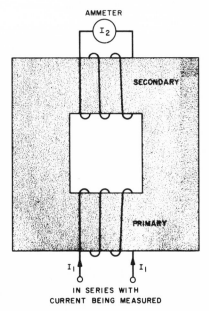

AMMETER

I_2

SECONDARY

PRIMARY

I_1 I_1

IN SERIES WITH
CURRENT BEING MEASURED

Fig. 6-19 Use of current transformer.

plication, ratings, core materials, and a number of other variables.

The method of connecting a current transformer into a circuit is shown in Fig. 6-19. *When a transformer is being operated, the secondary circuit must always be kept closed.* Failure to keep the secondary circuit closed will result in excessive flux, appreciable iron losses, and overheating to such an extent that a moderate voltage may puncture the insulation. The primary is placed in series with the current branch being measured. The magnitude of the primary current is given by

$$I_1 = I_2 a$$

The turns ratio can be determined quickly with two d-c currents as shown in Fig. 6-20. The arrangement shown places the two variable resistors in parallel. When the resistors are adjusted so that the current through the galvanometer circuit is zero:

$$\frac{I_2}{I_1} = \frac{R_p}{R_s} = \frac{N_1}{N_2} = a$$

When two alternating currents are used, the resistors must be noninductive. The currents must also have the same frequency and waveform and must have a fixed phase difference. As discussed previously, losses produce a phase difference between applied and output voltages (and, therefore, currents). By using alternating currents in the turns ratio test, the inherent phase shift in the current transformer (β in Fig. 6-17B) may be found. For this determination, the circuit in Fig. 6-20 is altered to produce the potentiometer-like arrangement in Fig. 6-21. All resistors should be noninductive. Resistances r_p and r_s are on the order of 500 ohms overall, and C is a variable capacitor of about $1\,\mu f$. The turns ratio is given by

$$a = \frac{R_s(R_p + r_p)}{R_p(R_s + r_s)\sqrt{1 + \omega^2 r_p^2 C^2}}$$

and the phase angle by

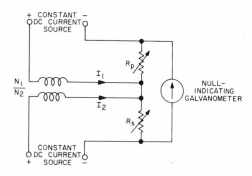

Fig. 6-20 D-c method for determining transformer turns ratio.

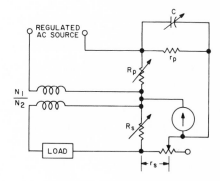

Fig. 6-21 A-c method for determining turns ratio and phase difference.

$$\tan\,(\Delta - \gamma) = \omega C r_p = (\Delta - \gamma)\;\text{radians}$$

It is advisable to plot two sets of characteristic curves for commonly used instrument transformers. These two sets are given in Fig. 6-22. One set is the ratio-correction-factor (rcf) curves. The manufacturer marks a turns ratio on all transformers. An rcf curve gives the ratio by which the marked turns ratio must be multiplied in order to get the true ratio for various power factors. The set consists of curves for different percentages of rated current for the transformer.

The second set of curves is the phase-angle curve showing the angle between I_1 and I_2 at various power factors and percentages of rated current.

Reference to these curves saves valuable time in using instrument transformers. The apparatus for checking angle and ratio can

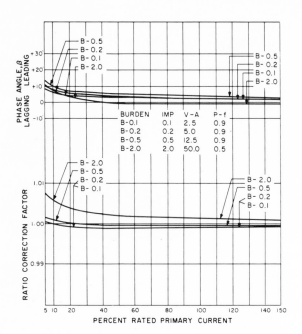

Fig. 6-22 Current transformer correction curves. The angle β indicated is illustrated in Fig. 6-17. (Courtesy, General Electric.)

BURDEN	IMP	V-A	P-f
B-0.1	0.1	2.5	0.9
B-0.2	0.2	5.0	0.9
B-0.5	0.5	12.5	0.9
B-2.0	2.0	50.0	0.5

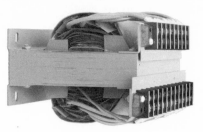

A
VARIABLE – VOLTAGE

B
UNFUSED

C
FUSED

(A) ADDING SECONDARY TURNS

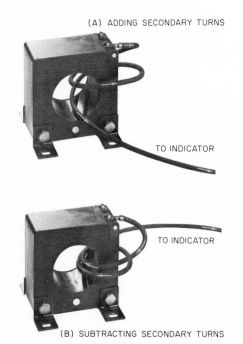

TO INDICATOR

TO INDICATOR

(B) SUBTRACTING SECONDARY TURNS

D
THREE – PHASE

Fig. 6-23. Varying secondary turns. The number added or subtracted is the number of times the conductor actually passes through the window. In either case, the other secondary terminal should go directly to the indicating device. The arrows indicate the direction of conventional flow. (Courtesy, General Electric.)

Fig. 6-24 Typical potential transformers. Various voltages are obtained from the model in (A) by tapping the winding with a sequence of terminals, each providing an additional quarter volt. (Part A, Courtesy, Nothelfer Winding Laboratories, Inc.; others, Courtesy, General Electric.)

be set up occasionally to insure that the transformer characteristics have not deviated from those represented by the original set of curves.

VARIABLE-RATIO CURRENT TRANSFORMERS[*]

The window type of current transformer illustrated in Fig. 6-23 can be utilized as a variable turns-ratio transformer. The turns ratio is varied by (1) looping the primary cable through the transformer window, (2) looping the conductor used to connect the secondary winding to the indicating device through the window.

Primary turns *can be added by* looping the primary cable through the transformer window. To calculate the exact number of turns, count the number of times the primary cable actually passes through the window.

Secondary turns can be added or subtracted by changing the direction in which the secondary conductor passes through the transformer window. This is shown in Fig. 6-23.

Primary and secondary conductors should not come in contact.

POTENTIAL TRANSFORMERS When the potential transformer is used the voltage actually measured is given by

$$V_1 = aV_2$$

The transformer is connected as shown in Fig. 6-25, with the primary in parallel with the voltage being measured.

It should be noticed that the voltages just designated are terminal voltages, not induced voltages E_1 and E_2. The actual turns ratio given by $E_1/E_2 = N_1/N_2$ is of lesser importance here than the working turns ratio:

$$\frac{V_1}{V_2} = \frac{N_1}{N_2}$$

By once more consulting Fig. 6-17, it can be seen that this turns ratio may be con-

*General Electric *Apparatus Handbook*, Sec. 7930, p. 143.

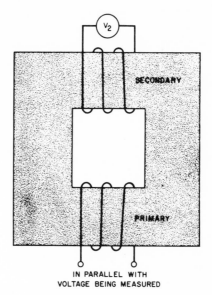

Fig. 6-25 Use of potential transformers.

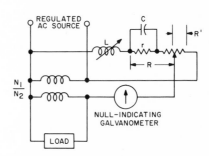

Fig. 6-26 Method for determining turns ratio and phase angle of potential transformers.

siderably different from the actual turns ratio, since certain potential drops will occur in the primary and secondary resistances and reactances.

An absolute method for determining the working turns ratio and the phase angle between V_1 and V_2 is given in Fig. 6-26. In using this method, the galvanometer tap is moved until a null is approached; then inductor L is varied to obtain a true null reading. The working turns ratio is then given by

$$\frac{V_1}{V_2} = \frac{R + R'}{R}$$

and the phase angle between V_1 and V_2 (angle γ in Fig. 6-17) by

$$\sin \gamma = \omega(L - Cr^2)\left(\frac{1}{R'} - \frac{1}{R + R'}\right)$$

Correction factor and phase angle curves for the potential transformer are shown in Fig. 6-27.

VOLTAGE AND CURRENT SOURCES

Calibration, as well as many other electric measurement processes, requires that some form of excitation be applied to the equipment under test. This excitation consists of a stable voltage or current which may be modulated or unmodulated.

For calibration, the most reliable sources of direct current and voltage are the various types of storage batteries and cells already discussed. When such a source is used with appropriate divider and multiplier networks, almost any range of values may be obtained.

The production of alternating currents and voltages of required stability creates a multitude of technical problems. These problems arise from the inherent transient and random nature of any variable waveform. The inherent inconsistencies are further complicated by practical design considerations, such as tuning over a wide frequency range, modulation processes, freedom from harmonics, and constancy of output amplitude over the entire frequency range. The ever-increasing need for reliable and more accurate sources has resulted in many technological advancements in this particular field.

Before proceeding with a discussion of alternating waveforms, it is necessary to classify the different frequencies into general categories. This will facilitate the subsequent classification of equipment and associated problems. Table 6-2 gives the classification which will be used throughout this manual.

Table 6-2 Frequency Classification of Alternating Waves

Category	Frequency limits	Transmission medium
VLF	3 kc–30 kc	Open wires
LF	30 kc–300 kc	Open wires
MF	300 kc–3 mc	Open wires
HF	3 mc–30 mc	Open wires
VHF	30 mc–300 mc	Open wires and co-axial lines
UHF	300 mc–3 kmc	Open wires, coaxial lines, and wave-guides
SHF	3 kmc–30 kmc	Waveguides
EHF	30 kmc–300 kmc	Waveguides

The VLF through VHF categories are generally classified as *radio frequencies*, and the UHF, SHF, and EHF categories, as *microwave frequencies*. The UHF category is subdivided into the P, L, and S bands of frequencies, and the SHF category is subdivided into the X and K bands. The term *audio frequencies* generally applies to waveforms having an upper frequency limit of 20 kc, although the actual *hearing range* of a human being stops well below this limit.

MODULATION   *Modulation* is the process by which some property of an r-f signal is varied in accordance with intelligence to be transmitted. In *amplitude modulation* the

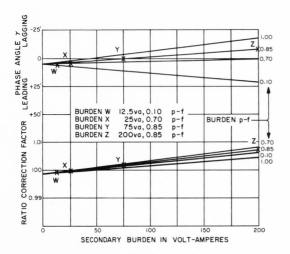

Fig. 6-27 Potential transformer correction curves. The angle γ is shown in Fig. 6-17. (Courtesy, General Electric.)

amplitude of the signal is varied, as the name suggests. Similarly, the instantaneous frequency of an r-f signal is varied in *frequency modulation*, and the phase is varied in *phase modulation*.

For transmitter and receiver tests, it is necessary to have a reliable modulated test waveform. For this reason, most laboratory r-f oscillators are provided with some form of amplitude or frequency modulation. Sine-wave and pulse-amplitude modulation are common for tests of normal voice equipment and newer pulse communication equipment. Sine-wave frequency modulation is employed to simulate voice fm systems.

A second form of frequency modulation is employed in special r-f generators known as *sweep-frequency oscillators*. Here, the modulating frequency is very low, and the frequency deviation (limits of the band swept through) is very large. For example, an oscillator may range back and forth over a band of 20 kc at a rate of 60 complete sweeps per second. The 20-kc band is equivalent to a deviation of $\pm$ 10 kc about a central frequency, and the 60-cycle sweep rate is the modulating frequency.

Laboratory oscillators are usually arranged so that the modulation is produced by internal circuitry. Provisions for the use of external modulation signals are also made.

Voltages ranging as high as 100 volts or more exist within the circuitry of r-f oscillators. The output, however, is usually only a few microvolts. The strong fields set up by the large internal potentials must not interfere with the *working* output potential.

Electric and magnetic r-f fields can also originate from external sources—natural phenomena and man-made devices.

Electromagnetic shielding is accomplished by using good conductors, such as copper or aluminum. The ratio of field strengths on both sides of the conductor is given by

$$\text{ratio} = 1.31 \, a \, \sqrt{f\gamma} \; db$$

where a is shield thickness in centimeters,

f is field frequency in cps, and γ is the relative conductivity of the shield conductor.

Ideally, a completely closed metal box would have characteristics approaching a perfect shielding device. But the use of such a box is not practical. Shafts for making adjustments, input and output leads, and access ports must be used in all equipment. Each of these represents an imperfection in the shield.

Leads passing through shield walls have resistance-capacitance filters to bypass leakage r-f energy to ground. Shaft ends are covered with a knob having a metal insert directly in contact with the shield material. Access lids are generally composed of a layer of insulation "sandwiched" between two conducting layers, both of which are in contact with their respective sides of the shield.

The existence of leakage fields can be determined by exploration with a coil of 4 or 5 turns connected to a sensitive-receiver input. For this check, turn the laboratory oscillator being tested to its smallest possible output voltage, and short the output terminals. There should be negligible pickup by the receiver exploring coil. This coil-receiver arrangement can also be used to determine the existence of external interference fields.

External fields are best eliminated by using a *screen room* for the tests or calibrations involved. Such a room is constructed of copper or aluminum screening (or sheets). All power leads into the room have appropriate r-f filters attached. All doors, hatches, vents, etc., also have special shielding precautions taken in their design and construction.

REGULATED POWER SUPPLIES Because of their good frequency control, convenience and economy, modern public utility 60-cycle a-c power lines serve as the primary power source for most equipment. Direct-current voltages are obtained from this source by the use of rectifiers.

Rectifiers may be used to supply voltages

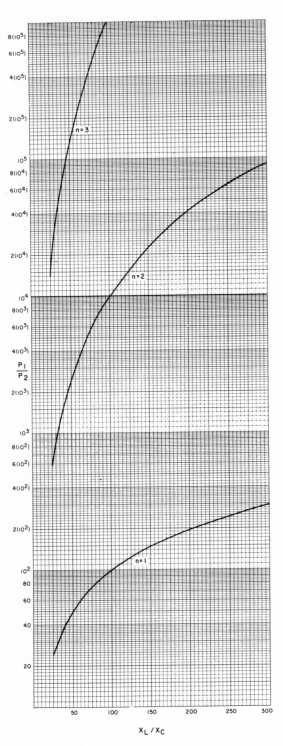

Fig. 6-28 Inductor-input filter performance characteristics.

up to, and above, 200 kilovolts. For this reason, *operators should observe all safety precautions at all times. Only one hand should be used to make internal adjustments.*

Rectified d-c has a pulsating or ripple waveform. Filters must be used to smooth this ripple to the degree of smoothness required by the application.

Single-stage or multiple-stage inductor-input filters have the relative performance characteristics shown in Fig. 6-28. In this figure, P_1 is the percent ripple without filtering and P_2 is the percent ripple after filtering. The curves are a plot of

$$\frac{P_1}{P_2} = \frac{(X_L - X_C)\,n}{X_C}$$

where n is the number of identical stages and X_L and X_C are the reactances of the components in one stage.

Capacitor-input filters provide more economical operation because the rectifier conducts only during a small portion of each input cycle. During the voltage peaks of each cycle, the capacitor charges, drawing current from the rectifier. During the rest of the cycle, no current is drawn—instead, the capacitor discharges into the load. This is illustrated in Fig. 6-29.

The actual output of capacitor-input filter is very difficult to predict on a theoretical basis. Operation is dependent on the capacitance value, the supply frequency, the load resistance, and the internal rectifier resistance. The best design procedure makes use of trial and error to achieve the desired results.

In many instances, a constant or nearly constant voltage amplitude is desired from the rectifier. For comparison, *regulation* is defined by the equation:

$$\% \text{ voltage regulation} = \frac{V_{\text{no load}} - V_{\text{specified load}}}{V_{\text{specified load}}}$$

Gas-filled tubes in parallel with the load provide a means of obtaining a high-current, regulated voltage, because the voltage drop across an ionized gas tube is very nearly

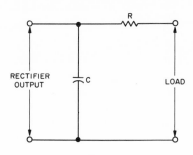

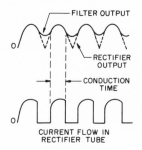

Fig. 6-29 Capacitor-input filter and waveforms.

constant. The d-c voltage, however, will be of a relatively low magnitude.

FREQUENCY MULTIPLIERS AND DIVIDERS A large number of electronic circuits are inherently nonlinear, or can be forced to be nonlinear in their operating characteristics. An application of this nonlinearity is employed in frequency division and multiplication circuits. Frequency multiplication is accomplished by producing oscillations rich in harmonics and then filtering out all but the desired frequency. The frequency division process utilizes submultiples of the fundamental frequency.

Any R-C oscillator can be used to produce oscillations which are a submultiple of some reference frequency. This is accomplished by *locking* the R-C device to the control signal as shown in Fig. 6-30. With such a system, high frequencies can be stepped down to frequencies as low as 1 cps.

If pulses are added to the timing waveform of an astable or monostable multivibrator, the circuit operation can be locked to some submultiple of the synchronizing frequency. The superposition of these pulses on the timing waveform is shown in Fig. 6-31. The amplitude of the pulses is given by

$$E_t = \frac{2\,(E_i - E_c)}{2\,N + 1}\ \text{volts}$$

where E_i and E_c are the peak timing wave voltage and grid bias voltages, respectively, and N is the division factor (number of pulses introduced). Variations in the feed-

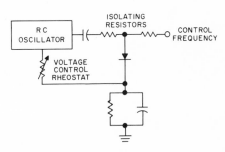

Fig. 6-30 R-c frequency divider.

Fig. 6-31 Timing waveforms for multivibrator frequency divider.

back resistors and capacitors will change E_i so that the circuit must be checked occasionally for continuous operation as a divider.

A triggered blocking oscillator can be very easily adapted to produce an output which is a submultiple of the input. This is accomplished by setting the variable cathode resistor so that a desired number of input pulses (N) must add together before the grid will go above cutoff and produce an oscillation. The number N is the division factor.

Since a multivibrator output is rectangular in shape, it is very rich in harmonic con-

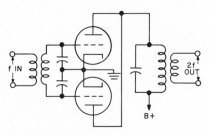

(A) FREQUENCY DOUBLER

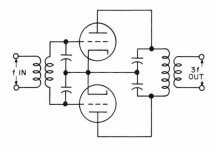

(B) FREQUENCY TRIPLER

Fig. 6-32 Class C R-f frequency multipliers.

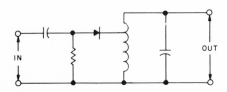

Fig. 6-33 Diode frequency multiplier.

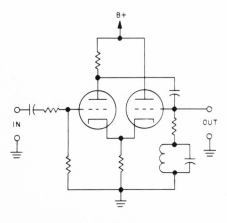

Fig. 6-34 Frequency multiplier-divider circuit.

tent. This is explained mathematically in Appendix D-3. Filters tuned to the desired harmonic will leave only the required output frequency. Multivibrators are extensively used for this purpose up to a fundamental operating frequency of 1 mc.

Above 1 mc, Class C oscillators are generally used for frequency multiplication, since their outputs are also rich in harmonics. The plate circuit is tuned to the desired harmonics. The tube is biased well below cutoff, and a large amplitude r-f input voltage is used to obtain the short tube conduction angle necessary for the high harmonic content in the plate circuit. Figure 6-32 shows a Class C–operated frequency doubler and tripler. These circuits are commonly used to produce microwave frequencies from radio frequencies.

Semiconductor diodes can be used over the same frequency ranges as Class C oscillators. Their output magnitude is low, although multiplication factors of from 3 to 5 are practical. The tank circuit in Fig. 6-33 is tuned to the desired harmonic frequency.

An oscillator which will divide and multiply the input frequency is shown in Fig. 6-34. The tank circuit is tuned to the desired output frequency. This circuit is not limited to integral multiples and submultiples of the input frequency. It will also produce fractional multiples, such as $\frac{3}{2}$ and $\frac{2}{3}$.

MAGNETIC FLUX MEASUREMENTS

Magnetic measurement cannot be made by the simple process of inserting the leads on an instrument into a magnetic circuit as the leads of voltmeters and ammeters are placed in electrical circuits. For such measurements, fundamental physical principles of the interrelation between electrical currents and magnetic fields are utilized in a variety of ways.

BALLISTIC GALVANOMETER It was shown at the beginning of this chapter that the deflection of a ballistic galvanometer is directly proportional to the electrical charge flowing through the galvanometer. Since charge and flux are related by a constant of proportionality, the deflection is a measure of the flux, as indicated by the relation:

$$\phi = K\theta \text{ webers}$$

where ϕ is the flux, K is a constant dependent upon construction of galvanometer, and θ is the galvanometer deflection.

Calibration of the instrument for magnetic measurements can be accomplished by determining the value of K. The circuit arrangement for this determination is shown in Fig. 6-35. Initially, switch number 1 is open and switch number 2 is closed. This allows the flux of the standard solenoid to build up to a steady value without damaging the galvanometer. The solenoid current is adjusted to any desired value. Switch number 1 is closed and the deflection of the galvanometer is read. The value of the constant is then given by the equation:

$$K = \frac{N_1 N_2 I A 10^2}{R\theta}$$

where N_1 is the number of turns/meter of the standard solenoid, N_2 is the total number of turns of the exploring coil, I is the solenoid current in amperes, A is the cross-sectional area of the solenoid in square meters, R is the total resistance of the galvanometer-exploring coil circuit, and θ is the deflection in meters.

Once this constant has been evaluated, the galvanometer may be used to make flux measurements by arranging it and the specimen under test as shown in Fig. 6-36. The coils are wrapped about the test specimen. The exciting current, and therefore the flux, is controlled by the rheostat. After desired steady conditions are reached, the switch in the galvanometer circuit is closed and the reading for θ in meters is taken. The flux can then be computed by the galvanometer equation given previously. *It must be re-*

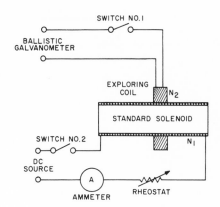

Fig. 6-35 Constant determination for magnetic measurements.

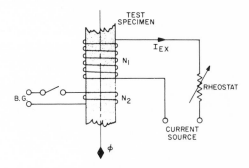

Fig. 6-36 Flux measurement with ballistic galvanometer.

membered that the actual value of flux in the specimen is inversely proportional to N_2. Thus the equation for calculating flux more appropriately becomes

$$\phi = \frac{K\theta}{N_2} \text{ webers}$$

GAUSSMETER A gaussmeter is an instrument that provides direct readings of *flux density*. It is used to measure the fields of ordinarily inaccessible air gaps.

Figure 6-37 shows a gaussmeter particularly adapted to the problem of small air gaps. The essential parts are a long, thin shaft, upper and lower jewel bearings, a control spring, a pointer and calibrated scale, and a small cylindrical magnet attached to

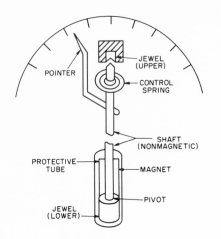

Fig. 6-37 Basic gaussmeter.

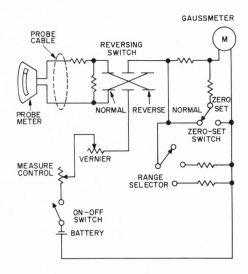

Fig. 6-38 Typical fluxmeter circuit.

the lower jewel by a pivot. Protruding from the back of the instrument, the magnet and lower jewel assembly are protected by a thin-walled tube. At the center of the assembly is the shaft, which extends up through the instrument and terminates at the upper jewel. Obviously, this construction results in a moving system, with the protrusion in the rear acting as a probe suitable for insertion within a magnetic field. Diameters of the probe are made in the range of

0.052 in. to 0.090 in., and probe lengths are available from 1¼ to 5 in. To offset the magnetizing influence of the various fields to be measured, the cylindrical magnet is made of highly coercive material. This property keeps the flux density of the magnet high and substantially constant, whether in the presence of external fields or not. When the probe is placed within an air gap, the interaction between the field of the magnet and that of the gap produces a torque which turns the shaft against the opposing action of the control spring. The instrument case must be rotated until the positive deflection of the meter is maximum. In this position, the probe magnet is perpendicular to the external field, and the scale reading provides a true measurement directly in gausses. The instrument is constructed so that the pointer indicates the direction of external field when the case is rotated to a zero-reading position.

FLUXMETER Instruments known as fluxmeters operate on a different principle. The primary components are a meter calibrated directly in gausses (maxwells/cm²), a second meter that is used as a probe, an internal battery, and various resistances and potentiometers. Figure 6-38 shows a representative circuit. Note that the probe meter is in series with the gaussmeter and a measuring control, R_1 (various shunting resistors for changing ranges may be switched in or out). It follows that all or a known fraction of the current flowing through the probe meter passes through the gaussmeter. Although the gaussmeter is a conventional moving-coil type, the probe meter departs from this construction in one important respect. It lacks completely an internal magnet and pole pieces. Otherwise, the probe meter is like any conventional moving-coil meter. No reading will be obtained, therefore, unless a magnetic field is supplied from some external source. Clamps are provided to hold the meter in a position that maintains the field at right angles to the coil—the same relationship that exists when pole pieces are included. Now if current is passed through the moving coil, the coil will rotate in accordance with the amount of the current and the strength of the magnetic field. To produce a standard deflection, less current is necessitated when the field strength is high. It is on this principle that operation of the device is based. Regardless of the magnetic field, the amount of current flowing in the probe meter is adjusted by means of the measuring control so that standard deflection is produced. If the field strength is high, relatively little current is needed, and the corresponding deflection of the gaussmeter is small. If the field strength is low, more current must flow through the probe meter to produce the standard deflection, and the corresponding deflection of the gaussmeter is great. Thus the deflection of the gaussmeter is a measure of field density —small deflections indicating relatively large field strengths.

Fluxmeters and gaussmeters may be calibrated by inserting the probe into the air core of a standard solenoid.

QUESTIONS

1 Describe the operation of a tangent galvanometer.

2 How is a ballistic galvanometer usually damped for short current pulse measurements?

3 What is the general method used for calibrating a gaussmeter or a fluxmeter?

4 What is meant by the term, variable ratio current transformer?

PROBLEMS

1 If 36 gage nichrome wire which has a cross-sectional area of 25 circular mils is used to construct a slide-wire potentiometer similar to that shown in Fig. 6-8, what is the resistance per foot of the wire?

2 If the slide-wire potentiometer described in Question 1 is exactly 3 ft long, and has a voltage of 2 volts across it, what is the amount of current in the slide wire?

3 What is the resistance per inch of the slide-wire potentiometer of Question 1?

4 If a voltage of 1.665 volts is impressed across the unknown voltage terminals of the slide-wire potentiometer described in Question 1, what will the resistance be between point A and the point at which the galvanometer nulls?

5 If you were to construct a volt scale for the slide-wire potentiometer of Question 1, how many volts would 1 in. represent?

6 How many inches up from point A would the null point be for the voltage given in Question 4?

7 Assuming you could read the scale accurately to $\frac{1}{64}$ in., what would be the smallest increment of voltage you could measure on the slide-wire potentiometer of Question 1?

8 Add another resistance to the top of the voltage divider network shown in Fig. 6-11 so that a tap for 500 volts is provided. What value resistance must be added to accomplish this?

9 What is the total resistance value of the voltage divider after the extra resistance of Question 8 is added?

10 Add another resistance to the top of the volt-box network shown in Fig. 6-12 so that a multiplication factor of 500 is provided. What is the total series resistance of the volt-box network now?

11 What is the value of the resistance added in Question 10?

12 If it were necessary to shunt a 50 μa meter, that has an internal resistance of 2720 ohms, so that a current of 50 ma would produce full-scale deflection, what would the ohms value of the shunt be?

EXERCISE: Use of the Laboratory Potentiometer*

MATERIAL REQUIRED

1 Weston Model 64 d-c voltmeter calibrator

2 Weston Model 1 voltmeter, 1000 ohms/volt, 3/7.5/15/30/150 volts

3 K-3 Universal Potentiometer, Leeds and Northrup 7553

4 Volt box, Leeds and Northrup 7592

5 Standard cell, Leeds and Northrup 7308

6 Working battery, Leeds and Northrup 7597

7 Galvanometer, Leeds and Northrup 2430C

8 Circuit patching unit, Philco No. 368-35311

9 No. 6 dry cell, 1.5 volts

10 Resistor, 100,000 ohms, ½ watt (2 required)

11 Resistor, 1000 ohms, ½ watt

12 Clip leads

PROCEDURE

Part 1   Standardizing the K-3

1 Connect the equipment as shown in Fig. 6-39.

2 Set the SC dial on the K-3 to the voltage listed on the certification tag of the standard cell.

3 Set the selector switch to either STD position.

4 While observing the galvanometer, tap GA SEN key 1, and adjust the COARSE control. Tap the key after each step adjustment of the dial, until a reversal of null current is indicated.

5 Adjust the FINE dial in small increments, tapping key 1 after each adjustment, until a slight overshoot of the null point is observed. Turn the FINE dial back to the point which gives the smallest deflection of the indicator.

6 Repeat the FINE dial adjustment for keys 2, 3, and 4, until there is no deflection whatsoever when key 4 is tapped.

7 Obtain a final balance by locking down key 4 (pressing and turning slightly), then adjusting the FINE dial while tapping the REV key.

8 If during the standardization, the FINE dial reaches its clockwise limit, advance the COARSE dial one step in the clockwise direction and then readjust the FINE dial following the foregoing procedure.

* Based on techniques recommended by the manufacturer. (Courtesy of Leeds Northrup Company.)

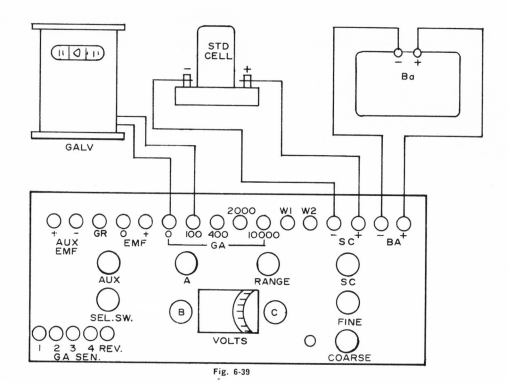

Fig. 6-39

9   Unlock tap key 4.

NOTE   Do not disturb the COARSE and FINE dials until the next standardizing.

Part 2   Zero Adjustment

10   Strap the EMF, G and + terminals with a small piece of copper wire.

11   Set the RANGE, A, B, and C controls for a dial reading of 000.0000 with C' at its counter-clockwise limit.

12   Remove the screw cap above the dial window.

13   Set the selector switch to EMF.

14   Balance the potentiometer using the tap key procedure previously stated, while adjusting C and C'.

15   When a precise zero is obtained, release the tap keys, but do not disturb C or C'.

16   Adjust the screw above the window until the scale zero line is directly under the hairline.

17   Replace the screw cap and remove the shorting strap from the EMF terminals.

Part 3   Low-Voltage Measurement

18   Set up the equipment as shown in Fig. 6-40, with the K-3 still connected as in Fig. 6-39.

19   The voltage to be measured is known to be approximately 7.5 millivolts.

20   Set the range knob to the low (X.01) range.

21   To obtain a preliminary balance, first rotate knobs A, B, and C to 0.015X99.

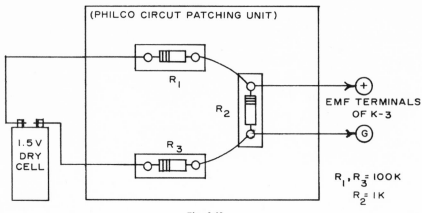

Fig. 6-40

22   Adjust knob A counterclockwise over its range of 15 steps, tapping GA SENS key 1 after each step until the galvanometer deflection reverses.

23   Rotate knob A back 1 step.

24   Adjust knob B counterclockwise over its range of steps, tapping GA SENS key 1 after each step until the galvanometer deflection reverses.

25   Rotate knob B back 1 step.

26   Repeat the preceding procedure for a final balance with knobs C and C'.

27   When making the final balance adjustments, first adjust knob C to an approximate balance point; then adjust knob C' to obtain a final precise balance. Tap GA SENS key 1 after each small adjustment until only a very small deflection of the galvanometer results. Then tap keys 2, 3, and 4 in numerical succession, at the same time adjusting knob C', until there is no deflection of the null indicator when key 4 is tapped.

28   Lock down tap key 4 by turning it slightly and tap the REV key. Adjust knob C' until there is no deflection when the REV key is tapped.

29   Release tap key 4.

30   The actual voltage drop across R2 can now be read directly from the dial.

Part 4   Voltmeter Certification

31   Set up the equipment as shown in Fig. 6-41, and connect the POTENTIOMETER terminals of the volt box to the EMF terminals of the K-3.

32   Using the screw face on the front of the Model 1 voltmeter, mechanically zero the instrument.

33   Set all controls on the voltmeter calibrator to zero, and turn the POWER switch to ON. Allow approximately five minutes for the unit to warm up.

34   Set the FUNCTION switch on the calibrator to V-UA.

35   Set the V-UA switch on the calibrator to 150.

36   Set the volt box to MULTIPLY BY: 1000; MAX VOLTS: 150.

37   Adjust dials A, B, C, and C' on the K-3 for an indication of 0.150000 volt.

38   Set the DIVIDE switch on the calibrator to 150.

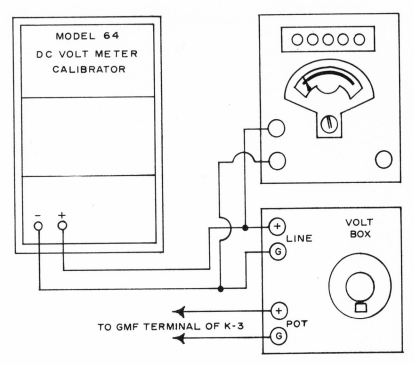

Fig. 6-41

Applied emf	High limit	Low limit	Actual reading
150-v Range			
150 v	150.375	149.625	
75 v	75.375	74.625	
30-v Range			
30 v	30.075	29.925	
15 v	15.075	14.925	
15-v Range			
15 v	15.0375	14.9625	
7.5 v	7.5375	7.4625	
7.5-v Range			
7.5 v	7.51875	7.48125	
3.75	3.76875	3.73125	
3 v			
3 v	3.0075	2.9925	
2.25	2.2575	2.2425	
1.5	1.5075	1.4925	
0.75	0.7575	0.7425	

Fig. 6-42

39   Tap GA SENS key 1 on the K-3 and adjust the SUBDIVIDER control on the calibration for a null on the galvanometer.

40   Tap through key 4 until the output of the calibrator is precisely 150 volts, as indicated by the zeroed galvanometer.

41   Read the Model 1 meter deflection. It should read within $\pm$ 0.25% of 150 volts.

42   Repeat Steps 34 through 41 for 75 volts, and check the meter deflection at midrange. The deflection should read 75 volts $\pm$ 0.25% of 150 volts.

43   Repeat Steps 34 through 42 for the 30-, 15-, 7.5-, and 3-volt ranges. The meter deflection should read within $\pm$ 0.25% of 30, 15, 7.5, or 3 volts, respectively.

44   For a linearity check of the meter on the 3-volt scale, check readings at 0.75, 1.5, 2.25, and full-scale deflection.

45   Fill out the calibration check sheet of Fig. 6-42.

Voltage, Current, and Impedance Equipment: Measurements and Calibration Techniques

7

The most fundamental electrical measurements are those of voltage, current, and impedance (including "pure" resistance, capacitance, and inductance). The instruments used in measuring these quantities form the building blocks for the more complex equipment used in power, frequency, attenuation, and other special measurements.

Most of the various instruments for the measurement of voltage and current are derived from the Weston galvanometer movement. These adaptations consist of various resistance and reactance networks, rectifiers, amplifiers, and thermoelectric converters. The Weston movement also provides the basic null-indicating device essential to most impedance measuring equipment.

A unidirectional current or voltage may be either steady (d-c) or pulsating, or it may have an alternating waveform superimposed on the d-c level. *Regardless of the form, measuring devices respond to the average value.*

An alternating current or voltage is a succession of surges, increasing in one direction from zero to some peak value and decreasing back to zero. The process is then repeated in the opposite direction. The complete transition—from zero to peak value, back to zero, then to peak value in the opposite direction and back to zero—is called a cycle.

For purposes of measurement three values of an alternating waveform are important. These are: (1) peak value—the highest value obtained; (2) r-m-s, or effective value —the a-c current value equal to the value of d-c current which has the same heating effect; and (3) the average value. For the sine wave, the r-m-s value is 0.707 times the peak value and the average value is 0.636 times the peak value. The values of more complex waveforms can be related to the sine wave by a constant known as the *form factor*. More information on this, as well as peak, r-m-s, and average values, is given in Appendix D-1.

In any electrical circuit, voltage and current are dependent upon impedance magnitudes and characteristics within the circuit. For this reason, accurate impedance measurements are essential to the prediction and evaluation of circuit performance.

The impedance-measuring equipment covered by this section is useful for d-c measurements, as well as for a-c measurements at frequencies where circuit elements may be considered to be lumped constants —the resistances, inductances, and capacitances may be separately represented.

With these restrictions the definition of impedance is given by the usual Ohm's law relationship:

$$Z = \frac{V}{I}$$

where the value is specified in both magnitude and an angle (θ), which is the lead or lag angle between voltage and current.

D-C INSTRUMENTS

Theoretically, a current-measuring device should have zero ohms internal resistance. If this were true, it would have no loading effect when connected into the circuit being measured, thereby revealing the true value of current flowing in the circuit. Practical instruments, however, have a definite amount of resistance, although it may be only a few ten-thousandths of an ohm.

A voltage-measuring device, theoretically, should have an infinite resistance so that no energy would be absorbed from the circuit under test. Such an instrument would measure the true voltage value under test. Circuit effect is unavoidable in practical instruments, but infinite internal resistance can be approached by devices using electron tubes.

Because of the effects of local magnetic and electrical fields, it is advisable to take at least two readings when making d-c calibrations—one with the voltage source connected in one direction, and the other with the source connected in the reverse direction.

AMMETERS When a galvanometer is calibrated in units of current, it is known as an ammeter, milliammeter, or microammeter, according to the magnitude of current required to produce full-scale deflection. In these applications, the meter is inserted in series with the conductor through which the current flows. Although the encasement of an ammeter is usually insulated from its electric circuits, the connection of the instrument into a circuit should be made at a point which is as near ground potential as possible. This practice minimizes the danger of insulation breakdown or injury to personnel. If an

ammeter is connected incorrectly, there may be serious damage both to the meter and to circuit components.

The accuracy of an ammeter reading (observed current value/actual current value) is given by

$$\text{accuracy} = \frac{R_c + R_m}{R_c}$$

where R_c is the normal circuit resistance without ammeter and R_m is the over-all resistance of the ammeter, its internal circuitry, and any auxiliary circuitry used with the ammeter connection. The ratio will approach 1 (observed value = actual value) only as R_m approaches zero.

Direct-current ammeters are most easily calibrated with a potentiometer. Current value is determined by measuring the potential difference between the terminals of a standard resistance and calculating the current by use of Ohm's law. The result is then compared with the reading of the ammeter in question, which is also inserted in the circuit.

A good source of constant current is required. Lead storage cells or Edison cells will provide this. A rheostat (or rheostats) can be placed in the circuit to control the current value. The circuit arrangement is given in Fig. 7-1.

A more direct method consists of obtaining a standardized current from an advanced-type potentiometer, such as the Leeds and Northrup K-3. This method allows calibration of instruments over a range of 0–15 amps with an accuracy of ± 0.035%.

Volt boxes or voltage divider networks should be used when appropriate.

VOLTMETERS A voltmeter is simply a galvanometer in series with a large resistance. This resistance, called a "multiplier," must be sufficient to limit the current to a safe value when the instrument is placed across a voltage source. By Ohm's law the current

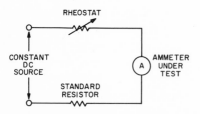

Fig. 7-1 Potentiometer method of calibrating d-c ammeters.

through the meter is proportional to the impressed voltage. Therefore, different values of resistance are required for different magnitudes of voltage.

Generally, the ratio of the total resistance of the voltmeter to its full-scale reading in volts is used to specify the instrument. This is the familiar *ohms-per-volt* ratio, and is called the "voltmeter sensitivity." Its reciprocal is the current in amperes required for full-scale deflection. Most frequently, these ratios vary from 100 ohms per volt to 25,000 ohms per volt and correspond to currents from 10 ma to 40 microamperes.

When a meter and a number of resistance multipliers (voltage dividers, actually) are contained within the same encasement, the instrument is known as a multirange voltmeter.

An extremely large ohms-per-volt ratio can be obtained with an electronic voltmeter. The electronic tube (or tubes) and associated circuitry in this type of instrument provide a very high shunting resistance across the circuit under test and increase the relative sensitivity. The power drain on the circuit by an electronic voltmeter is on the order of a few hundred-thousandths of a microwatt.

The simplest method of calibrating d-c voltmeters is to compare the meter reading with the voltage as measured by a potentiometer (Fig. 7-2). For voltages below the standard cell voltage (0–1.6 volts, approximately), the comparison is made directly against the standard cell. Potentiometers similar to the K-3 can make this comparison with an accuracy of ± 0.01% + 20 microvolts (μv) to ± 0.015% + 0.5 μv.

For voltages higher than 1.6 volts, a volt box or voltage divider arrangement must be used along with the potentiometer. An accuracy of ± 0.035% is still possible with the K-3 to 750 volts.

Be certain that one side of the line voltage used to make the calibration is grounded.

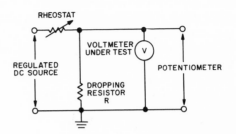

Fig. 7-2 Potentiometer method of calibrating d-c voltmeters.

TRANSFER INSTRUMENTS

Certain instruments may be used for the measurement of both a-c and d-c quantities. Their sensitivity is not high enough, as a rule, to dictate their use over sensitive d-c ammeters and voltmeters. They may, however, be calibrated with d-c quantities and may then be used to calibrate more common types of a-c instruments. For this reason they are called "transfer instruments."

ELECTRODYNAMOMETERS The electrodynamometer differs from a moving-coil galvanometer because the movable portion is suspended in the field of a fixed coil rather than that of a permanent magnet.

The commonly used commercial electrodynamometer is of the Siemens type. In this instrument, the movable coil is supported by a torsion spring, which brings the coil back to its initial position after the current is removed. Large quantities cannot be measured with this instrument.

The current path through the fixed and movable coils is shown in Fig. 7-3. The magnetic field for each coil changes every half cycle when a-c flows. The arrangement is such, however, that the direction of the torque does not change. The magnitude of the torque is proportional to the square of the instantaneous current, although the scale can be (and usually is) graduated in terms of effective values.

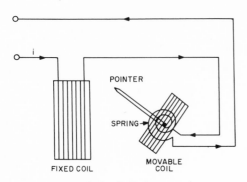

Fig. 7-3 Current path in electrodynamometer.

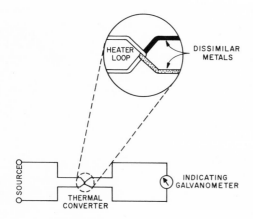

Fig. 7-4 Thermocouple ammeter. Magnified area shows details of thermal converter.

Series resistor and shunt resistor networks are used with the electrodynamometer, to adapt it for current and voltage measurements, just as they are used with ammeters. The sensitivity of the basic meter movement is low—10 to 30 ohms per volt.

Direct-current calibration of the electrodynamometer is accomplished by the methods previously described for ammeters and voltmeters. After calibration, the instrument can be used to measure a-c quantities or to calibrate a-c ammeters and voltmeters up to a few kilocycles, although moderately priced electrodynamometers must be used below 100 cps.

ELECTROSTATIC VOLTMETERS In instruments of this category, the force of an electrostatic attraction between bodies charged to different potentials (capacitance effect) is used to indicate voltage values. The magnitude of the force depends on the geometry of the system, the relative potential of the system components, and the dielectric cooefficient of the medium separating the parts.

If properly designed, an electrostatic instrument does not disturb the circuit conditions being measured. There are no frequency or waveform errors and no heating effects. When used with a-c voltages, the instrument reading gives the r-m-s value. Instruments are available which register voltages up to 50,000 volts with an accuracy of ± 1%.

As with the electrodynamometer, electrostatic instruments can be calibrated by d-c methods and then may be used to calibrate a-c instruments.

THERMOCOUPLES This type of instrument uses a thermal converter arrangement, in conjunction with a moving-coil galvanometer, as an indicator, to form a thermocouple galvanometer. These instruments are available for use with d-c currents, as well as with a-c currents as high as 100 megacycles. Accuracy can be as good as 0.5% at the lower frequencies. Current ranges from a few milliamperes to a few hundred amperes are available. The device can also be used as a voltmeter with a usual sensitivity of about 500 ohms per volt and with ranges from 0.5 to 150 volts.

The circuit arrangement of the thermocouple instrument (Fig. 7-4) takes advantage of the Seebeck effect. When two dissimilar metals are joined at both ends, opposing emf's develop within the loop. The net emf varies directly with the difference in the temperatures of the two junctions. The junction at the thermal converter is heated by the current being measured. The other junction (galvanometer connection) is maintained at a constant temperature. Since it is the heating effect of the measured current which accounts for the galvanometer indication, the instrument reads d-c or effective a-c values equally well.

At high frequencies, skin effect produces a positive error in the readings, but this error can be kept to less than 1% at 30 megacycles by proper design.

The particular advantage of the thermocouple instrument, as with other transfer instruments, is the fact that it can be calibrated with dc and then can be used to calibrate low-frequency a-c instruments.

A-C INSTRUMENTS

There are a number of devices capable of furnishing readings directly on the basis of alternating current. One such movement is the electrodynamometer movement already discussed.

A less expensive instrument is the repulsion-type, moving-iron-vane ammeter, shown in Fig. 7.5. It is used more extensively than the dynamometer types because of its lower cost. Current passing through the stationary coil magnetizes two iron vanes situated in the same plane, one fixed and the other attached to the movable pointer shaft. This arrangement insures an identical magnetic effect upon the vanes, despite the alternations of the current and of its associated magnetic field. Therefore, the net repulsive force acts upon the vanes and repels the movable one from the fixed member, causing the pointer to indicate a deflection on the scale. The amount of deflection is restricted by a spring, which stops the pointer and vane at a point where the magnetic and mechanical torques balance. The spring also returns the moving vane to its original position when current flow ceases.

The foregoing instruments can be used for either current or voltage measurements. When they are employed to measure voltage, however, their minimum current drain is often sufficient to disturb the actual relationships in the circuit under test. Further-

more, internal capacitance effects nullify usefulness at all frequencies but the power frequencies. In radio communications, it is therefore customary first to convert alternating voltage to direct voltage by rectification, and then to use a d-c voltmeter. These instruments usually employ copper-oxide rectifiers and a resistor in series with the meter. A copper-oxide rectifier makes use of a thin semiconducting layer, formed on a metal backing, and another metal plate in contact with the surface of the semiconducting layer. A rectifier block of this kind is shown in part A of Fig. 7-6. When an

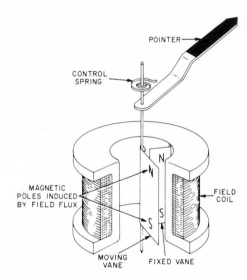

Fig. 7-5 Repulsion-type a-c meter.

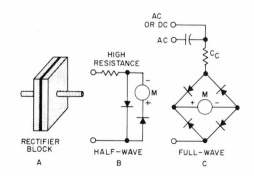

Fig. 7-6 Copper oxide rectifier and circuits.

electrical potential is impressed across the two plates, current will flow through the unit more readily for one polarity than for the other. This property arises from the contact condition between the metal backing and the semiconducting layer. This layer also acts as a dielectric between the plates. At high frequencies, the effective capacitance, which is dependent on the area of the metal plates, bypasses the rectifying contact and appreciably reduces the rectified direct current. The frequency range of uniform response is frequently extended by decreasing the area of the plates or by using crystal detectors. One possible circuit is shown in Fig. 7-6B, and another is shown in Fig. 7-6C. In the former, current is excluded from the meter during half of the signal cycle. Whenever the signal under measurement contains a d-c component, a blocking capacitor must be employed, as shown in Fig. 7-6C. In general, voltmeters employing rectification have ohms-per-volt ratios on the order of 1000 and a uniform response up to several thousand cycles per second.

Calibration procedures for a-c voltmeters

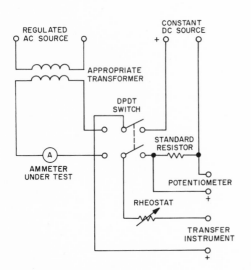

Fig. 7-7 Transfer instrument calibration of a-c ammeter.

are given in the discussion of vacuum-tube voltmeters.

Alternating-current ammeters may be calibrated by using a transfer instrument, as shown in Fig. 7-7. This arrangement provides a "running" calibration of the transfer instrument. If the transfer instrument calibration record shows that the instrument is reliable and has been calibrated within the required interval, the potentiometer and d-c circuitry to the right of the DPDT switch can be excluded.

If the ammeter under test is graduated in r-m-s values rather than effective values, the transfer instrument readings (effective) must be multiplied by an appropriate factor (Appendix D-1) to give the r-m-s values.

VACUUM-TUBE VOLTMETERS An instrument that incorporates an electromagnetic movement with an input circuit consisting of one or more vacuum tubes can be employed in a number of ways. Such a meter is characterized by greatly increased impedance and improved sensitivity as compared to a simple meter.

Of the various available vacuum-tube instruments, the vacuum-tube voltmeter has the widest scope of utility. According to the circuit arrangement, the instrument can be designed to respond to direct, r-m-s, peak, or average voltage. The readings also can be made proportional to the square of the r-m-s value. However, the scales of most vacuum-tube voltmeters are calibrated in r-m-s volts based on a pure sine wave. Hence, the readings obtained are valid only if the applied signal is a sine wave within the specified frequency range. If the meter responds to the square of the r-m-s value, the only requirement for accurate readings is that the harmonic content of the waveform be within the frequency range of the instrument.

Although most vacuum-tube voltmeters use a galvanometer or dynamometer type of movement with a pointer as an indicator, precision instruments have been developed which give the value in the form of a *digital read-out.* Such an instrument is shown in Fig. 7-8. The particular model shown provides a direct display of r-m-s values from 0.1000 to 1199.9 volts with an accuracy of 0.5% from 50 cps to 20 kc and 0.25% from 100 cps to 10 kc.

Vacuum-tube voltmeters, as well as other a-c voltmeters, can be calibrated by transfer instrument methods—particularly by using electrostatic voltmeters. They may also be calibrated directly against a standardized a-c voltage source. Comparison with electrostatic instruments permits an accuracy of ±1% up to 20,000 volts and slightly less accuracy up to 50,000 volts.

The circuitry for the transfer instrument method of calibrating a-c voltmeters is given in Fig. 7-9.

BRIDGES AND OTHER NULL-INDICATING NETWORKS

In the measurement and calibration of impedance and its components (resistance, inductance, and capacitance), the most sensitive methods employ RLC networks arranged in such a manner that a null is formed between certain points. When this null occurs, a balance exists between branches of the network. The conditions of balance permit the unknown quantities to be calculated in terms of the known circuit elements.

The null detector may be a galvanometer, a set of headphones or a speaker (if frequencies are audible), an oscillograph, an oscilloscope, or any other electronic null indicator. *The use of an electronic device permits a more accurate determination of the null point.*

Fig. 7-8 Model 350 digital read-out voltmeter. (Courtesy, Ballantine Laboratories, Inc.)

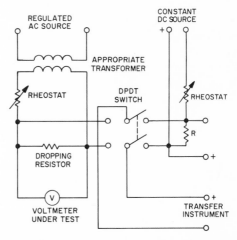

Fig. 7-9 Transfer instrument calibration of a-c voltmeter. Resistor R is a standard resistor. If the transfer instrument has a good record of reliability and has been calibrated within the proper interval of time, it may be used without simultaneous d-c calibration. This would allow the exclusion of the circuitry to the right of the DPDT switch.

BRIDGES The general bridge network is illustrated in Fig. 7-10.

Resistances, inductances, and capacitances may be combined in an infinite number of ways to produce bridge-networks. Those which are of primary importance in measurement and calibration work are shown in Table 7-1, along with balance conditions and remarks on specific use. The elements being calibrated or measured are indicated by the subscript x.

The discussions of bridges in this manual

Table 7-1   Bridge Arrangements

A. Resistance measuring

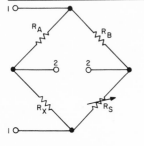

$$R_X = \frac{R_A}{R_B} R_S$$

Most universally used circuit for resistance measurement. Commercial models can be used to make measurements from 1 ohm to 1 megohm with accuracy of ± 0.25%.

1. WHEATSTONE

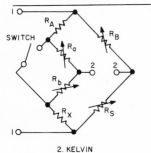

$$R_X = \frac{R_A}{R_B} R_S$$

Used for measuring small resistances as low as 0.001 ohm with accuracy of ±2%. The relationship $R_A/R_b = R_B/R_S$ must be maintained for the given balance equation. This is accomplished by varying R_A and R_B until a null is obtained with the switch closed. The switch is then opened and R_a and R_b are adjusted for null. The process is repeated until a final null is obtained with the switch open or closed.

2. KELVIN

B. Capacitance measuring

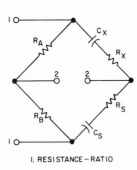

$$C_X = \frac{R_B}{R_A} C_S$$

$$R_X = \frac{R_A}{R_B} R_S$$

It is advisable to use a fixed resistance ratio and variable standards. The balance is obtained by alternately varying C_s and R_s. If the Q of the unknown reactance is greater than the standard Q, it will be necessary to place a variable resistor in series with the unknown reactance to obtain balance. The resistance of the unknown reactance is then given by $R_x' = R_x - R_s'$, where R_x is calculated from the balance equation and R_s' is the value of resistance which must be added in the unknown branch.

If the unknown capacitance has a high Q, it is permissible to vary the resistance ratio when a variable standard capacitor is not available. R_s may still have to be varied to obtain final balance.

1. RESISTANCE – RATIO

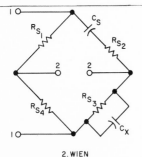

$$C_X = \left[\frac{R_{S_1}}{R_{S_4}} - \frac{R_{S_2}}{R_{S_3}} \right] C_S$$

Allows capacitance determination to high degree of accuracy when frequency and resistance standards are employed.

2. WIEN

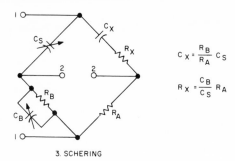

$$C_X = \frac{R_B}{R_A} C_S$$

$$R_X = \frac{C_B}{C_S} R_A$$

Available as a commercial unit for measurements from 100 picofarads to 1 microfarad with ±0.2% accuracy. Other ranges provide smaller accuracies. This is the most widely used capacitance bridge. The dial of C_x is graduated in terms of direct readings for C_x in commercial units since the resistance ratio is maintained at a fixed value.

3. SCHERING

C. Inductance measuring

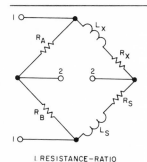

$$L_X = \frac{R_A}{R_B} L_S$$

$$R_X = \frac{R_A}{R_B} R_S$$

$$Q_X = \frac{\omega L_S}{R_S}$$

See precautions for capacitance resistance-ratio bridge (B-1).

1. RESISTANCE–RATIO

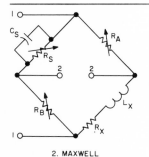

$$L_X = R_B R_A C_S$$

$$R_X = \frac{R_B}{R_S} R_A$$

$$Q_X = \omega R_S C_S$$

Particularly suited for inductance measurements, since comparison against a capacitor is more ideal than against another inductor. Use for measurements of low-Q coils only. Commercial bridges measure from 1 microhenry to 1000 henrys with ±2% error. A variable standard capacitor may be used with fixed R_A and R_B, but poorer accuracy is the result.

2. MAXWELL

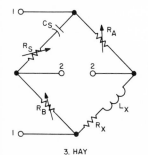

$$L_X = \frac{R_S R_A C_S}{1 + (1/Q_X)^2}$$

$$R_X = \frac{R_B R_A}{R_S} \cdot \frac{1}{Q_X^2 + 1}$$

$$Q_X = \frac{1}{\omega R_S C_S}$$

Desirable for measurement of high-Q coils. At low Q's the disadvantages lie in the fact that measurements depend on Q_x, the losses of the unknown inductors, and frequency. Commercial bridges measure from 1 microhenry to 100 henrys with ±2% error.

3. HAY

Table 7-1   Bridge Arrangements (cont.)

D. Incremental inductance measuring

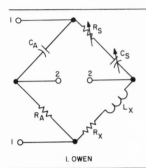

$$L_X = R_A R_S C_A$$

$$R_X = \frac{C_A}{C_S} R_A$$

Values of C_x are usually much higher than can be obtained with standard air capacitors.

I. OWEN

E. Mutual inductance measuring

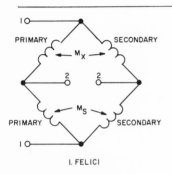

$$M_X = M_S$$

Uses variable standard mutual inductor. The secondaries of standard and unknown inductors must be connected so that they will have oppositely induced emf's.

I. FELICI

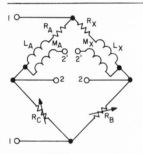

DETECTOR AT 2-2:

$$M_X = \frac{R_B}{R_C} M_S = \frac{L_X}{L_A} M_S$$

DETECTOR AT 2'-2':

$$L_X = \frac{R_B}{R_C} L_A$$

$$R_X = \frac{R_B}{R_C} R_A$$

Uses variable standard mutual inductor. When detector is connected to terminals 2-2, L_x and R_x may be determined; when it is connected to terminals 2'-2', M_x may be evaluated. Suffers in accuracy for low values of M_x.

2. MODIFIED CAMPBELL

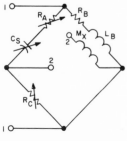

$$M_X = \frac{R_C L_B}{R_C + R_A}$$

OR

$$M_X = R_B R_C C_S$$

Accuracy better than with modified Campbell bridge. Disadvantage lies in the fact that L_B and R_B must be determined by use of other instruments.

3. CAREY-FOSTER

---

refer to Table 7-1. The detector terminals of all bridge circuits shown are marked 2-2, and the input terminals are marked 1-1.

Although any component in a bridge circuit may be variable, the variables shown in the tabulated circuitry are preferred for reasons of accuracy. When the bridges are used as normal measuring devices, the standards may be replaced by workable precision components. For calibration, however, the comparisons must be made against standards. All component elements must be checked occasionally, to insure operation within specified and desired tolerances.

Quality commercial instruments employ every known method of eliminating effects due to stray electromagnetic and electrostatic phenomena. When bridge circuits are constructed in the laboratory, these interferences can be large enough to upset all measurements entirely.

Grounded shields must be placed around all components. The detector may be coupled to terminals 2-2 by a shielded output transformer; Fig. 7-11 shows the grounding arrangement. A switch is also shown with variable impedances across the input. With the switch in the "a" position, an initial bridge balance can be obtained. With the switch in the "b" position, Z_5 and Z_6 can be adjusted for balance. The alternate adjustments are made until balance is obtained in either of the switch positions.

The sensitivity of a bridge is defined by the ratio of the voltage obtained at terminals 2-2 to a small change ΔZ_x in the unknown. Maximum sensitivity is obtained if

$$\frac{Z_1}{Z_2} = \frac{Z_3}{Z_4} = 1$$

where the branch impedances are arranged as in Fig. 7-10.

TWIN-T AND BRIDGED-T NULL NETWORKS The twin-T, or parallel-T, and bridged-T networks shown in Fig. 7-12 are also capable of providing a null indication when certain

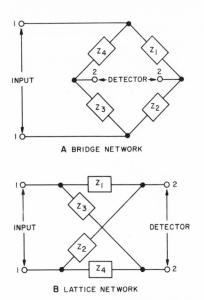

Fig. 7-10 Bridge networks. The lattice network in part B is identical to the bridge arrangement in part A.

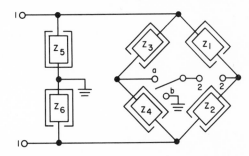

Fig. 7-11 Shielding and grounding of bridge elements.

balance conditions exist. For this arrangement, one input terminal and one output terminal are common. This eliminates the need for a shielded output transformer. Other grounding connections are also eliminated by this arrangement. Stray capacitances and residual reactances are minimized. This enables the use of higher frequencies than possible with ordinary bridge networks. The twin-T is commonly used in the arrangement shown in Fig. 7-13 for determining the components of Z_x in terms of two variable standard capacitors. Bridged-T networks are employed when measuring twin capacitors (letting one element of the twin be Z_1, the

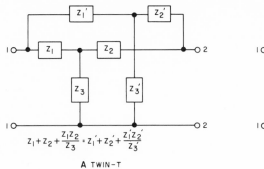

A TWIN-T

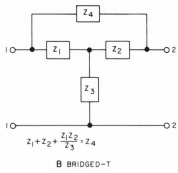

B BRIDGED-T

Fig. 7-12 Null-indicating T-networks.

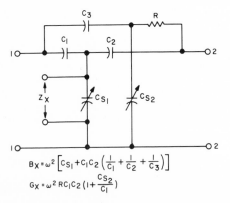

Fig. 7-13 Twin-T impedance network. Z_x may be capacitive or inductive. B_x and G_x are the susceptance and conductance of the unknown admittance ($1/Z_x = \sqrt{G_x^2 + B_x^2}$).

current-carrying electrons and molecules of the material, the state of molecular agitation must be taken into consideration. Molecular agitation, of course, is given by a measure of temperature.

In general, the resistance at any temperature (°C) can be determined by

$$R_t = R_{20}\left[1 + \alpha_{20}\left(t - 20°C\right)\right] \text{ ohms}$$

where R_{20} is the resistance at 20°C and α_{20} is the temperature coefficient of resistance at 20°C. If the resistance is given for some temperature other than 20°C, the equation can be used to solve for R_{20}, and this value can be used to find the solution at other temperatures. A list of temperature coefficients of resistance is given in Appendix C-7.

D-C TERMINAL RESISTANCE   There are many methods for comparing d-c resistances. One of the most accurate is the potentiometer method shown in Fig. 7-14A. The current flowing in the circuit must remain constant. With most potentiometers the leads will have to be switched back and forth between R_x and R_s to make measurements. The value of the unknown resistance is given by

$$R_x = \frac{V_x}{V_s} R_s$$

If the K-3 potentiometer is used, the connections may be made as shown in Fig. 7-14B. The advantage of the potentiometer

other Z_2) against a standard at Z_4 as well as for making measurements on iron-core coils carrying a-c current biased at a d-c level.

Twin-T and bridged-T networks must be balanced first without the unknown impedance and then with the unknown impedance connected.

RESISTANCE MEASUREMENTS

Resistance is the property of an electrical conductor which tends to prevent electron flow while, at the same time, converting electrical energy into heat energy. Since this is due, in most part, to collisions between method is that R_x is determined *directly* in terms of a standard.

Bridge methods may be used to compare resistors within the limits of precision of bridge elements. Faith in this method is dependent on calibration and reliability of the instrument used.

If a standard decade resistance box is available, the substitution method may be used (Fig. 7-15). The rheostat is used to adjust the current with R_x in the circuit. The decade resistance box is then switched in and adjusted until the current is the same. The reading of the decade resistance box is the value of R_x.

A-C TERMINAL RESISTANCE

For a-c frequencies up to 1000 cps, standard resistors used for most d-c comparisons can still be used. Thus the calibration of terminal resistance may be made by the procedures already described.

For higher frequencies and for measuring resistance as the power-loss component of complex impedances, the various universal bridge circuits must be employed.

Measurements up to 1,000,000 megohms (including insulation resistance) can be made with a megohm bridge. Vacuum tubes are used to amplify the very small currents involved and to indicate the null point.

An ohmmeter consists of a galvanometer, batteries, and resistors of known value connected so that an unknown resistance can be measured by comparison with a standard. Basic circuit arrangements are shown

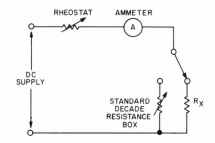

Fig. 7-15 Substitution method of comparing resistors.

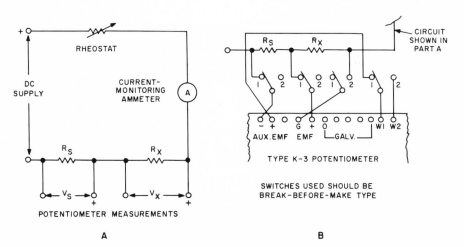

Fig. 7-14 Potentiometer method of comparing resistors. As shown in part B, the comparison can be made with the K-3 without changing leads. The value of R_s should be such that the drop across it is equal to one of the 15 AUX EMF values available. V_s can be checked with all switches in the number one position as shown. V_x can be read by placing the switches in the number two position and making the usual A, B, C, and C' dial adjustments. It will be necessary to use the REV EMF on the selector knob. A null-indicating device is connected as usual. (Courtesy, Leeds and Northrup.)

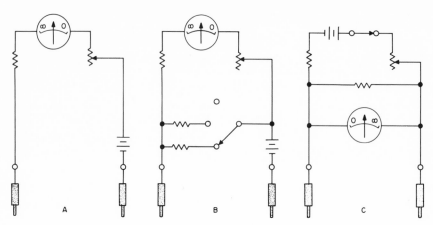

Fig. 7-16 Basic ohmmeter circuits.

in Fig. 7-16. In part A the unknown resistance is in series with the battery and the meter, which is both in series and in parallel with the standard resistances. When the test leads are open, no current flows through the meter, and the meter is mechanically set to indicate ∞. When the test leads are shorted, there should be a full-scale deflection of the meter, and the series resistor R is adjusted accordingly. Any conductor having an intermediate value of resistance will produce a corresponding deflection on the meter when the conductor is connected to the test leads. An appropriately calibrated scale allows the resistance under measurement to be evaluated.

The markers on a resistance scale are crowded near the ∞ point, and are spaced increasingly farther apart in the vicinity of the zero-resistance marker. Because of this nonlinear spacing, reasonably accurate readings are provided over approximately half of the scale only. If the instrument is to cover a wide range of resistance, different values of internal multipliers and shunts must be used—one set for each scale. There is a switching arrangement for this purpose, as illustrated in Fig. 7-16B. The sensitivity of the meter movement limits the highest measurable resistance for a particular battery voltage. An external series battery and

standard resistor can extend the range of any ohmmeter.

When the value of resistance to be measured is less than approximately half of an ohm, higher accuracy is afforded by shunting the unknown resistor across the meter, as shown in Fig. 7-16C. In this circuit, full-scale deflection corresponds to ∞, so that adjustment of the variable resistor must be made with the test leads open.

Severe damage to an ohmmeter can occur if it is used while power is applied to the equipment under test. If there are filter capacitors in the equipment, they must be discharged before any measurements are taken. When an ohmmeter is not in use, the internal battery will run down unless the test leads are open in the series type, or the switch is open in the shunt type.

Ohmmeters are not precision measuring devices. They find widest application in nominal trouble-shooting measurements. Calibration can be accomplished by measuring standard resistor or standard decade values and noting the instrument reading.

CAPACITANCE MEASUREMENTS

Any two conductors separated by a dielectric constitute a capacitor. A difference of charge between the two conductors permits energy to be stored in the dielectric medium. This phenomenon, known as "capacitance," is measured by the ratio of stored charge to the voltage between the conductors:

$$C = \frac{Q}{V} \text{ farads}$$

where Q is in coulombs and V in volts.

Because of imperfections in all dielectrics, the energy cannot be stored indefinitely. The power is lost through an effective series resistance between the conductors. The power factor, or dissipation factor, of a capacitor is

$$\text{p. f.} = \omega R_s C$$

Instead of a series resistor, the effective resistance may be considered in parallel with the capacitor, in which case the power factor is

$$\text{p. f.} = \frac{1}{\omega R_p C}$$

TERMINAL CAPACITANCE The bridges indicated in Table 7-1 can be used to measure terminal capacitance, and, with standard and precision components, they can be used to calibrate terminal capacitance.

An absolute method is illustrated in Fig. 7-17. A large source voltage of single, fixed frequency f_o is applied across the series capacitor and thermocouple ammeter. The reactance of C_x must be considerably larger than the ammeter impedance. If these conditions are met, the capacitance is given by

$$C_x = \frac{1}{\omega_o V}$$

where V is the supply voltage in volts and $\omega_o = 2\pi f_o$.

Shunt and series substitution circuits are shown in Fig. 7-18. The standard variable capacitor (C_1) in the shunt arrangement is tuned for maximum deflection of the microammeter without C_x connected. C_x is then connected, and C_s is readjusted to a value (C_2) which gives a lower peak of the microammeter. The unknown capacitance is given by

$$C_x = C_1 - C_2$$

For the series arrangement, C_x is placed

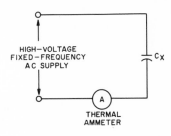

Fig. 7-17 Absolute method of capacitor measurement.

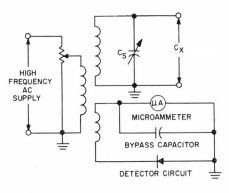

A. SHUNT METHOD

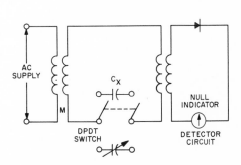

B. SERIES METHOD

Fig. 7-18 Substitution methods for capacitor comparison.

in the circuit, and the input frequency is adjusted for maximum deflection of the detector. C_s is then placed in the circuit and is adjusted for the same detector reading. At this point:

$$C_x = C_s$$

DISSIPATION FACTOR The losses of a capacitor are usually represented by a simple series resistor (R_x in the bridge circuitry of Table 7-1). If it is desirable to represent the losses by a parallel resistance in circuit analysis:

$$R_p = \frac{1}{\omega^2 R_s C^2}$$

where R_s is the series resistance.

Commercial bridges usually have a resistance dial graduated directly in terms of dissipation factor.

ELECTROLYTIC CAPACITORS A d-c polarizing voltage may be required in order to get a

true capacitance and dissipation factor value for electrolytic capacitors under operating conditions. Commercial bridges usually have built-in circuitry for this purpose.

Initial application of a d-c voltage to a good electrolytic capacitor will cause a sudden current surge. This surge will rapidly decrease to a smaller steady value, which is known as the *leakage current*. With the steady current flowing, the capacitor is *polarized*.

The leakage current value can be determined separately by the circuit arrangement of Fig. 7-19. The shorting switch should be closed initially to protect the milliammeter from the sudden current surge. After a few minutes have elapsed, the leakage current may be read. Table 7-2 gives a general idea of the amount of leakage current allowable.

TABLE 7-2 Leakage Current for Electrolytics

Rated voltage (volts)	Allowable leakage current (ma/μf)
15–100	0.1
101–299	0.2
300 and over	0.5

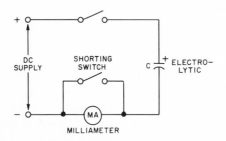

Fig. 7-19 Leakage current determination for electrolytics.

DISTRIBUTED CAPACITANCE The inherent electrostatic force between any two conductors separated by a dielectric medium produces a *distributed capacitance* in all coils. This capacitance exists between each turn as illustrated by Fig. 7-20. Because of this distributed capacitance, coils will go into a state of self-resonance at frequencies which are not necessarily integral multiples of the fundamental. For analytical purposes, the distributed capacitance is lumped together and represented by a single capacitor (C_e) in parallel with the coil.

A direct method of measuring C_e is shown in Fig. 7-20. The input is set to some initial frequency (f_1), and the standard capacitor (C_s) is adjusted for resonance. At this point, minimum current will be indicated on the meter. The input frequency is then changed to a value equal to $2f_1$, and C_s is again adjusted for resonance. The distributed capacitance can then be computed from

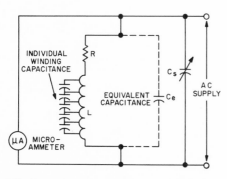

Fig. 7-20 Determination of distributed capacitance.

$$C_e = \frac{C_1 - 4C_2}{3}$$

where C_1 and C_2 are the values of C_s for the two resonant conditions.

There is also a bridge method for determining C_e, as shown in Fig. 7-21. At balance (both switches closed),

$$C_e = \frac{R_b}{R_a} C_s$$

The procedure consists of discharging the two capacitors by closing switch 2 with switch 1 open. The switch conditions are then interchanged until the detector shows that a steady current has been reached. Both switches are then closed simultaneously. Adjustment of R_a and R_b must be made and the switching procedure must be repeated until no deflection of the indicator occurs.

INDUCTANCE MEASUREMENTS

The self-inductance of a coil is defined by

$$L = E \; \frac{di}{dt} \text{ henrys}$$

Because of distributed coil capacitance (see preceding discussion), the measured inductance of a coil is a function of frequency and is called the apparent inductance, L_a. The true inductance is given by

$$\omega L = \frac{L_a}{\omega L_a C_e + 1}$$

where C_e is the distributed capacitance.

True inductance may also be defined in terms of the geometry and physical make-up of the magnetic circuit:

$$L = \frac{\mu \mu_0 N^2 A}{L} \text{ henrys}$$

where N is the number of turns and A and L are the cross-sectional area and mean length, respectively, of the magnetic circuit. The factor μ is the relative permeability of the core material, defined in terms of the d-c magnetization curve as shown in Fig. 7-22,

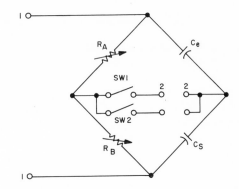

Fig. 7-21 Bridge for determining distributed capacitance.

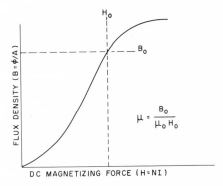

Fig. 7-22 D-c magnetization curve.

and is a nonlinear quantity. The factor μ_0 is the permeability of free space.

If a cyclic magnetizing force (alternating current) is applied to the magnetic circuit, a hysteresis loop such as a-j-k-l-m-n-a of Fig. 7-23, will result. Further, if the magnitude of the alternating current is successively decreased, the intermediate hysteresis loops in the figure can be plotted. The line drawn through the vertices of these loops (a-b-c-d-e-f-g-l) is the a-c, or normal, magnetization curve, which defines the a-c permeability as shown. If μ_{ac} is substituted in the preceding equation, the true a-c self-inductance of a coil, transformer, etc., may be computed.

In electronic circuitry, it is often necessary to operate an inductor or transformer with both a direct bias current and an alternating "working" current. Such operation introduces a second concept of inductance—incremental inductance. The direct current produces a steady magnetizing force which tends to bias the core at some point on the d-c magnetization curve, as shown in Fig. 7-24A. When the alternating current is applied, a hysteresis loop will be produced, with the d-c bias point at its center and with a vertex on the normal magnetization curve. The slope of a line drawn through these two points defines the incremental permeability, as illustrated in Fig. 7-24B. This value of permeability will give the incremental inductance when used in the previous equation.

By way of clarification and summary, the a-c permeability and a-c inductance of a coil are defined for cyclic operation without a d-c level of inductance, and the incremental permeability and incremental inductance are defined for cyclic operation when a d-c level of inductance is present.

It must be remembered that these values change as the magnetizing current magnitude changes. If the cyclic change is not great, a constant mean-inductance value may be assumed. Manufacturers of commercial equipment will provide the d-c and normal magnetization curves for their products, along with other helpful information.

A third concept of induction—mutual inductance—exists when two or more coils are in close proximity. Mutual inductance is defined by the equation:

$$M = \frac{E_2}{di_1/dt} = \frac{E_1}{di_2/dt} \text{ henrys}$$

This relationship shows that the mutual inductance is the ratio of the voltage induced in one coil to the changing current in the other coil. Mutual inductance and self-inductance are related by a constant, the *coefficient of coupling*:

$$k = \frac{M}{\sqrt{L_1 L_2}}$$

In this equation, L_1 and L_2 are a-c values or incremental values, whichever are appropriate.

SELF-INDUCTANCE TECHNIQUES The terminal self-inductance of inductor components may be calibrated by use of the bridge circuits given in Table 7-1. This will also allow the determination of losses by the evaluation of an equivalent series resistance (R_x in tabulated circuitry) and Q.

INCREMENTAL-INDUCTANCE TECHNIQUES Commercial bridges for incremental inductance measurements are uncommon. An Owen bridge is shown in Table 7-1 along with its limitations and can be constructed with standard parts. Other bridges may also be constructed. All of the bridges, however, will have serious limitations and will require the use of complex corrective circuitry.

The circuit shown in Fig. 7-25 provides the simplest and most direct method of obtaining incremental inductance. An initial observation is made with the DPDT switch connecting the thermoammeter in the circuit so that

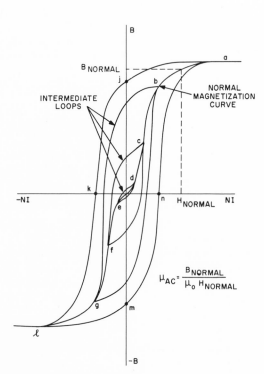

Fig. 7-23 A-c magnetization curve.

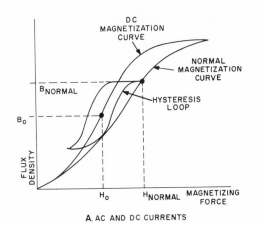

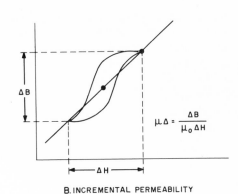

A. AC AND DC CURRENTS

B. INCREMENTAL PERMEABILITY

$$\mu_\Delta = \frac{\Delta B}{\mu_0 \Delta H}$$

Fig. 7-24 Illustration of incremental permeability.

no direct current is applied. The a-c input voltage is varied until the proper alternating current (I_{ac}) flows through the coil. This will give a voltage reading on VTVM$_2$.

The d-c circuitry is then placed in operation and adjusted until the d-c ammeter, which must be an instrument that will not be affected by alternating current, reads the desired value of direct current. The a-c input voltage must be readjusted to some value V_{ac} so that VTVM$_2$ will have the same reading as without the direct current flowing. The incremental inductance is given by

$$L = \frac{V_{ac}}{\omega I_{ac}} \text{ henrys}$$

where $\omega = 2\pi f$.

MUTUAL-INDUCTANCE TECHNIQUES Bridge methods for obtaining calibrated values of mutual inductance are given in Table 7-1. The Felici method provides a simple, direct approach. The modified Campbell bridge gives very good accuracy and is particularly useful when the self-inductance values are not known.

UNIVERSAL IMPEDANCE BRIDGE

The instrument shown in Fig. 7-26 is a typical commercial impedance bridge. It will measure any impedance placed across its termi-

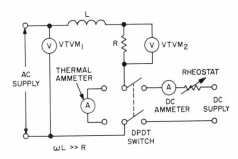

Fig. 7-25 Determination of incremental inductance.

Fig. 7-26 Universal Z-Y bridge. (Courtesy, General Radio Co.)

111

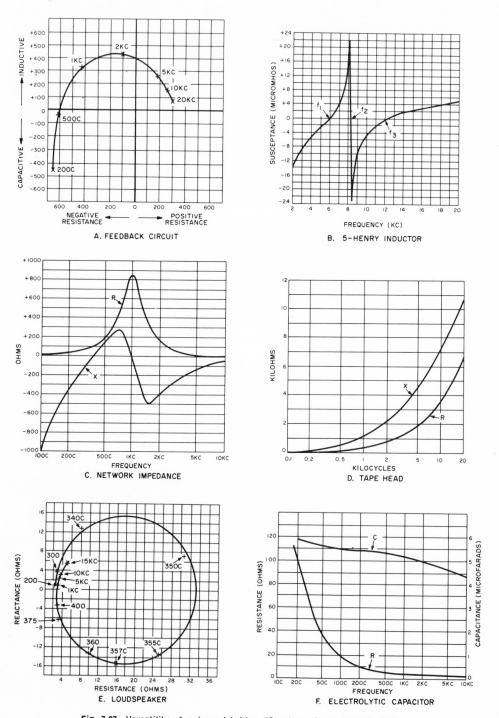

Fig. 7-27 Versatility of universal bridge. (Courtesy, General Radio Co.)

nals. From short circuit to open circuit, real or imaginary, positive or negative, a bridge balance can easily be obtained. Good accuracy is obtainable over a very wide range.

Figure 7-27 shows the variety of information that may be obtained by the use of this bridge. Part A is the input impedance of a feedback circuit showing the negative resistance characteristic. Part B shows the susceptance variation of a 5-henry inductor, along with the resonant effect produced by distributed capacitance at f_2. Part C shows the impedance components of an RLC network (any "black box" type of problem). Parts D and E show the impedance characteristics of a tape recorder head and loudspeaker, respectively. The bridge is particularly suited to measuring electrolytic solution characteristics and electrolytic capacitor characteristics (part F).

QUESTIONS

1 What limits the upper frequency operation of a copper oxide rectifier type of a-c voltmeter?

2 In a shunt-type ohmmeter, a full-scale reading is indicative of what resistive value?

3 Under what theoretical conditions would a current-measuring device reveal the true value of current flowing in a circuit and avoid drawing power from the measured circuit?

4 How is the sensitivity of a voltmeter specified?

5 Describe the principles involved in electrostatic voltmeters.

EXERCISE 1   Wheatstone Bridge Measurements

MATERIAL REQUIRED

1 Decade resistor, Eico 1171 (3 required)

2 Multimeter, Simson 360, Series III

3 Galvanometer, G. M. Labs

4 Key Switch, Philco 368-35318

5 Dry cell, No. 6 1.5 volts (2 required)

6 Several resistors, unknown values

PROCEDURE

1 Determine the approximate resistance of one resistor with the multimeter.

2 Set up the equipment as shown in Fig. 7-28.

3 Set decade's one and two to 500 ohms.

4 Set decade three to the approximate resistance of R_x.

5 Tap the key switch while observing the galvanometer. If the galvanometer does not deflect, the actual value of R_x is the present setting of the decade 3.

6 If the galvanometer did deflect, adjust the setting of the most significant digit of decade 3. Tap the key switch after each adjustment, until the galvanometer deflection is to the opposite side. Then set the most significant digit to the value just before the deflection change.

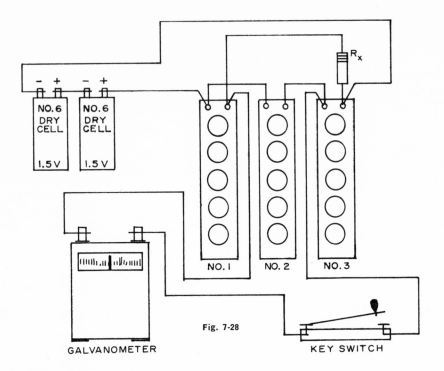

Fig. 7-28

GALVANOMETER   KEY SWITCH

7 Now adjust the next most significant digit until the galvanometer deflection again reverses. Set this digit to the value just before the galvanometer reversal.

8 Continue this adjustment until the units digit balances the galvanometer.

9 Since decade 1 and decade 2 are set to be equal, the unknown resistance, R_x, will equal the setting of decade 3. Under this arrangement, the bridge is limited to 99.9997.

10 To check higher values, decade 1 and 2 should be unequal.

11 To increase the range to 999,999 ohms, set decade 1 equal to 10 times decade 2. To increase the range to 9,999,999, decade 1 should equal 100 times decade 2. Under these conditions,

$$R_x = \left(\frac{R_{decade\ 1}}{R_{decade\ 2}} \right) R_{decade\ 3}$$

12 Repeat the measurement for several other resistors.

EXERCISE 2   Wien Bridge for Capacitance Measurements

MATERIAL REQUIRED

1 Audio oscillator—HP 200CD or equivalent

2 Oscilloscope

3 Resistor 400 ohms, ±1% (2 required)

4 Decade resistor, Eico 1171 or equivalent, (2 required)

5 Decade capacitor, Eico 1180 or equivalent

6 Unknown capacitor (approximately 0.05μfd)

PROCEDURE

1 Set up the equipment as shown in Fig. 7-29.

2 Initially connect the oscilloscope vertical input leads across the output of the oscillator.

3 Set the oscillator for an output of 1000 cps and adjust the oscilloscope synchronizing circuits for a stable display.

4 Reconnect the vertical input leads as shown in the figure.

5 Set R_{s2} to 1000 ohms.

6 Vary C_s for a reduction in amplitude of the signal on the scope.

7 When the minimum point has been reached, vary R_{s3} to reduce the amplitude further.

8 When the minimum signal is achieved, repeat Step 6, then repeat Step 7. Continue to repeat these until no further reduction in the scope trace is possible. It may be found that there is a considerable amount of back and forth adjustment of the decades, but this is not unusual.

9 When the final adjustments are completed, record the settings of C_{s1} R_{s2} (should be 1000 ohms as preset) and R_{s3}.

10 Using the values of Step 9, determine the unknown capacitance by the formula:*

$$C_X = \left(\frac{R_{s1}}{R_{s4}} - \frac{R_{s2}}{R_{s3}} \right) C_s$$

* In this case $R_{s1}/R_{s4} = 1$, simplifying the formula to

$$C_x = \left(1 - \frac{R_{s2}}{R_{s3}} \right) C_s$$

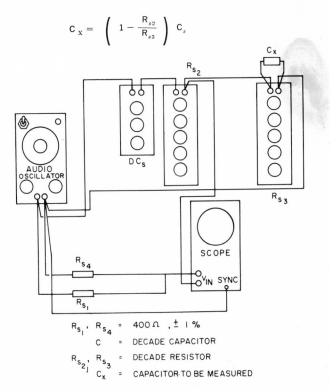

$$
\begin{aligned}
R_{s_1}, R_{s_4} &= 400\,\Omega \ , \pm 1\ \% \\
C &= \text{DECADE CAPACITOR} \\
R_{s_2}, R_{s_3} &= \text{DECADE RESISTOR} \\
C_x &= \text{CAPACITOR TO BE MEASURED}
\end{aligned}
$$

Fig. 7-29

EXERCISE 3   Use of the Universal Impedance Bridge*

MATERIAL REQUIRED

1   Z-Y bridge, General Radio 1603-A

2   Null detector, General Radio 1232-A

3   Audio signal generator, HP-205A6

4   Decade resistor, GR-1432T or equivalent

5   Decade indicator, GR-1490C or equivalent

6   Decade capacitor, GR-1419M-N or equivalent (3 required)

7   Connecting leads

PROCEDURE

1   Set up the equipment as shown in Fig. 7-30.

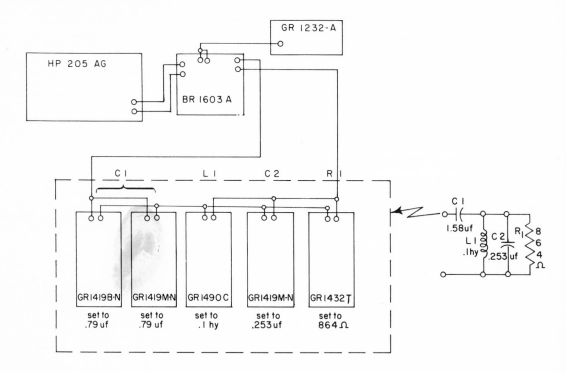

Fig. 7-30

2   Adjust the output of the generator for 100 cycles at 30 volts, into 5000 ohms.

3   Set the controls of the Z-Y bridge as follows:

Control	Setting
f_o	0.1kc
Measurement	Z Initial balance normal

4   Set the controls of the Null detector as follows:

Control	Setting
Gain	Off
Meter	Log

* Based on manufacturer's operating instructions. (Courtesy of General Radio Company.)

Control	Setting
Filter frequency	20–200C
Filter tuning	10

5 Set the GAIN control on the Null detector for a midscale indication on the meter.

6 Adjust the FILTER TUNING control for a maximum indication on the meter. Readjust the GAIN control if necessary to keep the meter on scale.

7 Using the INITIAL BALANCE ∆X or ∆G and the INITIAL BALANCE ∆R or ∆B controls balance the bridge, as indicated by a null on the meter.

8 Set the measurement switch to the Z MEASURE position.

9 Balance the bridge again, using the main X or G, and R or B controls.

10 The cartesian coordinate of the impedance of the network can now be read directly from the main dials, as $Z_x = R_x + jX_x$.

11 The impedance of the network can be determined at any other frequency up to 20 kc. IF the frequency chosen is not one of those listed on the f(dial, set the dial to the nearest frequency listed above the generator frequency. The imaginary coordinate (X_x) is equal to the reading of the X dial multiplied by f_o/f.

EXERCISE 4 Calibration of a Vacuum-tube Voltmeter*

MATERIAL REQUIRED

1 Vacuum tube voltmeter, HP 410B (to be calibrated)

2 Weston voltmeter calibrator models 63 and 64

3 Vacuum tube voltmeter HP 400D

PROCEDURE

1 Set up the equipment as shown in Fig. 7-31.

CAUTION AVOID A SHORT CIRCUIT ACROSS THE POWER LINES. To measure power line voltage, first connect only the upper (red) INPUT terminal to each side of the power line, in turn, leaving it connected to the side that causes a meter indication. Then connect the lower (black) input terminal (grounded internally) to the other side of the line. If this procedure is not followed, the power line may be short circuited through the grounded INPUT terminal of the voltmeter.

2 Set the following switch positions:

Control		Setting
AUTOTRANSFORMER (ON-OFF)		OFF
AUTOTRANSFORMER (DIAL)		MINIMUM
HP 400 D	ON-OFF	ON
HP 400 D	RANGE	300 v
HP 410 B	SELECTOR	+
HP 410 B	RANGE	1 v
MODEL 63	DIVIDE SWITCHES	ALL TO 0
MODEL 63	SUBDIVIDE	0
OUTPUT RANGE		0.75–30
MODEL 63	POWER	ON
MODEL 64	FRICTION-CALIBRATE	CALIBRATE

* Based on manufacturer's calibration procedure. (Courtesy of Hewlett-Packard Company.)

Control		Setting
MODEL 64	SUBDIVIDE	0
MODEL 64	DIVIDE	0
MODEL 64	VOLTS-ma	1.5
MODEL 64	MILLIAMPERES	1.5
MODEL 64	OUTPUT	OFF
MODEL 64	FUNCTION	v–μa

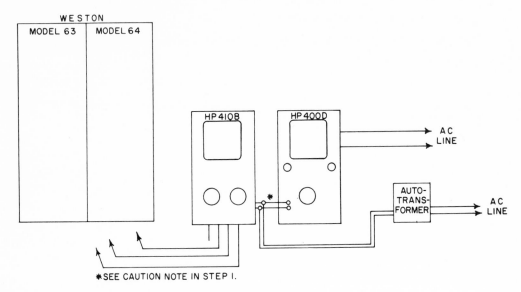

*SEE CAUTION NOTE IN STEP I.

Fig. 7-31

3   Set the autotransformer to ON and adjust for a reading of 117 VAC on the HP 400 D (See caution note in Step 1).

4   Allow 5 minutes for equipment warmup.

5   Short the COMMON and d-c leads of the HP 410 B together and adjust for a meter reading of exactly zero.

6   Switch SELECTOR switch to — and readjust zero if necessary.

7   Repeat Steps 5 and 6 until a final zero is obtained.

8   Set SELECTOR switch to +. Range switch should remain at 1 volt.

9   Connect COMMON lead of HP 410 B to — volts terminal of Model 64 calibrator. Connect d-c lead of HP 410 B to + volts terminal of Model 64.

10   Using COARSE ADJUST control and adjacent push button, zero set the NULL MONITOR of the Model 64.

11   Use FINE ADJUST control and adjacent push button for a final NULL MONITOR zero.

12   Set OUTPUT control of the Model 64 to DIR.

13   Increase DIVIDE switch up to 100. The applied voltage to the HP 410 B is now 1 volt.

14   If necessary, adjust R 32 through the back of the HP 410 B for a full-scale reading.

15   Set OUTPUT switch on Model 64 to OFF.

16   Set Range switch on HP 410 B to 3 V.

17   Set VOLTS-μA switch on Model 64 to 3.0.

18   Set OUTPUT switch on Model 64 to DIR.

19   Step DIVIDE switch up to 150. The applied voltage is now 3 volts. The HP 410 B should read within 1 small division of 3 on the 0–3 scale.

20   Set OUTPUT switch on Model 64 to OFF.

21   Set RANGE switch on HP 410 B to 10 V.

22   Set DIVIDE switch on Model 64 to 0.

23   Set VOLTS-μA switch on Model 64 to 15.

24   Set OUTPUT switch on Model 64 to DIR.

25   Step DIVIDE switch up to 100. The applied voltage is now 10 volts. The HP 410 B should read within 1.5 small divisions of 1.0 on the 0–1.0 scale.

26   Set OUTPUT switch on Model 64 to OFF.

27   Set RANGE switch on HP 410 B to 30 V.

28   Set VOLTS-μA switch on Model 64 to 30.

29   Set OUTPUT switch on Model 64 to DIR.

30   Step DIVIDE switch on Model 64 to 150. The applied voltage is now 30 volts. The HP 410 B should now read within 1 small division of 3 on the 0–3 scale.

31   Set OUTPUT switch on Model 64 to OFF.

32   Set RANGE switch on HP 410 B to 100 V.

33   Set DIVIDE switch on Model 64 to 0.

34   Set VOLTS-μA switch on Model 64 to 150.

35   Set OUTPUT switch on Model 64 to DIR.

36   Step DIVIDE switch on Model 64 to 100. The applied voltage is now 100 volts. The HP 410 B should now read within 1.5 small divisions of 1.0 on the 0–1.0 scale.

37   Set the OUTPUT switch on the Model 64 to OFF.

38   Set the RANGE switch on the HP 410 B to 300 V.

39   Set the VOLTS-μA switch on the Model 64 to 300.

40   Set the OUTPUT switch on the Model 64 to DIR.

41   Step DIVIDE switch on Model 64 to 150. The applied voltage is now 300 volts. The HP 410 B should indicate within 1 small division of 3 on the 0-3 scale.

42   Set the OUTPUT switch on the Model 64 to OFF.

43   Set the RANGE switch on the HP 410 B to 1000 V.

44   Set the VOLTS-μA switch on the Model 64 to 750.

45   Set the OUTPUT switch on the Model 64 to DIR. The applied voltage is now 750 volts. The HP 410 B should read within 1.5 small divisions of 0.75 on the 0–1.0 scale.

46   Set the OUTPUT switch on the Model 64 to OFF.

47   Set all RANGE and DIVIDE switches to their minimum values.

48   Remove leads from the Model 64.

49   Set the SELECTOR switch on the HP 410 B to AC, and the RANGE switch to 1 V.

50   Short the COMMON and a-c leads together and adjust a-c control for a precise zero on the meter.

51   Using the COARSE and FINE controls on the Model 63 Calibrator, adjust for a null on the NULL MONITOR.

52   Connect the COMMON lead of the HP 410 B to the $\pm$ terminal of the Model 63. Connect the a-c probe to the 1.5 terminal.

53   Adjust the C DIVIDE switch on the Model 63 to the 10 position. The applied a-c voltage is 1 volt. The HP 410 B should read within 1.5 small divisions of 1.0 on the Red 0–1.0 scale. If not, adjust R 35 for a proper indication.

54   Set the C DIVIDE switch on the Model 63 counterclockwise to 0.

55   Set RANGE switch on the HP 410 B to 3 V. Connect the a-c probe to the 3 terminal of the Model 63.

56   Adjust C DIVIDE switch on the Model 63 to 15. The applied voltage is now 3 volts. The HP 410 B should indicate within 1 small division of 3 on the Red 0–3 scale. If not, adjust R 39 for a proper indication.

57   Set C DIVIDE switch on the Model 63 counterclockwise to 0.

58   Set the RANGE switch on the HP 410 B to 10 V. Connect the a-c probe to the 15 terminal of the Model 63.

59   Adjust C DIVIDE switch on the Model 63 to 10. The applied voltage is now 10 volts. The HP 410 B should indicate within 1.5 small divisions of 1.0 on the Black 0-1.0 scale. If not, adjust R 40 for a proper indication.

60   Set C DIVIDE switch on the Model 63 counterclockwise to 0.

61   Set the RANGE switch on the HP 410 B to 30 V. Connect the a-c probe to the 30 terminal on the Model 63.

62   Adjust C DIVIDE switch on the Model 63 to 15. The applied voltage is now 30 volts. The HP 410 B should read within 1 small division of 3 on the Black 0–3 scale. If not, adjust R 36 for a proper indication.

63   Set the C DIVIDE switch on the Model 63 counterclockwise to 0.

64   Set the RANGE switch on the HP 410 B to 100 V. Connect the a-c probe to the 150 terminal on the Model 63.

65   Set the OUTPUT RANGE switch on the Model 63 to 75–150–300.

66   Adjust B DIVIDE switch on the Model 63 to 10. The applied voltage is now 100 volts. The HP 410 B should read within 1.5 small divisions of 1.0 on the 0–1.0 scale. If not, adjust R 37 for a proper indication.

67   Set B DIVIDE switch on the Model 63 counterclockwise to 0.

68   Set RANGE switch on the HP 410 B to 300 V. Connect the a-c probe to the 300 terminal on the Model 63.

69   Adjust C DIVIDE switch on the Model 63 to 15. The applied voltage is now 300 volts. The HP 410 B should read within 1 small division of 3 on the 0–3 scale. If not, adjust R 38 for a proper indication.

70   Set C DIVIDE switch on the Model 63 counterclockwise to 0.

71   Set the SELECTOR switch on the HP 410 B to OHMS.

72   Set RANGE switch to R $\times$ 10.

73 Adjust OHMS ADJ ∞ for a full scale reading (leads not shorted).

74 Set RANGE switch to R $\times$ 1. Meter should indicate full scale (∞). If not, adjust R 49 for a proper indication.

75 Shut all equipment OFF.

Equipment and Calibration Techniques
Associated with Waveforms

8

The most common graphical representation of a physical phenomenon is a plot of magnitude versus time. On a purely theoretical basis, the plotting procedure consists of using a formula which presents the magnitude as a function of time. By calculating a sufficient number of magnitude values for specific values of time, it is possible to draw a smooth curve representing the phenomenon on rectangular or other suitable coordinates.

The most common method of "automatically" recording the *actual magnitude* of a phenomenon in relation to time consists of first converting the phenomenon into a voltage and then recording the voltage waveform with a suitable electronic or electromechanical apparatus.

The basic periodic waveform is the sinewave. A pure sine wave is free from harmonics. The more complex waveforms are developed by adding in-phase and/or out-of-phase sine waves along with even and/or odd harmonics of the fundamental sine wave. A more detailed analysis of this process is given in Appendix D.

Because of the relationships just mentioned, two important periodic waveform measurements are apparant—relative phase and frequency determinations.

Although the horizontal axis represents time, periodic waveform duration is more frequently recorded in terms of angular measure. One cycle represents 360° (2π radians). This notation developed because of the rotating phasor concept of alternating voltages and currents. Alternative horizontal axis scales include angular velocity ($\omega = 2\pi f$)

and time units based on the cyclic period

$$(T = \frac{1}{f} = \frac{2\pi}{\omega}).$$

The relative phase angle between two waveforms may be determined by two different approaches—by measuring the angle between successive peaks of two or more waveforms, or by determining the angular difference between the waveforms as they pass through the zero reference point. A waveform which reaches the peak value first (or goes through zero first) is a *leading* waveform.

The frequency of the waveform is a measure of the number of cycles repeated per unit of time (usually 1 second). Since frequency is defined in this manner, the standards, measurements, and calibrations for frequency determinations can also be interpreted in terms of time.

This chapter is concerned with the following aspects of waveform measurements: waveshape, frequency, time interval, phase, and distortion.

WAVEFORM RECORDING EQUIPMENT

The exact shape of a voltage waveform (remember, this voltage may represent any physical phenomenon) may take on an infinite variety of patterns. Some of these are shown in Fig. 8-1. The waveforms shown are periodic; i.e., they are repeated at regular intervals. Nonperiodic, or random, forms also exist.

The signals in most communications systems are composed of various sinusoids added, subtracted, and multiplied to produce the resultant waveform.

Newer equipment employed in pulse communication systems, as well as the equipment used in digital computers, radar, television, facsimile, and control systems, uses signals of a more transient nature—pulses. In these cases the actual shape of the signals is important.

A standard rectangular pulse is shown in Fig. 8-2A. Fig. 8-2B shows a common waveform associated with pulse measurements. This waveform displays *overshoot*—distorted response to the abrupt application of the pulse—and *undershoot*—distorted response to the abrupt cessation of the pulse. Overshoot is defined by $E_{max} - E_f$ although there may be several damped cycles associated with this type of waveform. Undershoot is given by E_{min} unless the over-all waveform is biased at some d-c level other than zero; for the latter case, the overshoot becomes $E_{min} - E_{dc}$.

Another important factor shown in Fig. 8-2B is the *rise time* and *fall time* associated with the leading and trailing edges of the pulse, respectively. There is no universal standard definition for this factor. In this manual, these time measurements will be associated with the interval between $0.1 E_f$ and $0.9 E_f$. Rise- and fall-time limits must always be defined if they are to have exact meaning.

A third factor known as *sag*, is shown in Fig. 8-2C. Sag is the distorted response to the flat top of a pulse waveform, and is given in percent by

$$\% \, \text{sag} = \frac{E_i - E_f}{E_i} \times 100 \, \%$$

The actual sag curve is given by $K\epsilon^{-At}$, as shown, where $K = 1/A$ is the initial slope of the curve. Sag is, therefore, an exponential response produced by capacitive effects of circuitry.

Good waveform recorders must incorporate special design precautions to insure that the recorders themselves do not produce the

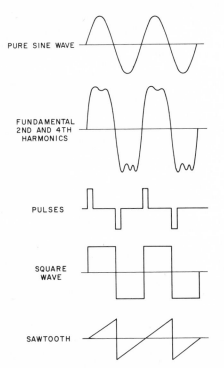

Fig. 8-1 Alternating waveforms.

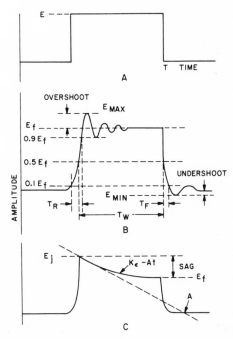

Fig. 8-2 Forms of pulse distortion.

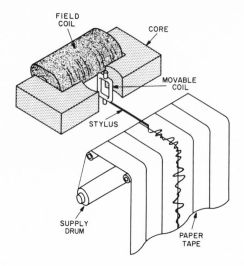

Fig. 8-3 Electromagnetic oscillograph.

distortions just described. The essential factors in choosing and calibrating a recorder are its individual frequency response, rise and fall time, and sag. These factors must be negligible, or at least accurately known, over the frequency and amplitude ranges that will be used.

DIRECT-READING OSCILLOGRAPHS   Recorders which produce permanent records of waveforms on paper tapes are known as *direct-reading oscillographs*. The picture on the paper tape is an *oscillogram*. Most of these instruments use an electromagnetic movement similar to the galvanometer movement —a coil of wire suspended in a magnetic field. A stylus is attached to the coil directly or through a system of levers. This stylus contains an instant-drying ink, or it may be heated if the paper tape is sensitive to heat. In some instruments, the stylus is replaced by a mirror, and a sensitive photographic tape is used to record the deflected light beam.

The response of the stylus or mirror is proportional to the instantaneous current in the wire loop if the mass of the sytem is small and if proper damping is employed. Under these conditions, the angular deflection is given by

$$\theta = K_1 BIN$$

where B is the flux density in the magnetic air gap, I is the current in the coil, and N is the number of turns in the coil. The constant K_1 depends on the construction of the movement.

The time axis for the recorded waveform is provided by driving the paper tape beneath the stylus at a constant speed.

The general construction of the electromagnetic oscillograph is shown in Fig. 8-3. The bottom end of the tape may be free (as shown), or it may be wound onto a take-up drum.

In use, the oscillograph requires auxiliary equipment such as power supplies, current shunts, and voltage dividers.

The upper frequency limit of these devices is in the vicinity of 6000 cps, with sensitivity (amount of deflection for specific input amplitude) decreasing as frequency increases.

Simultaneous examination of more than one phenomenon is possible by the use of multichannel oscillographs.

Calibration of the electromagnetic oscillograph consists of determining the machine constant (K_1), the frequency response, and the relationship between paper-tape speed and actual time measurements.

In calibrating the machine constant, it is more desirable to rewrite the previous deflection equation as

$$\theta = K_2 IN$$

In the form of the equation, K_2 represents both K_1 and B and allows the calibration to include variations in the field of the magnet used with the instrument. If an electromagnet rather than a permanent magnet is used to provide the field, the value of K_2 will be valid only for the particular field supply conditions used in the determination of the constant.

The circuit for determining the value of K_2 is illustrated in Fig. 8-4. The rheostat is used to control the current magnitude, which may be read on the calibrated ammeter. The switch is closed rapidly and is held closed long enough for the oscillograph to reach a steady value. At this point the current value should be read. The value of K_2 is given by

$$K_2 = \frac{\theta}{aIN}$$

where a is the experimentally determined current-transformer turns ratio (see Chapter 6). The deflection θ may be measured directly on the paper tape in terms of any convenient length unit.

The foregoing procedure will also show any damping and overshoot irregularities, since the closing and opening of the switch represents a rectangular pulse. Thus, the rise time, fall time, overshoot, undershoot, and sag can be determined from the plot on the paper tape.

Once K_2 has been determined, the relative frequency response can be calibrated. Specially designed resonant shunt circuits and equalizing networks are used to correct response irregularities and provide a relatively flat response over the range for which the device is to be used.

If a pure sinusoidal input of good frequency and amplitude stability from a variable-frequency generator is used to produce an oscillogram, the amplitude can be measured directly on the tape in any convenient length unit. This measurement can be made over the entire frequency range. *Adjustments must be made at the generator to insure that its output remains constant as frequency changes.* After each frequency change, sufficient time should be allowed for the generator (and oscillograph) to reach a stable steady state. A plot of relative amplitude versus frequency can be compared with a similar curve supplied by the oscillograph manufacturer.

The foregoing procedure also allows calibration of the tape speed, since frequency and time are inversely proportional. This calibration is accomplished by measuring the length L occupied by n cycles of a fixed frequency input f. The speed of the tape is given by

$$v = \frac{Lf}{n} \quad \text{length units/sec}$$

OSCILLOSCOPES *Oscilloscope* is the term commonly applied to the *cathode-ray* oscillograph. In this instrument, the oscillograph stylus is replaced by a beam of electrons. Deflection of this beam is accomplished by either an electrostatic or an electromagnetic device. Instead of tracing a permanent record on paper tape, the oscilloscope traces a temporary plot on a phosphorescent screen. All these components—electron beam, deflection system, and screen—are contained in a single cathode ray tube.

Luminescence is produced by the beam of high-velocity electrons impinging on the fluorescent coating, which is deposited on the inner surface of the tube face. The electrons are released initially by the cathode and are then attracted by the positive potential of the first anode. First, they must pass through an opening in the grid structure, a provision that helps to collimate the electron stream. The magnitude of negative voltage applied to the grid with respect to the cathode limits the number of electrons passing through, and therefore determines the intensity of fluorescence eventually produced at the screen. For a particular ratio of the potential at the second anode to the potential at the first, the electrons of the col-

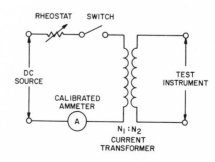

Fig. 8-4 Oscillograph K_2 determination.

limated beam will converge on the screen and form a sharply defined spot of light. This method of converging the electrons is called *electrostatic focusing.*

The position at which the spot appears is determined by the potentials on two pairs of deflecting plates. In each pair, the planes of the two plates are parallel, and between the pairs a right-angle relationship exists. In operation, the tube is oriented so that, when there is a potential difference across each pair of plates, one set will deflect the electrons along the vertical dimension and the other will deflect them along the horizontal dimension. This method of deflecting the moving electrons is called *electrostatic deflection.* When the plates are made long to increase the deflection sensitivity, the ends nearer to the screen are often divergent so that electrons will not be collected by the plates. The magnitude of the displacement on the screen is proportional to the deflection voltage, the length of the plates, and the distance of the plates from the screen, and is inversely proportional to the second anode potential.

Since the brightness of the light emitted by the screen depends on the kinetic energy of the bombarding electrons, there is a point below which the anode voltage may not be reduced. (The energy of the moving electrons varies directly with the second anode potential.) Many cathode-ray tubes therefore include a third anode between the deflection plates and the screen, so that sufficient energy may be imparted to the electrons without incurring excessive loss of deflection sensitivity. The post-deflection anode usually takes the form of a graphite coating on the inner wall of the tube.

Electrostatic tubes can respond to frequencies over 100 mc, and do not absorb a significant amount of power from the source of deflection voltage. For these reasons, an oscilloscope invariably employs an electrostatic cathode-ray tube.

A description of tubes utilizing electromag-netic principles of deflection and focusing is omitted, since these tubes are not employed extensively in measurement processes.

A block diagram of a simple oscilloscope is shown in Fig. 8-5. The associated circuits are provided to perform a number of functions. One group, the high-voltage power supply, furnishes the various potentials required to operate the cathode-ray tube. Note the intensity, focusing, and positioning controls. Direct-current operating voltages for the various other circuits are provided by a separate low-voltage supply, not shown in the block diagram. Another important section consists of sweep-generating circuits which produce a sawtooth sweep. This voltage, which later is applied to the horizontal deflecting plates, increases in amplitude at a constant rate. As a result, the lateral deflection of the electron beam is proportional to time. Furthermore, the frequency of the sweep generator can be varied, usually from about 15 to 20,000 cps. If desired, it is also possible to switch into the horizontal amplifier an externally generated sweep, or any other waveform.

The horizontal and vertical amplifiers develop sufficient signal voltage to insure ample deflections on the screen of the cathode-ray tube while absorbing negligible power from the source of the input signal. There is a gain control in each amplifier to adjust the amount of deflection. More expensive oscilloscopes incorporate a frequency-compensated input attenuator, to permit the application of greater-amplitude signals to the instrument without causing pattern distortion.

If a signal is applied to the vertical-deflection plates by the vertical amplifier at the same time a sawtooth sweep is applied to the horizontal-deflection plates by the horizontal amplifier, the display will be a pattern showing visually the variations of the signal with time. The permissible frequency range of the input signal is governed by the bandpass of the vertical amplifier, as well as by

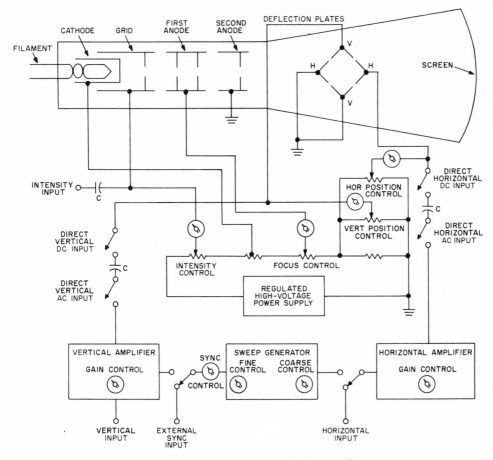

Fig. 8-5 Block diagram of a cathode-ray oscilloscope.

the highest frequency of the sweep generator. *A true representation of a complex waveform is possible only if the highest appreciable harmonic frequency lies within the bandpass of the vertical amplifier.*

The time scale (usually the horizontal axis) most commonly employed for an oscilloscope is produced by a sawtooth sweep voltage applied to the horizontal-deflection plates as mentioned above. Such an arrangement produces a waveform representation as shown in Fig. 8-6A. Special circuitry is usually employed to prevent the electron beam from producing a luminous trace when it returns from right to left. Another useful time base is shown in Fig. 8-6B. The circular

sweep is produced by applying two sinusoidal voltages of equal magnitude and frequency, but 90 degrees out of phase (usually produced from a single source by a phase-splitting network) to the respective deflecting electrodes. Here, the angle of rotation of the spot is proportional to time, with one revolution representing one deflection-wave cycle. The test voltage is applied to either of the deflection-plate pairs.

Grounding the oscilloscope cabinet is desirable for safety. Oscilloscope leads (and sometimes the entire test setup) must be shielded. A helpful system of grounding and shielding consists of operating all the equipment in the test setup on a bench surface

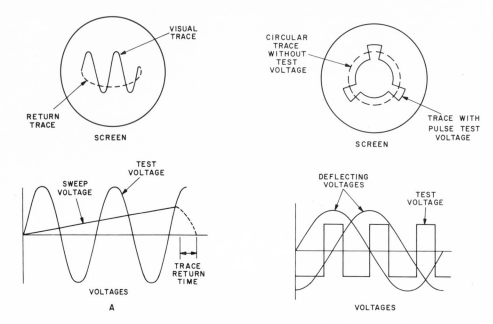

Fig. 8-6 Oscilloscope trace methods.

which has a large conductive sheet insulated from the bench itself. All ground connections can be made directly to this sheet. The arrangement and length of the oscilloscope input leads must be given careful attention.

Most oscilloscopes have an input impedance equivalent to that of a resistor and capacitor in parallel. When an oscilloscope is used to measure high-impedance circuits, the value of the resistive input impedance becomes important, since it may present an undesirable load to the equipment under test. The capacitive component is also important since it may result in high-frequency distortion.

Because of the preceding considerations, as well as distortion due to the effect of low-impedance coaxial cables (when used), an impedance-matching device of some sort must be used in order to obtain accurate results. Manufacturer's handbooks and specifications list the maximum ratings of input signal which may be applied to the various oscilloscope input terminals. Such external networks as attenuators, amplitude limiters,

and frequency or amplitude selectors may prove helpful in operating within these ranges.

Although oscilloscope traces are temporary by nature, the picture on the screen can be permanently recorded by photographic techniques. Regular camera, movie camera, and quick-printing (Polaroid) attachments are available.

A typical high-speed laboratory instrument, the Tektronix 545 oscilloscope, is pictured in Fig. 8-7. This oscilloscope's fast rise time, wide sweep-speed range, and 10-kilovolt accelerating voltage permit fast, easy analysis of fast-time waveforms.

By using plug-in preamplifiers, the instrument can be used in almost all laboratory-oscilloscope applications. The sweep speeds and vertical-deflection sensitivity can be precisely calibrated to permit accurate quantitative time and amplitude measurements. Detailed observation of a very small portion of the input waveform is made possible by accurately delayed trigger sweeps.

As is true of any other type of precision

measurement equipment, calibration of the oscilloscope is essential. Primarily this consists of amplitude calibration (vertical deflection) and time-base calibration (horizontal deflection).

Amplitude calibration is usually accomplished by impressing a known, controlled d-c voltage across the vertical input terminals. Initially the spot on the screen can be set to any convenient position. Usually the center position is a good starting point. The application of the d-c voltage will cause a deflection of the spot, and the spot will hold its new position as long as the voltage is maintained. Next, the deflection distance is measured directly on the screen. The vertical sensitivity (volts/millimeter, usually) can then be computed and compared with that quoted by the manufacturer. This check should be repeated by initially setting the location of the spot at various places about the screen. The latter procedure enables calibration of the linearity of the deflection throughout the entire movement range.

Amplitude calibration should be performed at each amplifier and attenuator setting of the input controls in order to determine changes in these devices, which, as a rule, maintain stable conditions for long periods of time. One sensitivity calculation for each setting is usually sufficient.

Methods exist for producing calibrating pulses or bright dots directly on the oscilloscope screen. The requirement for complex equipment, however, makes most of these systems impracticable from the standpoint of economics and testing time.

Sine waves are not desirable calibrating waveforms because of waveform distortions which may be introduced. Square waves are frequently used, since peak-to-peak measurements are easy to make and accuracy is high.

Time-base calibration can be accomplished with a continuous-wave sinusoid of accurately known and stable frequency characteristics. The calibrating signal is applied across the vertical input terminals. The sweep generator is triggered once, and the resultant trace is recorded by photographic methods. The total sweep time and the sweep sensitivity (time/unit length) are then computed from the number of calibration cycles recorded. This procedure can be repeated at each sweep control setting.

Timing *markers*, which are provided by *marker generators* may also be used for time-base calibration. These accurately spaced markers can be viewed directly on the screen, impressed on the trace of the vertical input signal. The markers, in the form of positive pulses, may be applied directly to the horizontal input terminals. They may also be applied to the electrode controlling the beam current (or to any intensifier electrode) to produce bright spots on the trace. The latter method of application provides an accurate time scale independent of imperfections in the over-all instrument. Marker generation becomes less reliable as sweep speeds are increased; therefore, it is more practical to use sine-wave calibrating signals for very short time intervals.

Fig. 8-7 Tektronix type 545 oscilloscope.

A simple method of calibrating the time duration of regularly repeated rectangular pulses requires only a calibrated communication receiver with a frequency coverage of several megacycles. The receiver is connected directly to the source of the pulses and is tuned across the frequency range. As the receiver is tuned, a frequency component will be encountered at intervals equal to the pulse repetition frequency. The amplitude of this component is minimum (null) at frequencies that are multiples of the reciprocal of the pulse duration. Thus the receiver operates as a spectrum analyzer.

After the time base is calibrated, the same conditions (power-line voltage, control settings, etc.) that were used during calibration must be maintained during operation.

Although the electromagnetic oscillograph is a more economic device for monitoring several different phenomena simultaneously, the monitoring of high-frequency information may require a higher frequency response than the usual 6000-cps limit of these recorders. Multichannel oscilloscopes, such as the one pictured in Fig. 8-8, are available for these applications. The model pictured in the figure has separate sweep circuitry and controls for each channel. Thus, the individual channel is calibrated as an ordinary oscilloscope would be.

Fig. 8-8 Multichannel oscilloscope. (Courtesy, Sierra Electronics.)

SYNCHROSCOPES   The synchroscope, which is widely used in radar testing, will be described in considerable detail, because an understanding of its action is important.

The synchroscope is an adaptation of the oscilloscope. A trace is produced by the synchroscope only when it is initiated by an input trigger, as contrasted with the continuous-sawtooth sweep provided by the oscilloscope. Synchroscope circuits are similar to oscilloscope circuits except for the signal channel and the sweep channel. The circuits for these channels in a typical synchroscope are shown in block form in Fig. 8-9.

The signal channel includes an input circuit, which is usually in the form of a 72-ohm adjustable-step attenuator. Various degrees of attenuation are available, and the knob is calibrated to indicate how much attenuation is present. Use of this attenuator insures that all signals, regardless of amplitude, produce about the same input level to the amplifier section. Following the attenuator is an artificial delay line, which is a low-pass filter with a cutoff frequency higher than the highest frequency to be passed and which has an impedance of 72 ohms. The delay line is terminated with a 72-ohm gain control. One purpose of this delay line is to delay the signal to be observed until the sweep trace has been initiated by a portion of the input signal which is not delayed. If the delay line were not used, the beginning portion of the waveform would not appear on the trace (as shown in Fig. 8-10) because a certain amount of time is required for the input signal voltage to rise to the level needed to trigger the sweep circuit. With the delay line in use, the signal does not reach the amplifier until ½ microsecond (μsec) after the trace starts; as a result, the entire pulse is seen. A secondary purpose of the delay line is to provide, by means of reflection, a series of accurately spaced pulses suitable for calibration of short time intervals. To accomplish this purpose, a switch is provided to cause a

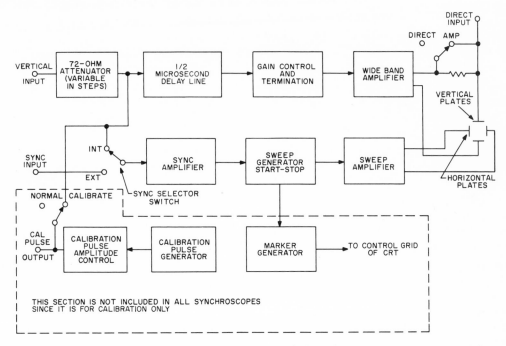

Fig. 8-9 Block diagram of a typical synchroscope.

mismatch in the termination of the delay line so that when a sharp pulse is fed into the line, a series of reflections will occur (Fig. 8-11). Since the time required for a pulse to travel to the end of the line and back is 1 μsec, a series of pulses, occurring 1 μsec apart, is produced. Of course, each successive pulse is smaller because of losses in the delay line, but a sufficient number are visible for most high-speed calibration purposes.

The gain control feeds a wideband (video) amplifier, which is connected to the vertical-deflection plates. In addition, an external connection is provided to the vertical plates.

The horizontal circuit consists of a sync switch for selecting either internal or external synchronization, a sync amplifier with a gain control, and a start-stop sweep generator, which will not develop a sweep voltage until a pulse of sufficient amplitude is fed in. The duration of the sweep, or the sweep speed, may be varied from a very few microseconds to about 250 μsec. The sweep generator is followed by a conven-

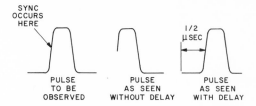

Fig. 8-10 Action of delay line.

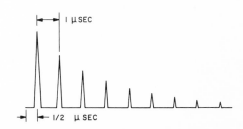

Fig. 8-11 Pulse reflections on an artificial line.

tional horizontal amplifier. Since the trace is triggered by the input signal, the synchroscope may be used to observe non-periodic pulses, such as those occurring in a radar system that has an unstable PRF.

In instruments of later design, it is common to find provisions for calibration of input voltages and sweep time. Voltage calibration is made by comparing the unknown voltage with a variable-voltage pulse of known value, generated internally. The calibrating pulse is adjusted to be equal in amplitude to the unknown voltage, and the value is read from the dial that controls the calibrating pulse. Sweep-time calibration is made with the aid of marker pulses produced by accurately adjusted tuned circuits. The marker pulses appear on the trace as a series of bright dots spaced at intervals chosen by the operator. In a typical synchroscope, marker intervals of 0.2, 1, 10, or 100 μsec may be selected in accordance with the time duration of the pulse to be observed; for greater accuracy, interpolation may be used.

The accuracy of the internal calibration voltages and sweeps can be checked with externally attached calibration signals, as discussed in connection with oscilloscopes. Many advanced oscilloscopes may be operated in a triggering mode to serve as synchroscopes.

FREQUENCY-MEASURING EQUIPMENT AND TECHNIQUES

In a previous discussion, frequency was defined as the number of repetitions (cycles) of a periodic phenomena occurring per unit time. Fundamental mechanical and electromagnetic oscillations are sinusoidal by nature. In making mechanical frequency measurements, the vibration is almost always converted to an electrical waveform, as discussed in Chapter 9. This section is devoted to equipment associated with the measurement of electrical and electromagnetic phenomena.

BRIDGE METHODS Null-indicating bridges (see Chapter 7) which are dependent upon fre-

quency for their balance equations can be used to measure frequency. The Hay bridge (C-3, Table 7-1) can be used, although it is usually modified slightly when primarily applied to frequency measurements. Commonly employed frequency bridges are listed in Table 8-1.

Special consideration must be given to grounding and shielding, as was true of impedance bridges discussed previously. The power consumed by a frequency bridge should be very small. An accuracy of 0.5 to 1% can be obtained.

WAVE METERS The absorption frequency meter, or wave meter, consists of an indicating device and an inductor and capacitor, either or both of which may be variable. As a rule, the capacitor is the variable element, and the band of frequencies covered by the instrument is determined by the coil in use. When tuned to the frequency of the transmitter and loosely coupled to the tank coil, a device of this type will absorb a small amount of energy. The presence of this energy can be indicated in several ways. When a flashlight lamp is used, resonance is indicated by maximum brilliance of the lamp. If improved sensitivity is desired, the lamp may be replaced by a vacuum-tube voltmeter or by a crystal detector and d-c milliammeter.

A well-made instrument will provide accuracies of 0.25 to 2.0%. Although not suitable for precise measurement, the less expensive absorption wave meter is nevertheless an extremely useful general-purpose instrument. For example, it is valuable for detecting the presence of r-f energy in unwanted places and for making approximate measurements of frequency, such as the measurement of parasitic oscillations during the neutralization of an amplifier. Other uses are (1) checking the fundamental frequency of an oscillating circuit, (2) determining the amplitude and order of harmonic frequencies, and (3) providing a relative measure of field strength.

Table 8-1 Commonly Used Frequency Bridges

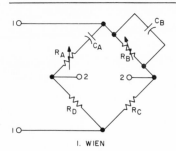

I. WIEN

$$f = \frac{1}{2\pi\sqrt{R_A R_B C_A C_B}}$$

OR

$$f = \frac{1}{2\pi R_B C_B}$$

Measures frequencies to 20 kc. In practice R_C, R_D, C_A, and C_B are kept constant with $C_A = C_B$ and $R_D = 2R_C$. R_A and R_B are equal and are varied simultaneously in equal increments. Under these conditions, the second balance equation is valid. Accuracy of 0.5% is possible. A frequency range of 10 to 1 can be covered with a single set of components with various ranges obtained by changing the values of C_A and C_B.

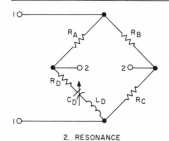

2. RESONANCE

$$f = \frac{1}{2\pi\sqrt{L_D C_D}}$$

At balance, series resonance exists between L_D and C_D, so that this branch is purely resistive. R_D is the inherent resistance of the inductor, capacitor, and branch wiring.

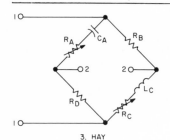

3. HAY

$$f = \frac{R_C}{2\pi\sqrt{L_C(R_B R_D C_A - L_C)}}$$

Modification of inductance bridge (see C-3, Table 7-1) by placing a variable resistor in series with the inductor. The total resistance R_C includes the inherent inductor resistance. Used from 50 to 5000 cps with $L_C = 1/2\pi$ henrys, $C_A = 1/2\pi$ microfarads, and $R_D = R_B = 1.414$ kilohms.

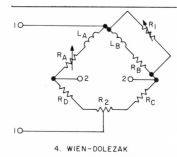

4. WIEN–DOLEZAK

$$R_1 = R_C \frac{1 + \dfrac{R_B L_A}{R_A L_B}}{\dfrac{R_D}{R_C} - \dfrac{L_A}{L_B}}$$

$$f = \frac{R_A}{2\pi\left[L_A L_B\left(\dfrac{R_D}{R_C} - \dfrac{L_A}{L_B}\right)\right]^{\frac{1}{2}}}$$

$$\times \left[1 - \left(\frac{R_B}{R_A}\right)^2\left(\frac{R_D}{R_C}\right)\left(\frac{L_A}{L_B}\right)\right]^{\frac{1}{2}}$$

Frequency range is from a few cycles to 2000 cps. Usually used with $L_B = 1000$ microhenrys and $L_A = 100$ microhenrys. R_B should be 150 ohms, and the ratio R_D/R_C should be 0.353. The latter is accomplished by tapping R_2 at the proper point. When balance occurs under these conditions, $f = R_A (1 - 795/R_A^2)^{1/2}$.

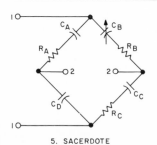

5. SACERDOTE

$$\frac{R_B}{C_D} = \frac{R_A}{C_C} + \frac{R_C}{C_A}$$

$$f = \left[\frac{(1 - C_A C_C / C_B C_D)}{R_A R_C C_A C_C}\right]^{\frac{1}{2}}$$

If the first equation is satisfied by fixing the values of R_A, R_B, R_C, C_C, and C_D, and if C_B can be varied from $C_A C_C / C_D$ to infinity, the frequency range will extend from zero to $(1/2\pi \, R_A R_C C_A C_C)^{1/2}$.

Table 8-1 Commonly Used Frequency Bridges (Cont.)

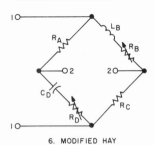

$$R_D = \frac{1}{R_B}\left(R_A R_C - \frac{L_B}{C_D}\right)$$

$$f = \frac{R_B}{2\pi\left[L_B C_D\left(R_A R_C - \frac{L_B}{C_D}\right)\right]^{\frac{1}{2}}}$$

R_A and R_C are kept equal. Balance can be obtained at $f = R_B$ if $R_A = R_C = 594.4$ ohms, $C_D = 1$ microfarad, and $L_B = 100$ millihenrys. Other combinations are also possible. Frequency ranges from 25 to 5000 cps can be obtained.

6. MODIFIED HAY

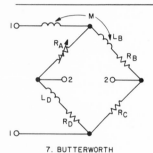

$$M = \frac{(L_B R_D + L_D R_B)}{(R_C + R_D)}$$

$$f = \left[\frac{R_A R_C - R_B R_D}{4\pi^2 L_D (M + L_B)}\right]^{\frac{1}{2}}$$

Usually $L_B = L_D$ and M is fixed by satisfying the first equation. This bridge has an infinite frequency range.

7. BUTTERWORTH

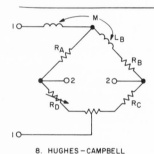

$$M = \frac{R_D L_B}{R_A + R_B + R_C + R_D}$$

$$f = \frac{\sqrt{A}}{2\pi L_B}\left[\frac{R_A(B - R_D)}{R_D} - R_B\right]^{\frac{1}{2}}$$

$$A = \sqrt{R_A + R_B + R_C}$$

$$B = R_C R_D$$

Excellent for very low frequencies—10 to 120 cps. Values of A and B are fixed. M must be variable in order to satisfy the first balance equation. Suggested values for the frequency range quoted are: $R_A = 5$ ohms, $B = 4$ ohms, $R_B = 25$ ohms, $L_B = 0.1$ henry, M variable from 0.28 to 1.7 millihenrys, and R_D variable from 0.1 to 0.6 ohm.

8. HUGHES—CAMPBELL

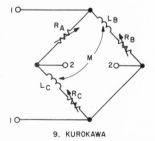

$$R_B = R_C$$

$$M = \frac{R_C(L_B + L_C)}{R_A}$$

$$f = \frac{R_C}{2\pi\sqrt{L_B L_C - M^2}}$$

Frequency range is from a few cycles to 5000 cps.

9. KUROKAWA

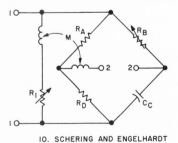

$$M \approx \frac{C_C R_1 R_B R_D}{R_A + R_D}$$

$$f = \frac{1}{2\pi}\left[\frac{R_1 R_A}{M C_C R_B(R_A + R_D)}\right]^{\frac{1}{2}}$$

Used for measurements in the audio-frequency range.

10. SCHERING AND ENGELHARDT

Occasionally, a measurement is possible even when the power available from the circuit being tested is not sufficient to actuate the indicator of the wave meter. In the case of circuits that incorporate a grid or plate current meter, the indications of these meters will change when the wave meter is tuned through resonance. The coupling should be loose so that the mutual inductance between the tank and the wave meter does not appreciably change the frequency of oscillation.

HETERODYNE FREQUENCY METERS More accurate frequency measurements are possible with heterodyne frequency meters. To be most effective, such a meter must incorporate a small, fully shielded oscillator that covers the entire frequency range to be measured. The use of plug-in coils or switches is generally unsatisfactory because they introduce frequency instability. If the construction of the frequency meter is sturdy throughout, and if high-grade ceramics are used as insulators in the oscillator circuit, a precise frequency calibration will hold over a long period of time. The tuning element of the oscillator is usually equipped with a vernier type dial to permit accurate settings. In some cases, the divisions of the dial may be engraved directly in terms of frequency, but more often a calibration chart is used with the instrument.

An electron-coupled oscillator is well suited for heterodyne meters. By using a voltage-stabilized power supply and correctly proportioning the plate and screen voltages of the oscillator, it is possible to obtain extremely stable oscillations. Adequate power can be obtained from the plate circuit without impairing stability. Another desirable property of the plate circuit output is the presence of strong harmonics.

More elaborate heterodyne meters also include a quartz-crystal–controlled oscillator which is used to check the accuracy of multiple points on the graduated dial. Calibration checks insure accurate measurements.

A block diagram of the heterodyne meter is illustrated in Fig. 8-12. When the frequencies of the beating signals are exactly the same, the difference frequency is zero. Under this condition, a null would be indicated by a signal-indicating device; for example, no tone would be audible in a headset. Many heterodyne meters also include an antenna for picking up a radiated signal. In use, the instrument is placed near the source of the frequency to be measured, and the need for a direct connection between the instrument and the source is eliminated. The calibrated oscillator is then tuned for a zero-beat condition. When the zero beat is obtained, the unknown frequency is either the same as that of the calibrated oscillator or, as explained in the following paragraphs, it is a harmonic of the oscillator frequency. With the aid of the calibration chart, the dial reading of the frequency meter will indicate the frequency under measurement. Another procedure is to radiate the oscillator signal by means of the antenna and to beat it against the unknown signal in an external receiver.

When frequencies greater than the upper limit of the variable oscillator must be meas-

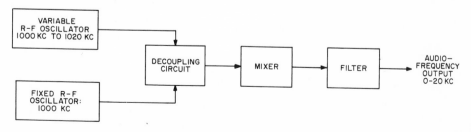

Fig. 8-12 Block diagram of beat-frequency oscillator.

ured, it is customary to beat harmonics of the oscillator against the unknown signal. The procedure is to turn the dial from the high end of the band and note where the first two strong beats occur. The difference of the frequencies corresponding to the settings for zero beat is divided into the higher frequency. The integer obtained from this division is then multiplied by the lower frequency to obtain the unknown frequency.

As an illustration, suppose that the range of the heterodyne meter in use lies between 100 and 200 kc. The first two strong beats produced by a signal higher than 200 kc in frequency occur at dial settings corresponding to 162.5 kc and 130 kc. Subtraction gives a difference of 32.5 kc. Division of this number into 162.5 kc yields 5. This means that the unknown frequency is the fifth harmonic of 130 kc and is therefore equal to 650 kc.

The drawback of the previously described method is the uncertainty that sometimes arises when harmonics of the unknown signal combine with the internal signal to produce exceptionally prominent beats. Although such beats usually are not pronounced enough to be misleading, the foregoing procedure must be modified to include a wavemeter or some other means of approximating the unknown frequency whenever confusion is possible. Knowledge of the approximate frequency then insures an exact measurement without danger of error.

For example, suppose that the second harmonic of the 650-kc signal assumed in the preceding illustration can produce beats as strong as those arising from the fundamental. In this event, a zero beat will be obtained at a dial setting of 144.5 kc, since the ninth harmonic of this frequency equals 1300 kc. Naturally, if the beat occurring at the 144.5-kc setting were used instead of the one at 130 kc, the subsequent calculation would result in an answer of 1300 kc. By knowing the approximate frequency in advance, however, it is still possible to make a true measurement. Under this circumstance, 1300 would be divided by 2, giving 650 kc as before.

ZERO-BEAT INDICATORS   Precision measurements based on the heterodyne principle necessitate the use of sensitive zero-beat indicators. Headphones may be acceptable to obtain an approximate indication of zero beat, but for greater accuracy visual methods of indication are required.

When exceptional sensitivity is required, an oscilloscope may be used. The sensitivity of the device increases with the amount of

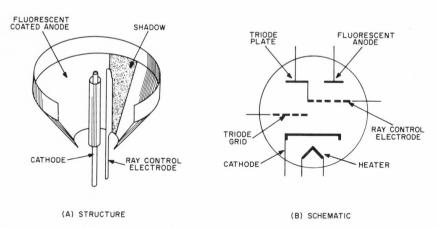

(A) STRUCTURE   (B) SCHEMATIC

Fig. 8-13 Electron-ray tuning-indicator tube.

amplification preceding the cathode-ray tube. No vertical deflection occurs at the zero-beat condition.

An effective indicator suitable for incorporation within a frequency meter utilizes an electron-ray indicator tube. This device is a simplified form of the cathode-ray tube. Figure 8-13 shows both the elementary structure and the schematic diagram. The cathode is mounted vertically and situated in the center of the envelope. Surrounding the cathode is a cone-shaped anode, or *target*, open at the top. This target is coated with a fluorescent material sensitive to electron bombardment. There is a light shield over the cathode so that the fluorescence of the inner wall appears as a ring encircling a dark round spot to an observer looking at the top of the tube. The third electrode is a long, thin wire parallel to the cathode and placed between it and the target. This wire is known as the vertical deflector, or the ray-control electrode. When this electrode is at nearly the same potential as the target, it has little effect on the ring of light. When its potential is appreciably less than that of the target, however, electrons in the vicinity of the wire are repelled. Under these circumstances, a portion of the target behind the wire does not glow. Furthermore, the greater the potential difference between the wire and the target, the greater the dark portion of the screen. This property enables the electron-ray tube to serve as an indicator of potential difference. In use, the tube is generally mounted in a horizontal position so that the shadow may be readily seen. The angular change of the shadow is from zero degrees, corresponding to no difference of potential between the ray-control electrode and the target, to about 90 degrees, corresponding to a maximum potential difference. The sensitivity of this simple device is excellent.

Other visual-type indicators are vacuum-tube voltmeters, rectifier-type audio-frequency voltmeters, and neon bulbs.

CATHODE-RAY OSCILLOSCOPES One of the quickest methods of determining frequencies

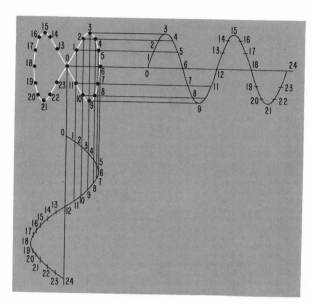

Fig. 8-14 Graphical production of Lissajous figure.

is by using *Lissajous* patterns produced on an oscilloscope screen. This particular pattern results when sine waves are applied simultaneously to both pairs of deflection plates. If one frequency is an integral multiple (harmonic) of the other, the pattern will be stationary. The production of a Lissajous figure is shown graphically in Fig. 8-14. The ratio between the number of pattern tangencies along the horizontal axis and the number along the vertical axis is the same as the ratio between the applied frequencies:

$$\frac{f_v}{f_h} = \frac{\text{number of horizontal tangencies}}{\text{number of vertical tangencies}}$$

where f_v and f_h are the frequencies applied to the vertical and horizontal axes, respectively. It can be seen that one of the frequencies must be known. This frequency is usually supplied by a local oscillator.

As stated previously, the two numbers comprising the ratio of the applied frequencies must be integers—1:1, 3:1, 3:2, 3:4, etc.—in order for the pattern to remain stationary. When the ratio is 1:1, or unity, the pattern is a straight line, a circle, or an ellipse, depending on the phase relationship

0°   22.5°   45°   67.5°   90°   112.5° 135° 157.5° 180°
360° 337.5° 315° 292.5° 270° 247.5° 225° 202.5°

Fig. 8-15 Lissajous patterns for 1:1 frequency ratio.

between the signals and their respective amplitudes. Figure 8-15 in which the two signals are assumed to be equal in amplitude, illustrates the various possibilities. Phase relationship will be discussed at greater length below.

In patterns of this type, there frequently is a slow drift from one pattern shape to the next, despite all attempts to keep the display stationary. This condition is attributable to a slight frequency instability in at least one of the applied signals.

There are many possible configurations for any ratio of applied frequencies. One consideration is whether the higher or lower frequency is applied to the horizontal-deflection plates. The most significant consideration, however, is the "phase" of the high-frequency signal with respect to the low-frequency one when the latter is beginning a cycle. Strictly speaking, "phase" in this usage is a misnomer, as the definition is normally in terms of a single frequency. Nevertheless, a cycle of the high-frequency signal is often well advanced at a time when a cycle of the low-frequency signal has just commenced, and for convenience this condition will be referred to as a "difference in phase."

Figure 8-14 shows the situation that exists when both applied signals start out together. The resulting pattern can be likened to a figure eight resting on a side. A tangent drawn against the top edge of the pattern would make contact at two places. Similarly, a line drawn against a vertical side would be tangent at only one place. Evidently, the horizontal tangencies correspond to the vertical-deflection voltage, and the vertical tangencies correspond to the horizontal-deflection voltage. Hence, the ratio of the vertical-deflection frequency to the horizontal-deflection frequency is 2:1. If the two signals were applied to the opposite set of plates, the pattern would be rotated 90 degrees.

An interesting situation exists when the high-frequency signal is shifted ahead 90 degrees in phase. As shown in Fig. 8-16B, the high-frequency signal may be at its maximum value when the low-frequency signal is beginning a cycle. When this condition occurs, the two loops are closed into the form of an inverted parabola (cup downward). Similarly, if the high-frequency signal is at its most negative value when the low-frequency signal is commencing a cycle, the pattern is an upright parabola (cup upward), as shown in Fig. 8-16D. This type of pattern is commonly referred to as a *double image*, since the electron beam, after reversing its direction, traces out exactly the same path. A double-image pattern is also called *an uncompleted loop, or closed pattern*. Fig. 8-16A and C represent intermediate phase relationships between the signals. Note how the loops gradually "close in" on themselves.

Each type of 2:1 Lissajous pattern, except the parabolas, is devolped for two different phase relationships. For example, the pattern of Fig. 8-14 is also generated when the high-frequency signal is 180 degrees out of phase with the low-frequency signal. These alternative phases are illustrated in Fig. 8-16 by the high-frequency signals to the right.

When a double image such as the parabola is developed, a somewhat different method of evaluating the frequency ratio must be employed. If the contact of an open line against a side of the pattern is counted as one-half, the correct ratio can be determined. As an illustration, consider a line drawn across the top and a line drawn against the right vertical side. There are two contacts against the top line, giving a total of 1. Against the vertical line there is only one contact, giving a figure of 1/2. The ratio of vertical-deflection-plate frequency to horizontal-deflection-plate frequency is therefore still 2:1 (1:1/2 = 2:1).

Suppose the horizontal line had been drawn against the bottom edge of the pattern. Here the rounded end, or closed loop, of the parabola clearly makes a single tangency with the line, again giving a figure of 1. Once more, the ratio is 2:1.

Analogous conditions hold when the frequency ratio is 3:1. Representations of the various patterns that may be obtained are shown in Fig. 8-17. If the signals applied to the deflection plates are interchanged, the resulting patterns are exactly the same except for a rotation of 90 degrees. In the case of the S-shaped curve, the frequency ratio is computed by the same procedure described for the parabolas of Fig. 8-16. To illustrate,

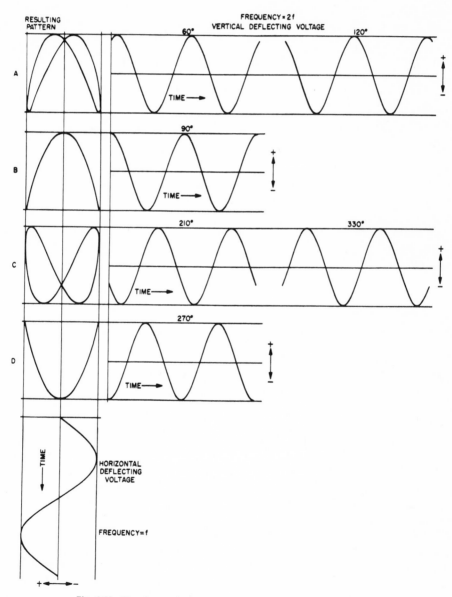

Fig. 8-16 Lissajous patterns for various phase relationships.

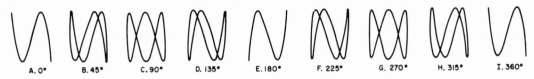

A. 0°   B. 45°   C. 90°   D. 135°   E. 180°   F. 225°   G. 270°   H. 315°   I. 360°

Fig. 8-17   3:1 Lissajous patterns.

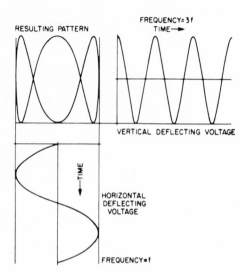

Fig. 8-18   Closed 3:1 Lissajous pattern.

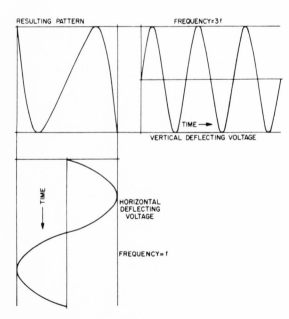

Fig. 8-19   Open 3:1 Lissajous pattern.

there would be a tangency and a contact with respect to a horizontal line drawn against the pattern shown at A in Fig. 8-17. This gives a figure of 3/2. If a vertical line were drawn, there would be a single contact, giving a figure of 1/2. The ratio of these two numbers is 3:1, consistent with the ratio of the frequencies.

Figures 8-18 and 8-19 show how the phase relationship of the signals affect the resultant Lissajous pattern. In Fig. 8-18, the high-frequency signal starts from its maximum amplitude as a cycle of the low-frequency signal is ready to begin. This results in a symmetrical pattern comprising three loops. As shown in Fig. 8-17, the same pattern is formed when the phase difference is 270 degrees instead of 90 degrees. Figure 8-19 shows how an S-shaped pattern is formed when the two signals are in phase. If the high-frequency signal began to swing negative as the low-frequency cycle began, the pattern of E in Fig. 8-17 would result.

There are two restrictions on the frequencies of the signals applied to the deflection plates. One has been mentioned previously—namely, the frequency must lie within the useful bandpass of the oscilloscope. The other restriction is that the relationship between the applied frequencies must not result in a pattern too involved for an accurate evaluation of the frequency ratio. As a rule, ratios as high as 10:1 and as low as 10:9 can be determined comfortably.

Up to this point only integral ratios, such as 1:1, 2:1, 8:1, and 10:1, have been discussed. In addition to the patterns for these ratios, there are many patterns for which the numerator and denominator of the ratio are whole numbers or integers. For example there are the 3:2 patterns of Fig. 8-20, the 5:3 patterns of Fig. 8-21, and so on. In every case, the methods for determining the ratio of the applied frequencies are the same as those described previously. As an example, consider the 5:3 ratio of Fig. 8-21. The pattern at A of the figure would make five tangencies against a horizontal line and three against a vertical line, leading to the correct ratio of 5:3.

If in Fig. 8-21B an open line is counted as a "half tangency" as described previously, the correct ratio can again be obtained. Thus, two and a half loops are counted along a horizontal side and one and a half loops along a vertical side. This is equal to a ratio of 5:3. As indicated by the double-image patterns shown in the various figures, all patterns of this type are characterized by two free ends.

A circular sweep trace may also be used as the basis of frequency comparison. Methods of producing a circular sweep are not complicated. As explained previously, the application of two sine-wave signals equal in amplitude but 90 degrees out of phase, to the vertical- and horizontal-deflection plates, respectively, results in the formation of a circle. If a single sine wave is applied to a phase-shifting circuit, such as the one in Fig. 8-22, it is possible to obtain two outputs equal in amplitude and 90 degrees out of phase if

$$R = 1/\omega C$$

where $\omega = 2\pi f$, the angular velocity of the input sine wave. The voltage across the capacitor will lag the voltage across the resistor by 90 degrees.

Variation of the grid-cathode potential changes the density of the electron stream within the cathode-ray tube, and in this manner determines the intensity of light emitted by the screen. When the grid bias of the tube reaches the cutoff potential, there is no electron stream, and fluorescence at the screen cannot occur. This familiar property can be utilized for the comparison of two

frequencies, provided that their ratio is an integer (1:1, 2:1, 3:1, etc.).

A circular pattern is obtained from the low-frequency signal, which is passed through an appropriate phase-shifting network and applied to the deflection plates. The high-frequency signal is applied to the grid. Sufficient bias must be present so that negative peaks of the sine wave will cut off the electron beam. The high-frequency signal does not have to be a pure sine wave; for example, it may be a square wave. Fig. 8-23 illustrates the effect of this type of operation. At A of the figure, the frequency ratio is 10:1, and so there are 10 blanks in the circle. At B of the figure, the frequency ratio is 20:1, and there are 20 blanks in the pattern. In other words, the number of blanks in the

Fig. 8-20 3:2 Lissajous patterns.

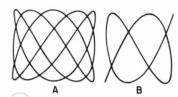

Fig. 8-21 5:3 Lissajous patterns.

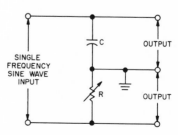

Fig. 8-22 Phase-splitting network.

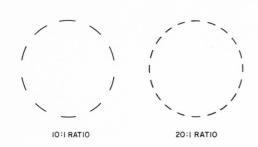

IO:I RATIO   20:I RATIO

Fig. 8-23   Spot-wheel patterns.

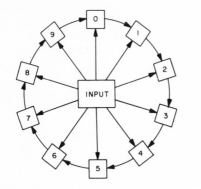

Fig. 8-24   Ring-type decade counter.

pattern is equivalent to the ratio of the frequencies. Because of their appearance, such displays are often called *spot-wheel patterns*.

ELECTRONIC COUNTERS OR SCALERS   The application of pulse counter circuits has led to the development of extremely versatile electronic counters. Use of these instruments in the area of frequency measurements has made other methods obsolete in terms of simplicity, speed of measurement, dependability, and accuracy. In the realm of pulse waveforms, frequency is more aptly termed *repetition rate*.

The most widely used counter circuit is the bistable multivibrator or flip-flop, discussed in Chapter 6. The frequency-division characteristics of this circuit were also discussed. When employed as a counter, the cascade chain is known as a "binary counter" since the count is based on powers of 2. Decimal notation is more familiar. Hence,

most counters utilize ring chain or binary decade counters.

The ring chain counter is shown in Fig. 8-24. Ten multivibrator units are used in cascade. In addition, the units are connected in parallel to a common pulse source. All multivibrators (except unit 0) are initially in the same state (state 1). Unit 0 is initially adjusted so that it is in the second stable condition (state 2). The first input pulse causes unit 0 to go to state 1 thereby providing a pulse to unit 1. This pulse causes unit 1 to change to state 2. The second input pulse causes unit 1 to change back to state 1, providing a pulse to unit 2, which then goes to state 2. The process continues around the chain, with each unit in state 2 utilizing an input pulse to revert to state 1. When this occurs, the output pulse from the reverting unit triggers the following unit so that this second unit goes to state 2—ready to accept the next input pulse. The tenth input pulse causes unit 9 to trigger unit 0 into its original state 2 condition, with all other units in state 1.

The binary decade counter employs a cascaded chain of four multivibrators. The count of this chain would ordinarily be 16 (2^4). However, feedback is used to *advance the count*, as shown in Fig. 8-25B. The end result is one output pulse for 10 input pulses.

The counting process of the foregoing circuits would be of no value if some indication of the state of the various units were not available. Hence, each *counting state* must also trigger an indicating device—usually a neon tube. For example, with the ring counter, each time a unit goes into state 2 it causes a neon bulb to light, representing the digits 1, 2, 3, 4, 5, 6, 7, 8, 9, and 0, respectively.

Counting circuits count equal-amplitude pulses. When preceded by appropriate limiting and wave-shaping circuits, however, the frequency (repetition rate) of any waveform can be measured.

Basic counter circuits are adapted to measure frequency by using the circuit shown in

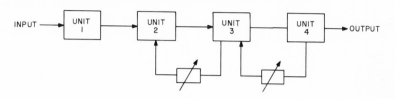

(A) BINARY COUNTER CASCADE WITH FEEDBACK

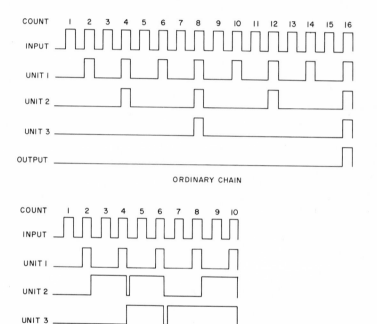

(B) PULSE PROPAGATION THROUGH COUNTER

Fig. 8-25 Principles of binary counter chains.

Fig. 8-26. The *signal gate* may also be a bistable multivibrator. It is manually or automatically set to a state which will allow the input pulses to reach the counter units at the beginning of the test. After a preset time interval, the timer pulses the signal gate to its second state, so arranged that the pulses are blocked from the counter units. The frequency is then given by

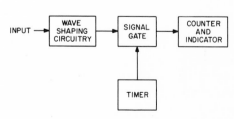

Fig. 8-26 Frequency measurement with electronic counter.

$$f = \frac{N}{T} \text{ cps}$$

where N is the number of cycles counted, and T is the time the signal gate was turned on (in seconds).

The error resulting from the use of this device depends upon the time interval over which the count was made. The longer the count interval, the greater the accuracy of the frequency measurement.

A typical counting-type instrument which may be used for frequency measurements (as well as other waveform applications to be discussed later) is shown in Fig. 8-27. The timing unit and signal gate device are an integral part of most packaged counting systems.

CALIBRATION OF FREQUENCY-MEASURING EQUIPMENT

This section discusses the comparison of an unknown frequency with standard frequencies, as well as the calibration of frequency-measuring equipment against a standard. Some of the techniques which will be described can be directly applied to the methods of the previous section in order to make them more accurate and more easily accomplished.

In recent years, the simple heterodyne meters described previously have become highly elaborate instruments called *frequency comparators*. The heart of such an apparatus is a standard frequency generator, usually a 100-kc crystal-controlled oscillator. The precision of this oscillator determines the accuracy of the instrument. Consequently, means

for checking the frequency against the transmissions of radio station WWV are included (see Chapter 4).

A block diagram of a frequency comparator is shown in Fig. 8-28. Sometimes there is a duplicate frequency standard so that it can be substituted automatically if the oscillator in use should fail. The standard signal is supplied to a series of four "locked-in" oscillators, as shown in the figure. Their purpose is to divide the standard frequency into submultiples of tenths and to isolate the frequency standard from other circuits. Frequency-dividing multivibrators can be used in place of the locked-in oscillators, although the precision of the latter is somewhat superior. The output of any oscillator can be selected as excitation for a harmonic generating stage, but as a rule the output from the 10-kc locked-in oscillator is utilized. If the frequency of a transmission is to be measured, the output of the harmonic generator is supplied to the appropriate receiver. The output of the receiver will then contain difference-frequency components obtained from the unknown signal and the two nearest harmonics of 10 kc. It is also possible to include a separate mixer in order to extend the range of the comparator to low frequencies, as shown in Fig. 8-28. The difference-frequency signals are applied to the interpolation oscillator, which is adjusted for zero beat. A reference to the dial reading of the receiver is the usual way of deciding which harmonic is closest in frequency to the signal being measured. In the event of any uncertainty, the display of the panoramic adapter can be consulted. In this display, the various signals appear as vertical pips, resulting in a resemblance to Fig. 8-29. Hence, the adapter indicates which harmonic is closest in frequency to the incoming signal. A 1-kc synchronometer is included to simplify checks of the standard frequency. This device, driven by a 1000-cycle synchronous motor, is capable of accurately counting the number of cycles produced by the standard oscillator during a designated time interval.

Fig. 8-27 Electronic counter.

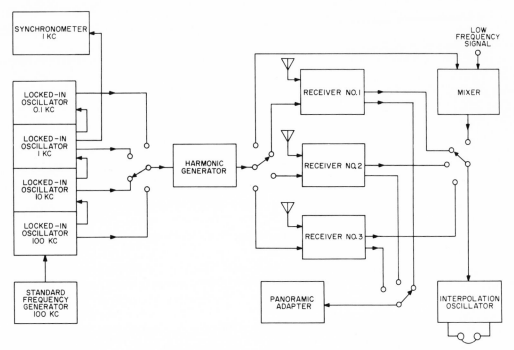

Fig. 8-28 Block diagram of frequency comparator.

Readings are facilitated by a large, illuminated 24-hr dial with a long sweep hand. There also is a microdial contactor that operates once each second. Calibrated in hundredths of a second, it makes comparisons with time signals accurate to one part in ten million over a 24-hr interval. The usual procedure is to compare the synchronometer indication with the time signals transmitted by station WWV. This indicates how accurately the standard frequency has been maintained during the period between transmissions. Phasing of the microdial mechanism is accomplished by means of a panel control. A 60-cycle motor is provided to start the 1000-cycle synchronous motor when a push button on the panel is operated.

When an exceptionally high degree of accuracy is desired with a frequency meter (or when the meter is to be calibrated), a frequency standard supplemented by a multivibrator is employed to provide equally spaced harmonic points. Unless the unknown frequency coincides exactly with one of these

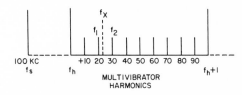

Fig. 8-29 Frequency relations between known harmonics and unknown signal.

harmonics, it is necessary to evaluate the frequency by an interpolation procedure. One excellent method utilizes a calibrated audio oscillator. As illustrated in Fig. 8-30, the output of a standard 100-kc generator may be supplied to a 10-kc multivibrator. The resulting harmonics applied to the heterodyning device, preferably a receiver, will therefore be 10-kc apart. A signal furnished to the receiver will beat against the harmonics to produce many new frequencies, the lowest of which is not greater than 5000 kc. This can be verified by referring to Fig. 8-29. The standard frequency, f_s, is 100

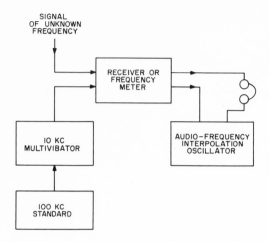

Fig. 8-30 Equipment setup for audio-frequency interpolation.

kc, a standard harmonic is represented by f_h, and the next harmonic by f_{h+1}. Similarly, the unknown frequency is designated by f_x, and the nearest multivibrator harmonics by f_1 and f_2. When the beat signals are supplied to the calibrated audio oscillator, as shown in Fig. 8-30, the oscillator should be adjusted for a zero beat with the lowest-frequency beat signal. In order to attenuate a higher beat note attributable to the next closest harmonic, which is f_2 according to Fig. 8-29, the receiver should be tuned halfway between f_1 and f_2 so that the adjacent channel selectivity discriminates against f_2. The reading of the audio oscillator dial is either added to the frequency of the next lower harmonic, f_1, or subtracted from f_2, the next higher frequency. To determine whether to add or subtract, it is necessary to know the frequency of the signal under measurement to within 5 kc of the nearest multivibrator harmonic. In the situation portrayed by Fig. 8-29, the reading is added to f_1.

The foregoing procedure is especially valuable as a means of recalibrating a heterodyne frequency meter. There are several advantages. One is the unlimited number of calibration points that can be taken. A second advantage is the utility made of only one frequency standard. Note particularly that frequencies lower than the frequency of the standard can also be checked. A third advantage of this method is its high degree of accuracy. Harmonic or subharmonic points provide an accuracy equal to that of the standard, assuming that the multivibrator is well designed, whereas the accuracy of other points is the same as that of the interpolation oscillator. If there is good adjacent-channel selectivity in the receiver, only the harmonic nearest to the setting of the frequency meter will be appreciable in the output furnished to the oscillator, tending to reduce uncertainty. When the receiver is employed, therefore, the "unknown" signal input is from the frequency meter being calibrated (see Fig. 8-30). If the receiver is eliminated, the output of the multivibrator is fed to the frequency meter, which applies the necessary beat note to the interpolation oscillator.

It is possible, of course, to apply the standard signal directly to the heterodyne frequency meter. This method is satisfactory only when the standard frequency is so low that a sufficient number of harmonics for calibration purposes is present in the band covered by the meter.

Interpolation is still possible when an audio oscillator is not available. If the receiver has a calibrated dial and less accuracy is acceptable, the interpolation may be performed arithmetically. As illustrated in Fig. 8-31, the dial readings for f_1, f_x, and f_2 should be noted. Since f_1 and f_2 are known exactly, the unknown frequency, f_x, can be evaluated from the following relationship:

$$f_x = f_1 + (S_x - S_1)(f_2 - f_1)(S_2 - S_1)$$

where $S_1 =$ dial setting for f_1

$\qquad S_2 =$ dial setting for f_2

$\qquad S_x =$ dial setting for f_x

The reading of the calibrated scale must be a linear function of frequency. This does not mean that there must be equal spacings between successive markers on the scale, although a linearly calibrated dial is desirable.

There are a number of possible arrangements for obtaining a reading. In Fig. 8-32 the use of a frequency meter is indicated. The internal-oscillator signal is first set for zero beat against the unknown signal, and the dial reading is noted. Then the output of the standard generator, or of the multivibrator, if used, is applied to the frequency meter. The dial reading for the two nearest harmonics is now obtained, and the computation described in the preceding paragraph is performed. A receiver with an internal beat-frequency oscillator can be substituted for the frequency meter. When the frequency of a radio transmission is to be measured and the receiver has no bfo, the setup of Fig. 8-33 is satisfactory. Here the receiver is tuned to the station, and the oscillator of the meter is adjusted to produce zero beat in the headphones. The dial reading of the meter should be recorded. Without changing the setting of the receiver, it should be possible to zero-beat the frequency meter against the two nearest multivibrator harmonics. After the readings of the frequency-meter dial are noted, the received frequency may be determined by interpolation.

The oscilloscope provides a quick visual method of comparing a test frequency with a standard frequency. The comparison is accomplished by applying the standard frequency to one set of deflection plates and the test frequency to the other set. The Lissajous figures discussed previously can be used to determine the unknown frequency in terms of the standard.

The oscilloscope method is valid only when the unknown frequency is an integral multiple of the standard. If it is not an integral multiple, a special technique may be employed which consists of applying the test frequency combined with another frequency (from a calibrated interpolation oscillator) to the vertical-deflection plates and a standard frequency to the horizontal-deflection plates. Waveforms similar to those of Fig.

8-34 will result. The interpolation oscillator is adjusted until the pattern is stationary. At this point,

$$f_x = nf_s \pm f_o$$

where f_s and f_o are the standard- and interpolation-oscillator frequencies, respectively. The factor n is an integer representing the harmonic ratio and equal to twice the number of pulsations in the oscilloscope pattern.

To determine whether the incremental

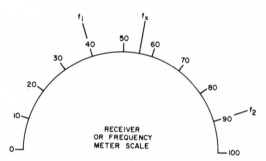

Fig. 8-31 Linear calibrated scale. Settings for known harmonics and unknown signal are as shown.

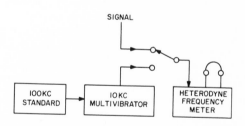

Fig. 8-32 Equipment setup for arithmetic interpolation.

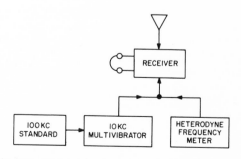

Fig. 8-33 Equipment setup for measuring frequency of received signal.

frequency, f_o, should be added or subtracted, f_x may be increased slightly and f_o varied until a stationary pattern is obtained again. If the new f_o reading is higher than the initial setting, the incremental frequency should be added; if lower than the original setting, it should be subtracted.

The accuracy of the oscillographic interpolation technique depends upon the accuracy with which the interpolation oscillator can be set and read. For this reason, in performing calibrations, it is desirable to check the interpolation reading with an electronic counter.

The standards mentioned in this section can be either primary or secondary standards. For most field and shop calibrations, secondary-standard generators are satisfac-

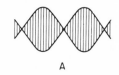

A

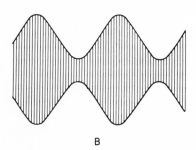

B

Fig. 8-34   Harmonic ratio pulsations on oscilloscope.

Fig. 8-35   Frequency divider and clock (synchronometer).

tory. If greater accuracy is desired, however, or if the secondary standard is to be calibrated, the primary United States frequency-standard broadcast by WWV or WWVH can be used. This standard was mentioned in the discussion of the frequency comparator (Fig. 8-28). In general, heterodyning methods and interpolation methods already discussed using an oscilloscope as a zero-beat indicator are best suited for primary standard comparisons. Table 4-2 lists the primary frequencies available. These frequencies can be multiplied or divided with the same precision as the original.

A special primary time-frequency reference standard setup is discussed in the following section.

TIME-INTERVAL MEASUREMENTS AND COMPARISONS

Since time is one of the fundamental dimensions chosen as a basis of the modern measurement system, the unit of time must remain constant, must be physically realizable to a high degree of precision, and must be permanently available for observation. Because of the direct relationship between time and frequency,

$$T = \frac{1}{f} \text{ seconds}$$

where f is in cycles per second. The United States frequency standard, which was discussed in detail in Chapter 4, is, of course, the primary time standard in this country.

Determination of time (with reference to oscillation periods) by use of an oscilloscope has already been discussed, as has the use of pulse generators to provide time markers.

A second method for producing time markers is to use the frequency divider and clock (synchronometer) pictured in Fig. 8-35. As previously stated in the discussion of frequency comparators, the synchronometer utilizes a 1000-cycle synchronous motor to drive the clock. A microdial contactor operates once each second to produce a tick (pulse).

These pulses can be applied to an oscillo-scope screen to provide a direct time scale just as the pulse generator markers were applied. They may also be applied *along with the pulse generator markers* to calibrate the latter. In this event, any adjustment of the advance-retard control of the synchronometer to achieve a superimposed pattern indicates a discrepancy in the time interval between the generator markers.

The Wien bridge (see Table 8-1) can be used to measure time intervals associated with sinusoidal waveforms. The period of the waveform at balance will be given by

$$T = 2\pi R_B \sqrt{C_A C_B \left[\frac{R_D}{R_C} - \frac{C_B}{C_A} \right]} \text{ seconds}$$

Electronic counters may also be utilized to measure waveform periods (especially low-frequency periods) and time intervals. These operations are illustrated in block diagram form in Fig. 8-36. The test signal opens and closes the signal gate at the beginning and end (respectively) of one cycle, or at the beginning and end of an integral number of cycles. During the time the gate is open, the counter counts the number of cycles transmitted from the frequency standard. The period can then be computed or, on most commercial equipment, read directly in seconds, milliseconds, or microseconds.

Figure 8-36B shows that the time interval measurement setup is similar in equipment arrangement and operating principle to the setup just considered. However, one input trigger opens the gate and a second trigger closes the gate. This permits adjustment of the two trigger pulses to include almost any time duration between the opening and the closing of the gate.

The instrument pictured in Fig. 8-27 contains the necessary internal circuitry to serve as a frequency counter, period timer, and time-interval measurer. The synchronometer can also be combined with a standard WWV receiver, a transfer oscillator (Fig. 8-37), and an oscilloscope as shown in Fig. 8-38 to

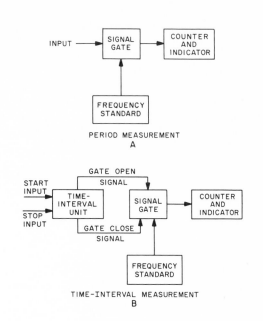

PERIOD MEASUREMENT
A

TIME-INTERVAL MEASUREMENT
B

Fig. 8-36 Time duration measurement with electronic counter.

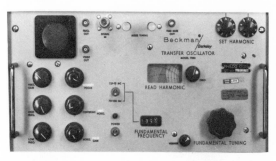

Fig. 8-37 Standard WWV receiver (top), and transfer oscillator (bottom).

produce a time-frequency standard system for calibration which, in turn, can be directly calibrated against the national primary standard. The units are usually rack-mounted vertically above one another to provide a convenient calibration console. An electronic

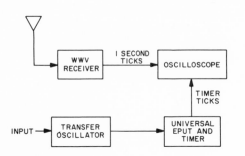

Fig. 8-38 Primary time and frequency standard (block diagram).

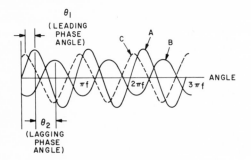

Fig. 8-39 Relative phase of waveforms.

counter and/or oscilloscope may also be included in the rack to increase the usefulness of the setup.

PHASE MEASUREMENTS

If two, or more, alternating voltages of equal frequency (or repetition rate in the case of nonsinusoidal waveforms) rise and fall in unison, they are said to be *in phase*. If they do not rise and fall together, however, a *phase shift* exists between the voltages, and they are *out of phase*. Figure 8-39 illustrates three out-of-phase voltages.

Phase measurements are relative measurements and have no meaning unless one of the waveforms is designated as a reference. In Fig. 8-39 waveform A is the reference waveform. A reference *point* along the waveforms must also be established. This point may be taken either as a peak in the waveforms or as a zero point in the waveforms. In the

figure, the lower amplitude waveform B is out of phase with A by the angle θ_2, since this is the angular difference between peaks (or zero points). The dotted waveform C is out of phase with A by the angle θ_1. Angle θ_2 is a *lagging* angle because the peak of B occurs after the peak of A (B lags A). The angle θ_1 is a leading angle because the peak of C occurs before (leads) the corresponding peak on A. The phase angle between waveforms B and C is given by $(\theta_1 + \theta_2)$. The angular phase difference actually represents a time difference between waveforms; the time difference is given by

$$T = \frac{\theta}{360f} \text{ seconds}$$

if f is in cycles per second.

OSCILLOSCOPE TECHNIQUES As stated previously, when two sine waves of the same frequency are applied to the deflection plates of an oscilloscope, the resulting Lissajous figure may be a straight line, an ellipse, or a circle. It is possible for a circle to be formed only when the amplitudes of the signals applied to the deflection plates are equal. If the signals are unequal in amplitude, an ellipse results instead. The axes of the ellipse are vertical and horizontal, assuming normal orientation of the cathode-ray tube. Excluding the consideration of signal amplitude, the property that determines the type of pattern formed is the phase difference between the applied signals. Figure 8-40 shows the phase relationship necessary for each of these patterns.

From Fig. 8-40 a number of useful properties can be deduced. For example, when two signals are in phase, the resulting pattern is a straight line in the first and third quadrants. Similarly, two signals 180 degrees out of phase produce a straight line lying in the second and fourth quadrants. When the angle formed with the horizontal axis is 45 degrees (or 135 degrees), the maximum amplitudes of the two signals are equal. An increase in the maximum vertical-deflection voltage causes the angle formed with the horizontal axis to increase. When the horizontal deflection voltage is greater than the voltage applied to the vertical deflection plates, the angle formed with the horizontal axis is less than 45 degrees.

A circle is displayed if there is a 90-degree phase difference between the two signals, assuming that the relative amplitudes are equal. If the vertical-deflection signal is larger, an ellipse with a vertical major axis is formed. (The major axis of an ellipse is the line that joins the two farther extremities; the minor axis joins the two nearer extremities.) Similarly, when the horizontal-deflection voltage predominates, the major axis of the resulting ellipse is horizontal. In the case of ellipses resulting from phase differences other than 90 degrees, a change in the relation between the deflecting voltage has a similar effect. Accordingly, the major axis rotates toward the horizontal axis of the display when the horizontal-deflection voltage increases, and it rotates toward the vertical axis when the vertical-deflection voltage increases.

Regardless of the relative amplitudes of the applied signals, an ellipse provides a simple means of computing the phase difference between the signals. This method is illustrated in Fig. 8-41. If the ratio of the Y-axis intercept (vertical), represented by Y_1, to the maximum vertical deflection, represented by Y_2, is calculated, the sine of the phase difference will be given by

$$\sin \theta = \frac{Y_1}{Y_2}$$

Reference to a sine table will then enable this ratio to be converted to a phase angle expressed in degrees and minutes. A similar ratio based on the X-axis (horizontal) intercept and the maximum horizontal deflection gives the same result:

$$\sin \theta = \frac{Y_1}{Y_2}$$

The direction in which these values are meas-

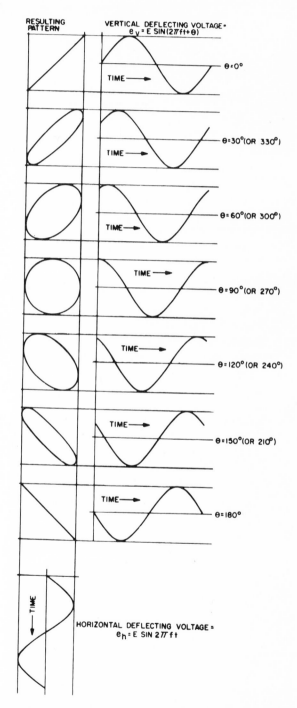

Fig. 8-40 1:1 Lissajous patterns, showing effect of phase relationships.

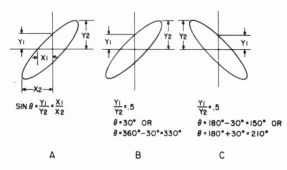

$$\text{SIN}\,\theta = \frac{Y_1}{Y_2} = \frac{X_1}{X_2}$$

$$\frac{Y_1}{Y_2} = .5$$

$$\theta = 30° \text{ OR}$$
$$\theta = 360° - 30° = 330°$$

$$\frac{Y_1}{Y_2} = .5$$

$$\theta = 180° - 30° = 150° \text{ OR}$$
$$\theta = 180° + 30° = 210°$$

A   B   C

Fig. 8-41 Computation of phase difference.

ured can be either positive or negative. The ratios are independent of the relative amplitudes of the signals.

B and C of Fig. 8-41 show how to interpret the phase angle according to the orientation of the ellipse. If the major axis lies in the first and third quadrants as shown in B, the phase angle is between either zero and 90 degrees or 270 degrees and 360 degrees. When the major axis passes through the second and fourth quadrants, the phase angle is somewhere between either 90 degrees and 180 degrees or 180 degrees and 270 degrees. In Fig. 8-41, the case of a sine equal to 0.5, corresponding to an angle of 30 degrees, is illustrated.

The ambiguity of two possible phase angles is not surprising. Whether a signal is 30 degrees or 330 degrees ahead of a second signal, the difference in phase is still 30 degrees. It is this difference that a Lissajous pattern can indicate, not which signal leads or lags the other. Fortunately, it is not difficult to learn which is the leading signal when the information is not known from other sources. Assume that a phase difference of 30 degrees is computed. If it happens that the signal applied to the vertical deflecting plates leads the horizontal signal by 30 degrees, an additional phase advancement of the vertical signal will reduce the eccentricity of the ellipse; i.e., it will be made to resemble a circle. On the other hand, if

the vertical signal lags by 30 degrees (equivalent to leading by 330 degrees), an advancement in phase will bring the two signals more nearly in phase. Consequently, the ellipse will contract until eventually it becomes a straight line.

There are a variety of circuits for shifting the phase of a signal; one circuit is shown in Fig. 8-42. One of the two signals under investigation, such as the signal to be applied to the vertical-deflection plates, can be impressed across a series circuit consisting of a rheostat and a capacitor. At the frequency concerned, the resistance of the rheostat should be about ten times the reactance of the capacitor. An output from the network can be taken from either the resistance, as shown in the figure, or the capacitor. In the event the signal developed across the capacitor is desired, the ground connection should be made to the input side of the capacitor. If the output is derived from the resistance, its phase will be advanced relative to the original signal; if taken from the capacitor, the phase will be retarded. Assume that the signal across the resistance is applied to the vertical input terminals of the oscilloscope. If the vertical signal leads the horizontal signal, the ellipse will become broader as the resistance of the rheostat is decreased. A circle will probably not be obtained, since the amplitude of the signal decreases as the resistance becomes less. This condition is illustrated by the vector diagram at B. If the maximum amplitude of the original signal is E, shown at (1), the amplitude at a phase shift of 45 degrees will be 0.7E, and the amplitude at a phase shift of 60 degrees will be 0.5E. This reduction of the signal is unimportant since the object is simply to find which of the two signals leads the others.

When an oscilloscope is used to determine phase relationships, several precautions must be observed. It is imperative, first of all, to know whether the circuits in the oscilloscope ahead of the deflection plates have unequal phase-shift characteristics. If there is a difference in phase-shift characteristics, the indicated phase relationship of the two signals under observation will be in error by the amount of the difference.

To determine the amount of phase error introduced by the oscilloscope circuits, simply apply a sine wave simultaneously to both the horizontal and vertical input terminals of the oscilloscope. If a straight line situated in the first and third quadrants is displayed, no phase shift is introduced by the oscilloscope amplifiers. In the event the straight line is in the second and fourth quadrants, a 180-degree phase shift is introduced by the amplifying stages of the instrument, probably because the numbers of the stages in the two sections are unequal. It is rather important to check this possibility, as the design requirements of the sections are not generally the same. The appearance of an ellipse, however, discloses an inherent disparity in the phase characteristics of the two amplifiers, rather than a mere difference of design. This phase difference, in degrees, must be added to, or subtracted from, the result of a phase measurement of two signals, according to which amplifier, the vertical or the horizontal, has the leading-phase characteristic. This check of amplifier characteristic, which should be made over the entire frequency range of interest, is especially important in the low- and high-frequency portions of the band passed by the amplifiers.

For an accurate determination of the sine of the phase angle, it is necessary that Y_1 and Y_2 in Fig. 8-40 must be measured properly. This means that the intersection of the Y and X axes must be placed in the center of the ellipse. In other words, the distance of the Y axis from the maximum horizontal deflection to the right must be equal to its distance from the maximum deflection to the left. A similar relationship must exist for the X axis.

Sometimes astigmatism in an oscilloscope may be so pronounced that accuracy in measuring Y_1 and Y_2 is difficult. In this situation,

the trace may be in focus over one region of the tube but out of focus over other regions. Wherever the trace is poorly defined, uncertainty arises over the measurement of distance. Preferably, an oscilloscope with an effective astigmatism control should be employed for phase measurements.

Errors in this method also result from the amount of harmonic content in the two signals. For a total harmonic content of 5%, errors of greater than 8 degrees may exist for angles over 45 degrees. Errors increase rapidly as a phase angle of 90 degrees is approached and may even be as great as 20 degrees at a phase angle of 70 degrees. For these reasons, other methods are utilized for more accurate determination of phase angles.

FREQUENCY MULTIPLICATION TECHNIQUES As previously mentioned, poor resolution places severe limitations on the Lissajous pattern method of determining phase angles—particularly at angles between 70 degrees and 90 degrees. However, measurements to within 1 minute accuracy can be obtained by frequency multiplication techniques.

It can be shown mathematically that when

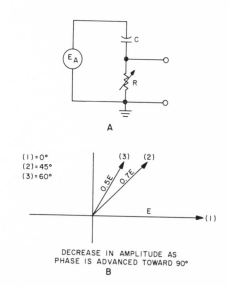

DECREASE IN AMPLITUDE AS
PHASE IS ADVANCED TOWARD 90°
B

Fig. 8-42 Phase-shift network.

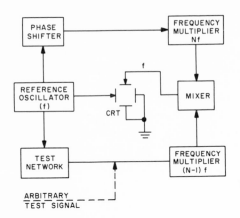

Fig. 8-43 Frequency multiplication technique.

a sinusoidal waveform is multiplied by an integer N, its phase angle is also multiplied by N, so that

$$\theta' = N\theta$$

Several methods exist for applying this concept to the oscilloscope patterns. If the test waveform is multiplied and the reference waveform is not, very complex Lissajous figures result. If both waveforms are multiplied by the same factor, the 1:1 pattern (ellipse) will result. This method also presents certain problems when used with conventional oscilloscopes.

A system with an accuracy of 1 minute for a multiplying factor of $N = 80$ is shown in Fig. 8-43.[*] Both frequency multiplication and heterodyning are employed. The upper path is for the reference waveform and the lower path for the test waveform. The test phase angle is shifted by a factor $(N-1)$. The mixer arrangement heterodynes the two new frequencies (Nf and $[N-1]f$) and applies the difference frequency (f) to the vertical-deflection plates. Since f is also applied to the horizontal-deflection plates, the Lissajous pattern will be the normal 1:1 ellipse. The inclination of the major axis will be $(N-1)$ times as great, however, resulting in

[*] R. A. Glaser, "The Accurate Measurement of Relative Phase," *Proceedings of the N. E. C.*, Vol. 3 (November, 1947), 593–602.

improved accuracy. The angle θ' is calculated by the method described previously, and the actual phase angle is found by

$$\theta = \frac{\theta'}{(N-1)}$$

The phase shifter shown in the circuit is used to compensate for differences in the phase shifts of the oscilloscope vertical and horizontal amplifiers.

The frequency multiplication method is generally used for calibration measurements.

ELECTRONIC SWITCH METHOD   A direct time (or angle) comparison of phase is made possible by the use of an electronic switch. This is a device that alternately applies two signals to an oscilloscope with such rapidity that both signals are simultaneously visible on the tube face. To ascertain the phase difference of two sine waves, it is necessary for one sine wave to be displayed directly under the other, as illustrated in Fig. 8-44. Any phase difference between the two signals can then be observed directly. If a measurement is required, the procedure to follow is simple. A convenient point on one of the waveforms must be selected as a reference, such as the point where one of the sine waves is zero and about to swing positive. At this point, the deflection of the other sine wave about the zero-voltage axis should be measured. The ratio of this distance to that of maximum amplitude is equal to the sine of the phase difference between the two signals. This relationship is illustrated in Fig. 8-44. Measurements along the time base can also be used to determine the phase shift in seconds. The angle is then found by the formula given in the introduction to this section.

ELECTRONIC COUNTER TECHNIQUES   Since phase angles and time intervals are directly related, it is possible to modify the electronic counter methods for frequency and time-interval measurement to give a direct reading of phase angle in degrees. Before application to the counter, the input waveforms must be converted to pulses, as is usual with counter techniques.

Figure 8-45 gives the block diagram for this process. The signal gate is opened when a reference cycle goes through zero on its positive-going portion. The gate is closed when a test signal cycle goes through zero on its positive-going portion. Thus, the gate is open for an interval equal to the phase difference between the two signals. The counter counts the number of pulses passed through the gate during this interval. If the pulse repetition rate is 360f, as shown, each count will represent 1 degree. Higher accuracies can be obtained with a greater PRF, limited only by the speed of the counter and the accuracy of the pulse generator. For example, the counter would read directly in minutes (of angle) if a PRF of 21,600f is used (21,-600f = 360f × 60 minutes/degree).

HARMONIC ANALYZERS

Almost all electronic devices have a certain amount of nonlinearity in their operating characteristics. Any time a nonlinear device is placed in an electronic circuit, new frequencies which are harmonics of the input frequency are produced. Occasionally this *harmonic distortion* is deliberately produced to a large degree, as in a harmonic generator or frequency multiplier. Faithful reproduction of a signal, however, is achieved only when the over-all distortion is low.

A measure of the distortion represented by a particular harmonic is simply the ratio of the amplitude of the harmonic to that of the

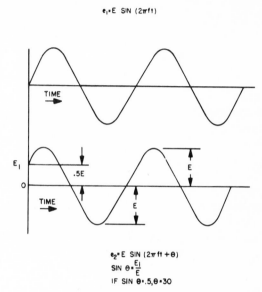

$$e_1 = E \; SIN \; (2\pi ft)$$
$$e_2 = E \; SIN \; (2\pi ft + \theta)$$
$$SIN \; \theta = \frac{E_1}{E}$$
$$IF \; SIN \; \theta = .5, \theta = 30$$

Fig.8-44 Direct phase comparison.

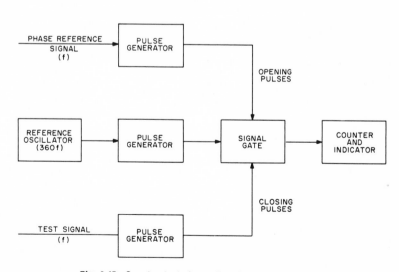

Fig. 8-45 Counter techniques for phase measurement.

fundamental frequency, expressed as a percentage.

Total harmonic distortion is expressed as the root-mean-square sum of all the harmonics present.

$$A_{HT} = \sqrt{A_1{}^2 + A_2{}^2 + \ldots + A_n{}^2}$$

where A represents the peak magnitude of a current or voltage, and the subscripts refer to each individual harmonic. The total percent harmonic distortion is found by dividing A_{HT} by the peak magnitude of the fundamental and converting the answer to a percentage. The same result can be achieved by letting A in the preceding equation be the magnitude of the individual percentages of each harmonic if this information is available.

TUNED-CIRCUIT HARMONIC ANALYZER The oldest method of determining the harmonic content of a wave makes use of a tuned circuit, which is shown in Fig. 8-46. The series resonant circuit, consisting of inductor L and capacitor C, is tuned to a specific harmonic frequency. By means of transformer T, this harmonic component is applied to an amplifier. The output of the amplifier is rectified and used to actuate a d-c meter. After a reading is obtained, L and C are tuned to the next harmonic, and another reading is taken. The parallel resonant circuit composed of L_1, R_1, and C_1 provides compensation for the variation in the a-c resistance of the series circuit, and

for the variation of amplifier gain over the frequency range of the instrument. Consequently, the sensitivity of the instrument is nearly the same at all frequencies.

Numerous modifications of the basic instrument just described have been developed. For example, equalizing networks are generally used in place of the compensating parallel resonant circuit. Frequently, the transformer is omitted, and the amplifier is excited by the voltage across either L, C, or R. The usual choice is the inductor L, since the increase of its impedance with frequency offsets the usual decline in the amplitude of the higher harmonics.

The tuned-circuit method has two principal drawbacks: One is the requirement at lower frequencies for using large component values in the tuned circuit. The other is the fact that the harmonics of the signal are often so close in frequency that they cannot be cleanly separated. Fortunately, various circuit refinements can lessen this difficulty. In many instances, it is inconvenient to measure each component individually instead of taking a single reading for the total harmonic distortion. The variation of the tuned-circuit impedance with frequency is also an often troublesome problem.

HETERODYNE HARMONIC ANALYZER In the widely used heterodyne type of analyzer, the difficulties of the tuned-circuit method are avoided by using a highly selective,

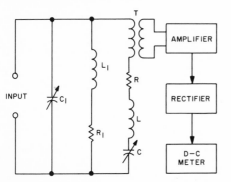

Fig. 8-46 Block diagram of tuned-circuit-type harmonic analyzer.

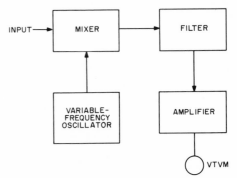

Fig. 8-47 Block diagram of heterodyne-type harmonic analyzer.

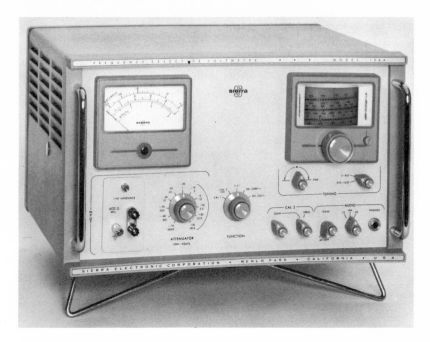

Fig. 8-48 Model 126A Frequency Selective Voltmeter. A wave analyzer when used with 126/PA High Impedance Probe. Probe impedance is 50 megohms. Instrument range with probe, −90 dbm to +2 dbm (24.5-microvolts to 1.0 volt), 5–1620 kc. Accuracy ±1.5 db. (Courtesy of Sierra Electronic Division, Philco Corporation.)

fixed-frequency filter. The output of a variable-frequency oscillator is heterodyned successively with each harmonic of the input signal, and either the sum or difference frequency is made equal to the frequency of the filter. As a result of converting each harmonic to a constant frequency, it is possible to use extremely selective filters, often of the quartz-crystal type. By such means, only the constant-frequency signal corresponding to the particular harmonic being measured is passed. The frequency of the filter must be higher than the highest harmonic to be measured.

The essentials of a heterodyne type of harmonic analyzer are shown in the block diagram of Fig. 8-47. A balanced modulator is commonly employed as the mixing device, since it offers a simple means of eliminating the original frequency of the harmonic. Another advantage is the low harmonic distortion generated by the balanced modulator as compared to that generated by other types of mixers. In addition to quartz-crystal filters, inverse-feedback filters also achieve excellent selectivity. A balanced vacuum-tube voltmeter usually serves as the indicating device. Some heterodyne analyzers are calibrated to give direct readings, and in others the harmonics of the impressed signal are compared with a reference voltage, usually by making the latter equal to the amplitude of the harmonic. A family of commercial direct reading instruments of the heterodyne type for use as harmonic and wave analyzers are known as frequency selective voltmeters. (Figs. 8-48 and 8-49) In these instruments only the difference frequency is selected so that the frequency of the input signal (harmonic or carrier) may be accurately read off on a calibrated dial. All frequencies that could cause a sum frequency response are excluded by a low pass filter in the input. Signal input level is read on a meter calibrated in dbm and volts. The level range for most of the instruments is −90 dbm to +32 dbm. Calibration accuracy is ±0.8 db or better.

DYNAMOMETER-TYPE ANALYZER As described in Chapter 7, a dynamometer is a device which compares the repulsive force between one moving coil and one or more stationary coils. For use as a harmonic analyzer, the dynamometer must have at least *two* stationary coils. The principle of the dynamometer has been adapted to analyzing waveforms of

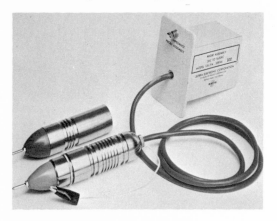

Fig. 8-49 Model 126/PA High Impedance Probe provides 50 megohm input impedance of wave analysis when used with the 126A Frequency Selective Voltmeter. Probe uses a subminiature triode in a cathode follower circuit. Power is obtained from the 126A. (Courtesy of Sierra Electronic Division, Philco Corporation.)

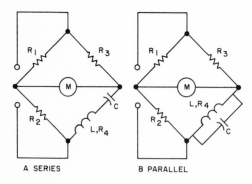

A SERIES   B PARALLEL

Fig. 8-50 Belfils resonance circuits.

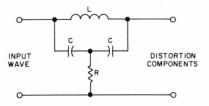

Fig. 8-51 Bridged-T suppression network.

rather low frequencies in the following manner:

First, the complex wave, after suitable amplification, is applied to one fixed coil of the dynamometer, and the output of a variable-frequency (search) oscillator is applied to the other. When the frequency of the search oscillator is extremely close to a harmonic of the waveform under analysis, the moving coil and the indicator attached to it oscillate at the difference frequency. The maximum deflection is proportional to the product of the currents in the two coils; i.e., the oscillator current and the harmonic-component current. By holding the oscillator current constant with the aid of a meter, the deflection of the pointer can be made proportional to the harmonic alone. A wave is analyzed, therefore, by varying the frequency of the search oscillator and noting both the frequency at which the beats occur and the amplitude of the deflection. Dynamometer analyzers can also be designed to give steady deflection. Instruments of the dynamometer type, however, are extremely limited in usefulness. One restriction is the inability to analyze frequencies above approximately 3000 cps. Another problem is the difficulty in keeping the oscillator signal exactly in phase with the waveform to be analyzed.

FUNDAMENTAL-SUPPRESSION ANALYZER The fundamental-suppression method of measuring distortion is employed whenever the predominant consideration is the total harmonic distortion, rather than knowledge of individual components. In this method, the input waveform is applied to a network that suppresses the fundamental component and passes the harmonic frequencies with a negligible attenuation. If a thermocouple or a square-law vacuum-tube voltmeter serves as the indicating device, the r-m-s value of all the harmonic components will be indicated. In other words, the reading will be in accordance with the relationship:

r-m-s value $= \sqrt{I_2{}^2 + I_3{}^2 + I_4{}^2 + \cdots}$

where I_2, I_3, I_4, etc., are the r-m-s values of the second, third, fourth, etc., harmonics. This quantity divided by the fundamental component, I_1, is equal to the total distortion.

There are a number of methods for removing the fundamental. One possibility is the use of a high-pass filter, which attenuates the fundamental drastically but passes the harmonic frequencies. It is also possible to employ some kind of bridge circuit, such as either form of the Belfils bridge shown in Fig. 8-50. If the resonant circuit of the bridge is tuned to the fundamental frequency, a meter placed across the null points will indicate the r-m-s value of the harmonics. Another alternative is a bridged-T circuit like the one shown in Fig. 8-51. In this network, the resonant circuit consisting of inductor L and capacitor C is tuned to the fundamental frequency, and resistor R is adjusted until the fundamental frequency is suppressed. The Q of the resonant circuit must be at least 3 to 5.

Figure 8-52 is a block diagram of a basic fundamental-suppression distortion meter. The first reading is obtained by placing the switch in position 1 and adjusting the network for minimum output. At this setting, the fundamental frequency is suppressed. Next, the switch is placed in position 2 and the attenuator is adjusted until the output indication is the same as before. The attenuator reading, in decibels, then gives the amount of r-m-s distortion below the amplitude of the fundamental.

Distortion meters based on the suppres-

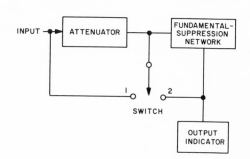

Fig. 8-52 Block diagram of fundamental-suppression analyzer.

sion of the fundamental are simpler and less expensive than instruments of the heterodyne type, but they cannot be used when the amplitudes of the individual distortion components must be known. A network that suppresses the fundamental, however, can be used to advantage in combination with other types of analyzers, such as tuned-circuit and heterodyne meters. Two benefits are gained. One is a reduction in the amount of harmonic distortion generated in the analyzer itself; the other is less stringent selectivity requirements. This is important when there is a frequency drift of the waveform being analyzed during the investigation. Finally, wave analysis can be accomplished quite accurately by means of an oscilloscope in conjunction with graphical methods, as will be described in Chapter 12. Such a system is known as a *spectrum analyzer.*

Since harmonic analyzers are frequency-selective devices as well as current (or voltage) indicators, they may be calibrated by employing frequency and current (or voltage) calibration techniques.

EXERCISE 1   Calibration of a Precision Laboratory Oscilloscope*

MATERIAL REQUIRED

1 Tektronix 545A with plug-in preamplifier (test instrument to be calibrated).

6 D-c voltmeter, John Fluke 823A or equivalent

* Based on manufacturer's calibration procedure. (Courtesy of Tektronix, Inc.)

2 Oscilloscope, triggered, with a bandpass to 10 mc

3 Variable autotransformer rated at 6.25 amp

4 Tektronix 180A time mark generator

5 Tektronix 107 square wave generator

7 A-c voltmeter, HP-400D or equivalent

8 Simpson 260, Series III or equivalent

9 Oscilloscope probe, attenuation of 10 to 1

10 Gain set adaptor, Tektronix EP-53A

PROCEDURE

1 Remove side and bottom cover plates from the 545A.

2 Preset the 545A front panel controls as follows:

INTENSITY	Full Left
HORIZONTAL DISPLAY	A
TRIGGERING MODE (A and B)	AC
TRIGGER SLOPE (A and B)	+ INT
STABILITY (A and B)	Full Left, but not PRESET
TIME/CM (A and B)	0.5 Millisec
VARIABLE	CALIBRATED (Full Right)
CALIBRATOR	OFF

Plug-in unit

Ac/Dc	Dc
Volts/CM	0.05
VARIABLE	CALIBRATED (Full Right)

3 Set the switch and shorting strap on the rear of the 545A as shown in Fig. 8-53.

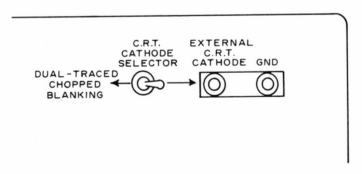

Fig. 8-53

4 Set up the equipment as shown in Fig. 8-54.

5 Set the range switch on the HP-400D to 300 volts, and the ON-OFF switch to ON.

6 Set the ON-OFF switch on the 545A to ON.

7 Adjust the autotransformer for a reading of 117 volts and allow 5 minutes for the warmup of equipment.

8 Set the differential voltmeter to read 150 volts and connect the positive lead to the chassis of the 545A. Connect the negative lead to the —150V check point on the terminal strip behind the sweep circuits.

9 Adjust the —150ADJ control for a meter reading of precisely —150 volts.

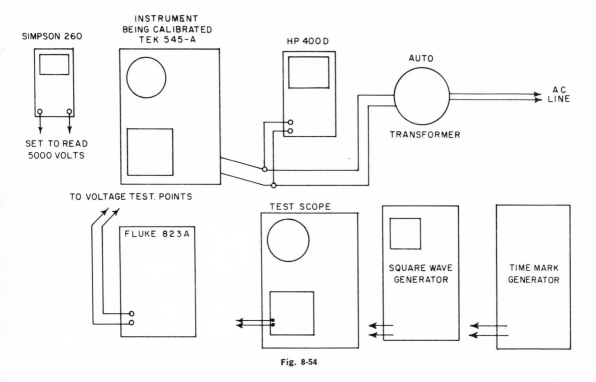

Fig. 8-54

10 Check the remaining power supply voltage on the terminal strip. The required accuracy is ±2%.

11 Set the test scope to AC, 0.05V/CM.

12 Connect the test scope, directly to each of the power supply terminals. The ripple should be less than 1/5 cm, peak to peak. (See Fig. 8-55.)

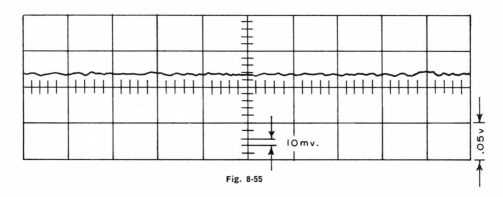

Fig. 8-55

13 With the differential voltmeter monitoring the 100-volt supply, vary the autotransformer down to 105 volts and up to 125 volts. The 100-volt supply should remain essentially constant. Reset the autotransformer to 117 volts.

14 Connect the differential voltmeter to the CAL TEST POINT in the lower left-hand corner

of the 545A's horizontal-circuit area. Adjust the CAL ADJ control just below the point for a reading of precisely 100 volts.

15   Set the Simpson 260 multimeter to read DC volts, 5000V full scale. Connect the positive lead to the chassis of the 545A. Connect the common lead to the high voltage test point above the neck of the CRT.

16   Adjust the H.V. ADJ control for a precise reading of −1350 volts.

17   Set the front panel controls as follows:

HORIZONTAL DISPLAY	A
TRIGGERING MODE	AC
TRIGGER SLOPE	+ INT
TIME/CM	0.5 Millisec
VARIABLE	CALIBRATED (Full Right)
VOLTS/CM (Plug-in)	0.2

18   Connect the output of the time mark generator to the vertical input of the 545A. Set the time mark generator to supply 500 μsec markers.

19   Adjust the intensity, triggering, and stability controls for a stable display.

20   Position the base line of the marker pulses below the visible area, so that only the vertical pulse line shows.

21   Adjust the GEOMETRY control on the inside control strip so that all the pulses appear as straight, parallel, vertical lines.

22   Set the A TRIGGERING MODE switch to DC.

23   Set the A TRIGGERING LEVEL control to 0, and the STABILITY control full left, but not to the PRESET position.

24   Set the HP-410B to read DC volts and connect to the junction of R19 and R20.

25   Stepping the voltmeter down to the lowest range, adjust the A TRIGGERING LEVEL control for a meter reading of exactly 0 volts. The A TRIGGERING LEVEL control should read exactly 0. If not, loosen the set screw and set the knob to 0.

26   Set the TRIGGERING MODE switch to AC, TRIGGER SLOPE to −EXT, and the TIME/CM to 0.5 MILLISEC.

27   Use a clip lead to ground the junction of R19 and R20.

28   Set TRIG SENS control on the inner control strip to midrange.

29   Connect a jumper from the CAL OUT jack to A TRIGGER INPUT, and set the CALIBRATOR to 0.1 volt.

30   Set the test scope to 0.5 V/CM, and TIME/CM to 0.5 MILLISEC.

31   Connect the test scope through the 10:1 probe to pin 6 of V45.

32   Adjust TRIG-LEVEL CENTERING on the control strip for a square wave of 1.5 cm on the test scope. Set the control to the center of the area which gives the 1.5-cm waveform.

33   Reduce CALIBRATOR to 0.2 MILLIVOLTS.

34   Set the test scope TIME/CM to 5 μsec/CM.

35   Slowly turn TRIG SENS control clockwise until the square wave reappears on the test scope.

36   Adjust the TRIG SENS control just to the point where the waveform is jitter-free.

37   Set the A STABILITY for a free running sweep, TRIGGER SLOPE to −INT, and the TRIGGERING MODE to DC.

38   Center the trace on the graticule.

39 Connect the HP-410B between ground and the junction of R22 and SW10A.

40 Adjust the INT. TRIG DC LEVEL ADJ on the sweep chassis for exactly 0 volts on the 410B.

41 Set the A TRIGGERING MODE to AUTO, and the TRIGGER SLOPE to +LINE.

42 Set the HP-410B to the 100-volt range and —DC function.

43 Connect the 410B between the wiper arm of the PRESET ADJUST potentiometer.

44 Set the PRESET ADJUST control full counterclockwise.

45 Slowly turn the PRESET ADJUST clockwise until the trace appears on the CRT. Record the HP-410B reading at this point.

46 Further advance the PRESET ADJUST control until the trace brightens. Record the HP-410B reading at this point.

47 Set the PRESET ADJUST for a reading midway between the two recorded voltages.

48 Set the HORIZONTAL DISPLAY to B, B TRIGGERING MODE at DC, and B TRIGGER SLOPE at +INT. Set the B TRIGGERING LEVEL at 0 and B STABILITY full left but not to the PRESET position.

49 Connect the HP-410B to the junction of R60 and R70.

50 Stepping the voltmeter down to the lowest range, adjust the TRIGGERING LEVEL control for exactly 0 volts. If the control knob does not read 0, loosen the set screw and adjust it to indicate precisely zero.

51 Set the B STABILITY for a free running sweep, the TRIGGERING SLOPE to —INT, and the TRIGGERING MODE to DC.

52 Center the trace on the graticule.

53 Connect the HP-410B between the junction of R72 and SW60A and ground.

54 Adjust the INT TRIG DC LEVEL control for exactly 0 volts.

55 Set the B TRIGGERING MODE to AC, and the TRIGGER SLOPE to —EXT.

56 Use a clip lead to ground the junction of R69 and R70.

57 Connect a jumper from CAL OUT to B TRIGGER INPUT and set calibrator to 0.2 volt.

58 Connect the test scope (5V/CM, TIME/CM—5 MILLISEC) through the 10:1 probe to pin 6 of V95.

59 Slowly adjust TRIG LEVEL CENTERING to the center of the area which gives a square wave of approximately 1.5 cm on the test scope.

60 Rotate TRIGGER SLOPE switch back and forth between —EXT and +EXT. If necessary, slightly readjust TRIG LEVEL CENTERING for a stable pattern in both positions of the switch.

61 Set B TRIGGERING MODE switch at AUTO and B TRIGGER SLOPE switch at + LINE.

62 Connect HP-410B on the —DC volts, 100V range between the junction of R214 and SW60B and ground.

63 Set PRESET ADJUST fully counterclockwise.

64 Slowly rotate PRESET ADJUST clockwise until the trace appears. Record the reading of the 410B at this point.

65 Further advance the PRESET ADJUST until the trace brightens. Record the 410B reading at this point.

66 Set the PRESET ADJUST for a reading midway between the two recorded voltages.

67   Set the front panel controls as follows:

HORIZONTAL DISPLAY	B
TRIGGERING MODE (B)	AC
TRIGGER SLOPE (B)	+INT
TIME/CM (B)	1 Millisec
5X MAGNIFIER	ON
VOLTS/Cm (Plug-in)	2

68   Connect the Tektronix 180A time mark generator to the 545A vertical input and set the 180A for marker pulses at 1 millisec and 100 μsec.

69   Adjust B triggering for a stable display.

70   Adjust the MAG GAIN control on the internal control strip to display 1 large marker every 5 cm, and 2 small markers every 1 cm.

71   Position the display with the HORIZONTAL POSITION control so that the first time marker is behind the center graticule line.

72   Set the magnifier to OFF and adjust the NORM/MAG REGIS control so that the first time marker is still behind the center graticule line.

73   Connect a jumper from the A SAWTOOTH to the vertical input, switch the HORIZONTAL DISPLAY to EXT X1, and turn the A stability full right.

74   Adjust the HORIZONTAL POSITION control counterclockwise to position a vertical trace to the left vertical graticule line.

75   Adjust the EXT HORIZ DC BAL control for no horizontal shift of the trace while turning the VARIABLE 10–1 control on the front panel.

76   Connect a jumper from CAL OUT to HORIZ INPUT, set the CALIBRATOR to 0.2 volt and turn the VARIABLE 10–1 control fully clockwise. There should be at least 1 cm of horizontal deflection.

77   Increase the CALIBRATOR to 2 volts.

78   Adjust the VARIABLE 10–1 control for exactly 10 cm of horizontal deflection.

79   Set HORIZONTAL DISPLAY to EXT X10, horizontal deflection should now be 1 cm $\pm 2\%$.

80   Connect a jumper from A SAWTOOTH to the vertical input.

81   Connect the CAL OUT to both the HORIZ INPUT and the A TRIGGER INPUT.

82   Set the front panel controls as follows:

HORIZONTAL DISPLAY	EXT X1
TRIGGER SLOPE (A)	−EXT
TIME/CM	1 Millisec
VOLTS/CM (Plug-in)	10

83   Adjust the A STABILITY and TRIGGERING LEVEL controls for a stable square wave. displayed vertically.

84   Adjust C330 for optimum square wave response.

85   Set HORIZONTAL DISPLAY to X10.

86   Increase the CALIBRATOR signal to 5 volts.

87   Adjust C301C for optimum flat top of the display.

88   Set the front panel controls as follows:

HORIZONTAL DISPLAY	B
TIME/CM (B)	1 Millisec
TRIGGERING MODE	AC

TRIGGER SLOPE	+INT
5X MAGNIFIER	OFF
VOLTS/CM (Plug-in)	2

89   Set the 180A for 1-millisec marker pulses and connect to the vertical input.

90   Adjust B triggering for a stable display.

91   Adjust SWEEP CAL for 1 time mark pulse per centimeter.

92   Set HORIZONTAL DISPLAY to A, TIME/CM (A) to 1 millisec, VARIABLE to CALIBRATED, and adjust A triggering for a stable display.

93   Adjust R1602 for timing identical to that of the B sweep in step 91, ±0.5%.

94   Adjust SWEEP LENGTH control for a sweep length of 10.5 cm.

95   With controls as in Step 88, check TIME BASE B sweep rates by the following table.

Time base B	Time mark generator	Markers displayed
1 millisec	1 millisec	1/CM
2 millisec	1 millisec	2/CM
5 millisec	5 millisec	1/CM
10 millisec	10 millisec	1/CM
20 millisec	10 millisec	2/CM
50 millisec	50 millisec	1/CM
0.1 sec	100 millisec	1/CM
0.2 sec	100 millisec	2/CM
0.5 sec	500 millisec	1/CM
1 sec	1 sec	1/CM

96   With controls as in Step 92, check TIME BASE B for sweep rates, following the foregoing table, with additional checks at

Time base A	Time mark generator	Markers displayed
2 sec	1 sec	2/CM
5 sec	5 sec	1/CM

97   Set TIME/CM (A) to 1 MILLISEC-CALIBRATED.

98   Set the 180A for 5-millisec markers and connect to the vertical input.

99   Adjust the A triggering for a stable display of 1 marker for every 5 cm.

100   Turn the VARIABLE control fully counterclockwise. The display should contain markers every 2 cm or less.

101   Set TIME/CM (A) to 0.1 millisec.

102   Set the 180A for 10-μsec markers and connect to the vertical input.

103   Adjust A triggering for a stable display.

104   Turn 5X MAGNIFIER to ON.

105   Horizontally position the trace so the first marker is behind the center graticule line.

106   Turn the TIME/CM (A) to 50 MICROSEC.

107   If first marker pulse is not behind center graticule line, adjust C330 to align it so. The first marker should be behind the graticule line for both the 0.1 MILLISEC and 50 MICROSEC positions.

108   Set 5X magnifier to OFF and TIME/CM (A) to 10 MICROSEC.

109   Make adjustments according to the following table:

Time/CM	Time mark generator	Adjust	Display
10 μsec	10 μsec	C160E	1 marker/CM
1 μsec	1 μsec	C160C	1 marker/CM

Time/CM	Time mark generator	Adjust	Display
0.5 μsec	1 μsec	C160A	1 marker/2 CM Position 2 marker to second line or graticule
0.1 μsec	10 MC	*C375 for linearity and C348 for time	1 cycle/CM
2 μsec	1 μsec	Check timing range	1 marker/CM
5 μsec	5 μsec	Check timing range	1 marker/CM
0.1 μsec	50 MC†	C364 and C384	1 cycle/CM

* C375 affects only the first part of the display. There is considerable reaction between C348 and both C160A and C160C. The adjustments of C348 and C160A should be repeated back and forth several times to obtain optimum linearity with correct timing, after which C160C should be readjusted if necessary.

† Couple 50MC from the time mark generator through a small capacitor (approximately 100 pf) directly to one of the vertical plates of the CM, C364 and C384 should be set as nearly at the same capacity as possible. It may be necessary to readjust C375 slightly in order to obtain the best possible linearity.

110   Set HORIZONTAL DISPLAY to B INTENSIFIED BY A.

111   Set the 180A for 500 μsec markers and connect to the vertical input.

112   Set TIME/CM (A) to 50 μsec, and TIME/CM (B) to 0.5 millisec.

113   Adjust B triggering for a stable display.

114   Rotate A STABILITY control fully clockwise. Note brightened portion of display.

115   Set DELAY TIME MULTIPLIER to 1.00.

116   Adjust DELAY START control until brightened portion starts at the first time mark (1 cm from the start of the trace).

117   Set DELAY TIME MULTIPLIER to 9.00.

118   Adjust DELAY STOP control until the brightened portion starts at the ninth time mark (9 cm from the start of the trace).

119   Repeat the foregoing procedure (Steps 115–118) until no further adjustment is required.

120   Set DELAY TIME MULTIPLIER to 1.00.

121   Set HORIZONTAL DISPLAY to A DEL'D BY B.

122   Adjust DELAY START control so the leading edge of the time mark is at the start of the trace.

123   Set DELAY TIME MULTIPLIER to 9.00.

124   Adjust DELAY STOP control until the leading edge of the time mark is at the start of the trace.

125   Set HORIZONTAL DISPLAY to B INTENSIFIED BY A.

126   Set TIME/CM (A) at 5 μsec and TIME/CM (B) at 50 μsec.

127   Set the 180A for 50 μsec markers and connect to the vertical input.

128   Adjust B triggering for a stable display.

129   Set A STABILITY fully clockwise.

130   Adjust the DELAY TIME MULTIPLIER control to place the start of the brightened portion of the trace at the first marker.

131   Set HORIZONTAL DISPLAY to A DEL'D BY B.

132 Adjust the DELAY TIME MULTIPLIER control so the leading edge of the time markers is at the start of the trace.

133 Record the DELAY TIME MULTIPLIER dial reading.

134 Set the DELAY TIME MULTIPLIER to a reading exactly 8.00 higher than the value obtained in Step 133.

135 Adjust C260C until the leading edge of the ninth time marker is at the start of the trace.

136 Repeat the forgegoing procedure (Steps 125–135) with TIME/CM (A) at 0.5 μsec, TIME/CM (B) at 5 μsec and 5 μsec markers applied. The adjustment should be made with C260A.

137 Set the HORIZONTAL DISPLAY to A DEL'D BY B, B STABILITY fully clockwise, and TIME/CM (A) at 0.1 MILLISEC.

138 Slowly adjust A STABILITY control until the sweep first appears.

139 Connect the test oscilloscope through the 10:1 probe to pin 3 of V133.

140 Set test scope to d-c coupling.

141 Adjust test scope vertical gain for a waveform of 4-cm amplitude.

142 Adjust LOCKOUT LEVEL ADJ control until the square wave portion of the displayed waveform is 2.4 division in amplitude. Be sure the A STABILITY is set to the point where the sweep just begins to run.

EXERCISE 2 Frequency Measurements with an Oscilloscope

MATERIAL REQUIRED

1 Oscilloscope

2 Audio Oscillator (2 required)

3 Potentiometer, 50,000 ohms

4 Capacitor, 0.1 μfd, 200 volts

PROCEDURE

1 Set up the equipment as shown in Fig. 8-56(A).

2 Adjust the variable resistor R for a perfectly circular pattern on the oscilloscope. This is indicative of the same frequency signal applied to both vertical and horizontal inputs of the oscilloscope, but a phase difference of 90°.

3 Using R, other variations in phase shift can be obtained similar to those of Fig. 8-15 of the text.

4 Set up the equipment as shown in Fig. 8-56B.

5 Set both oscillators to 1000 cycles.

6 If a stable circle is not obtained, vary one oscillator until the circular trace is established.

7 The dial error between the two oscillators can now be observed.

8 Turn oscillator #2 to the side so that the dial is not visible. Set the dial and range switch to arbitrary points.

9 Adjust oscillator #1 until a stable, readable Lissajous pattern is obtained.

10 Interpret the pattern to determine the frequency of the horizontal signal.

11 Repeat the procedure of Steps 9-10 for several other frequencies.

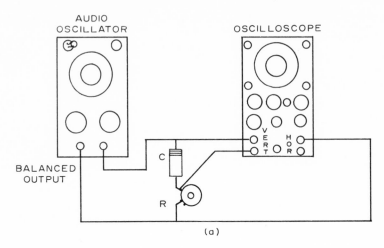

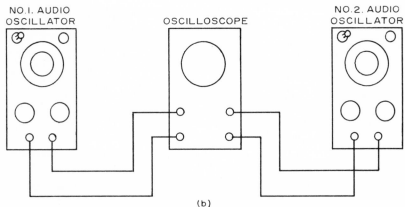

Fig. 8-56

EXERCISE 3 Standardizing the Counter and Adjusting Gate Length*

MATERIAL REQUIRED

1 WWV frequency comparator, LA-800D   2 Electronic counter, HP524C

PROCEDURE

1 Turn equipment on and allow a sufficient period for warmup.

2 Connect a balanced antenna, oriented to receive WWV, to the antenna input jack.

3 Set the WWV Frequency Selector switch to 5 mc.

4 Set the AUDIO-BEAT switch to AUDIO.

5 Adjust the AUDIO VOLUME control so that the audio note and time ticks of the stations are heard in the speaker.

* Based on manufacturer's procedures. (Courtesy of Lavoie Laboratories and Hewlett-Packard Company.)

6 Set the INTENSITY and FOCUS controls ¾ clockwise.

7 Adjust the ANTENNA TRIMMER control for best reception as indicated in the meter.

8 Set the FOCUS control for optimum CRT focus.

9 Adjust the XTAL. OSC TRIMMER control for a stable trace on the CRT.

NOTE Proper tuning of the crystal oscillator is indicated by a stable circular pattern that is not affected by time ticks or modulation.

10 Adjust the INTENSITY control so that the pattern is just barely visible.

11 On the 524C, make the following setups:

Control	Setting
Time unit	10 mc
Frequency standard	Internal

12 Connect the STD FREQ OUTPUT of the counter to the LOCAL STANDARD INPUT of the comparator.

13 Set the LOCAL STANDARD switch to the 2.5–10MC position.

14 Adjust the LOCAL STANDARD INPUT control to a position just sufficient to brighten the pattern on the CRT.

15 Set the AUDIO-BEAT switch to the BEAT position. A beat note will be heard.

16 Using the FREQUENCY STANDARD ADJ control on the counter, tune the beat note to its low pitch, where the frequency error is visible as a rotation of the pattern on the CRT. The standard should be tuned to the point at which the pattern ceases to rotate.

17 Disconnect the WWV comparator from the counter.

18 Set the following controls on the counter:

Control	Setting
Function selector	10 MC Chk
Frequency unit	1
Display time	Minimum (ccw)

19 Turn the counter off, remove the front panel plug-in unit, and turn the counter on again.

20 Adjust GATE LENGTH potentiometer R224 to center of the range which yields a reading of 10000.000.

EXERCISE 4 Calibration of Frequency Equipment*

MATERIAL REQUIRED

1 HP–524C Electronic counter

2 HP–525A Frequency converter

3 HP–330C Distortion analyzer

4 HP–400D Vacuum-tube voltmeter

5 HP-200CD Wide-range oscillator

6 600-ohm resistor (termination for oscillator)

PROCEDURE

1 Set up the equipment as shown in Fig. 8–57.

* Based on manufacturer's calibration procedure. (Courtesy of Hewlett-Packard Company.)

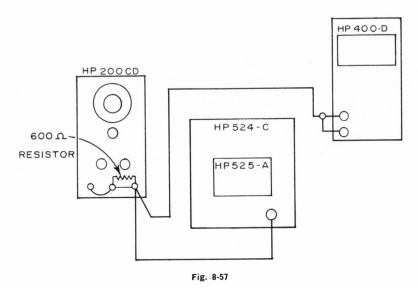

Fig. 8-57

2 Set the following controls on the equipment:

Control	Setting
	HP-524C
Power	ON
Frequency standard	INTERNAL
Function selector	FREQUENCY
Frequency unit	STD GATE TIME — SEC 1
Display time	Midrange
	HP-525A
Mixing frequency	0
Gain	Minimum
	HP-400D
Power	ON
Range	10 VOLTS
	HP-200CD
Power	ON
Range	X10
Frequency dial	5
Amplitude	Minimum

3 Adjust the amplitude control on the oscillator for a reading of 9 volts on the VTVM.

4 Increase the GAIN control on the HP–525A plug-in until the counter indicates a stable reading.

5 Turn the frequency dial of the HP–200CD to 60. The VTVM should read within ±¼ db of the reading established in Step 3, and the frequency should be within 2% of the dial indication.

6 If the counter indication does not fall within 2% of 600 cps, remove the cabinet from the oscillator and adjust C–6. Adjust for a counter reading of 599 cps, as replacing the cover will cause the frequency to increase.

7 Note reading on VTVM. If it differs from the reference in Step 3, adjust C-3 to correct for half the error.

8 Readjust C–6 for proper frequency.

9 Repeat Steps 7 and 8 until response is flat and frequency at 600 cps is within tolerance.

10 Set range control of 200CD to X100. Set dial to 5.

11 The counter should read 500 cps ±2%.

12 If the frequency is within 2% proceed to Step 20. If not continue with Step 13.

13 Adjust the frequency dial until within 2% of 500 cps.

14 Remove the center knob on the frequency dial.

15 Loosen the four screws which secure the dial plate to the drive shaft.

16 Set the dial to read 5.

CAUTION Do not disturb the drive shaft. The counter indication should stay within 2% of 500 cps.

17 Tighten the four securing screws.

18 Replace the knob.

19 Repeat Steps 7 through 12.

20 Check all numbered points on the dial, beginning at the high end. If some points exceed test limits (±2%) equalize the error by slipping the dial to get all points within these limits.

21 Set range control to X10K and the frequency dial to 60.

22 Adjust C–7 for a counter reading of 600kc ±2%.

23 Check frequency on remaining ranges. Errors should be no greater than ±2%.

24 When checking X1 range, set the counter to read 10 period average in milliseconds. The following chart lists the error limits.

Frequency	Period limits (milliseconds)
5	196.0
	204.0
10	098.0
	102.0
20	049.0
	051.0
40	024.5
	025.5
60	016.3
	017.0

25 Set up the equipment as shown in Fig. 8-58.

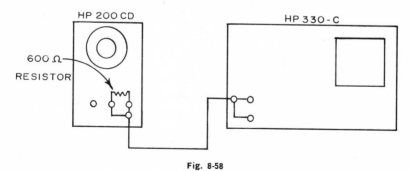

Fig. 8-58

26 Set the following controls on the equipment.

	HP-200CD
Power	ON
Range	X1
DIAL	20
Amplitude	Minimum

	HP-330C
Power	ON
AF — RF	AF
Frequency range	X1
DIAL	20
Function	Set level
Meter range	10 +20 100%
Input sensitivity	Minimum

27 Set the AMPLITUDE control on the HP–200CD to midrange.

28 Adjust INPUT SENSITIVITY on the HP–330C for a full-scale (1.0) meter reading.

29 Set HP–330C FUNCTION switch to DISTORTION.

30 Adjust FREQUENCY COARSE control until the meter pointer dips.

31 Adjust FREQUENCY FINE control for a further dip.

32 As meter falls to low end of scale, decrease RANGE switch accordingly.

33 Adjust BALANCE control to further dip the meter reading.

34 Repeat Steps 30 through 33 until the minimum reading is obtained.

35 The percentage of distortion can now be read from the meter in conjunction with the range switch.

36 Adjust R50 in the HP–200CD for minimum percentage of distortion.

37 Repeat Steps 26 through 35 for 50 cps.

38 Adjust R51 for minimum meter reading.

39 Connect the output of the HP–200CD, loaded by the 600–ohm resistor, to the HP–400D VTVM.

40 Set the range switch of the HP–400D to 30 volts.

41 Set the HP–200CD for an output of 1000 cps.

42 Set the AMPLITUDE control to maximum and adjust R11 for a reading of 11.5 volts on the HP–400D.

Electromechanical Equipment
and Calibration Techniques

9

Because of the high sensitivity of electrical indicating devices and the numerous operations (such as amplification, remote data transfer, and mathematical operations) which can be accomplished with the aid of electrical signals and electronic devices, such equipment is employed, together with suitable pickup devices, for the measurement of mechanical quantities. In general, the *electromechanical equipment* used for such measurements consists of three major systems: (1) a transducer, or pickup device, (2) an operational system, (3) a recording system.

The pickup device contains both mechanical and electrical components, combined in such a manner that the desired mechanical quantity is converted to an electrical signal. This signal may be an almost d-c voltage (or current), or it may be a rapidly changing a-c quantity of complex waveform. In any event, this signal is applied to an operational system, which may be simply a transmission wire. It may also be an amplifier, integrator, differentiator, etc., arrangement, or possibly a complex telemetry system. The resultant signal is then fed to a recorder system, which may be an oscillograph, oscilloscope, or computer memory. The recorder system may also be a voltmeter or ammeter, conveniently calibrated in terms of the measured quantity, with the human operator's pad and pencil doing the final recording.

Although these techniques extend to all areas of mechanical measurement, as discussed in Chapter 5, this chapter is concerned only with the shock, pressure, and vibration equipment frequently encountered in the field of aerodynamics, and with various temperature-sensitive electromechanical devices.

SHOCK AND VIBRATION EQUIPMENT

Many of the operating characteristics of modern machinery, particularly the machining of aircraft, rockets, and missiles, are affected by the mechanical vibrations set up by internal processes and external conditions. The actual measurement point may be in a small, inaccessible area, or it may be millions of miles away from the persons making the measurement. For these reasons, electromechanical devices capable of remote data transmission have come to be commonly used.

The devices discussed here are suited to measuring the displacement of an object in motion. Once a displacement has been converted to an electrical signal, the signal may be differentiated once to obtain a signal representing velocity, and if desired, it may be differentiated a second time to provide a signal representing acceleration. Electrical differentiating circuits are simple R-C networks such as the one shown in Fig. 9-1.

PICKUP DEVICES The three parameters in an electrical circuit which affect the flow of current are capacitance, inductance, and resistance. A change in any one of these

173

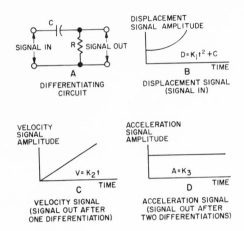

Fig. 9-1 Differentiation of pickup signals.

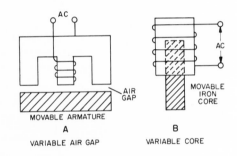

Fig. 9-2 Variable reluctance pickups.

tween the plates, there are three ways to incorporate a capacitor in a pickup device:

1. By changing the separation of the plates.
2. By changing the area of the plates.
3. By effecting a change in the dielectric properties of the medium between the plates.

Any of these actions may also be used in combination. Ideally, all three actions provide a linear relation between the measured quantity and the change in capacitance which is produced. In actual elements, this linearity is restricted to certain operating characteristics. This is true of nearly all pickup devices based on capacitive, inductive, or resistive elements.

Pickup devices operating on the magnetic principle of self-inductance or mutual inductance are also employed. Such devices are limited in their application. Within their limitations, however, they are very useful because of their inherently stable operating characteristics.

The self-inductance of a coil depends upon the number of turns of wire it contains, its shape and dimensions, and the permeability of the core. As the flux path is lengthened (length of coil increased), the inductance *decreases*. The shape of the coil and the number of turns are not readily variable. Therefore, most pickup devices of the self-inductance type depend solely on changes in permeability of the core. The changes in permeability cause corresponding changes in the reluctance (see Chapter 7) and, in turn, the inductance.

Figure 9-2 shows two methods of accomplishing such changes. In part A, the length of the air gap is changed. If the normal gap is very small (0.010 in. is typical), slight changes in this dimension will have a large effect on the coil inductance. In part B, the amount of core material inside the solenoid is varied to change the inductance.

An *inductance-ratio pickup*, such as that shown in Fig. 9-3, is a push-pull device. The winding is center-tapped to form two coils

quantities will produce a change in the magnitude or phase, or both, of the current flowing through the associated circuitry. Other electrical effects, such as piezoelectricity, photoelectricity, and changes in electrical characteristics due to magnetic and radiation fields, have also been utilized to measure the parameters associated with mechanical motion.

Capacitance variation pickups are among the oldest of electromechanical gaging methods. Since the capacitance of a parallel-plate capacitor is directly proportional to the dielectric properties of the separating medium and the surface area of the plates, and is inversely proportional to the distance be-rather than one. The core is normally centered, with an equal amount of material inside both coils. When the core moves, more material is projected into one coil, leaving less material in the other. This raises the inductance of one coil an incremental amount, while lowering the inductance of the other. Therefore, the device has a "push-pull" action. Although the double-coil pickup is more difficult to construct than a single-coil pickup, the sensitivity of this device is doubled, the response linearity is enhanced, and the error compensation for temperature changes, stray fields, etc., is simplified.

Mutual-inductance pickups are inefficient except in special arrangements. *Mutual inductance* is caused by a magnetic coupling between two coils. Varying the distance between the coils, or the orientation of one with respect to the other, produces a change in inductance. As compared with the total inductance, these changes are generally too small to be of practical value.

The circuitry associated with variable-inductance pickups may be a simple series circuit, such as that shown in Fig. 9-4A, or a series-opposition circuit, such as the one shown in Fig. 9-4B. The latter is preferred, since the simple series circuit requires a large d-c current to bias the coil to its proper operating characteristic. The third coil in the series-opposition circuit responds to the imbalance existing between the other two coils. This creates a difference potential that is proportional to the quantity being measured. Electronic amplification can be utilized in both types.

Variable-inductance pickups are ideally suited for use in bridge-type circuits (see Table 7-1); variable-capacitance and variable-resistance pickups are also adaptable to bridge-type circuits.

Pickups with a variable resistance element are most widely used in the field of aerodynamics because of their small size and because the change is effected uniformly in the entire mass of the resistance wire.

Resistance is an inherent property of any electrical conductor, the resistance value increasing with increases in conductor length and with decreases in conductor cross section. The resistivity (resistance per cubic unit of conductor material) is changed by variations in temperature. This latter pickup property, however, will be discussed in later sections.

Resistivity changes can also be brought about by internal stresses. These changes

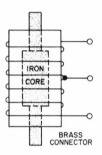

Fig. 9-3 Push-pull reluctance pickup.

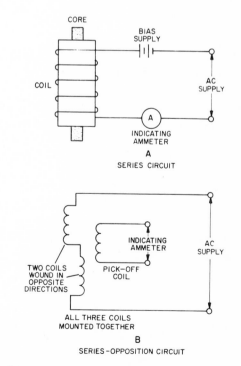

Fig. 9-4 Inductance pickup circuitry.

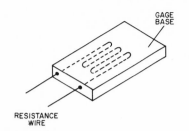

Fig. 9-5 Strain gage element.

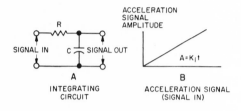

Fig. 9-7 Integration of pickup signals.

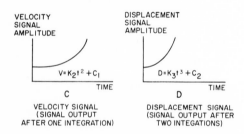

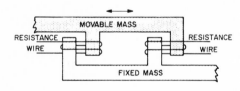

Fig. 9-6 Simple accelerometer.

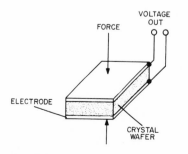

Fig. 9-8 Piezoelectric crystal pickup.

are not always computable beforehand. Hence, experimentally measured changes do not always conform to original design specifications based on length and cross section only.

The measurement of movement (or forces) must usually be accomplished in an indirect manner, using a resistance *strain gage* (Fig. 9-5), since the movement, as limited by the elastic constants of the material, is usually insufficient to permit direct measurement. The strain gage element shown in the figure is bonded to the surface of the object being studied, so that the strain applied to the work is transferred to the resistance wires (through the adhesive and base material) of the strain gage.

A second type of resistive pickup is used in the *accelerometer* (Fig. 9-6). A movable mass is suspended within fixed supports by fine resistance wires. This movable mass is subject to a force that is proportional to the applied acceleration, and this force, in turn, increases or decreases the normal strain on the resistance wires. The acceleration is thus converted to a variation in resistance. Further, if three mutually perpendicular sets of wires and movable masses are used, the acceleration is automatically resolved into its directional components.

Such an arrangement is ideally suited for the internal guidance measurements which must be made while missiles and aircraft are in flight. This is true because the acceleration components can be electrically integrated once to provide velocity information, and a second time to provide displacement information. Electrical integrating circuits are simple R-C networks, as shown in Fig. 9-7. Not only can the information be recorded for test purposes; it can also be fed to a computer for comparison with a predetermined flight path, for the determination of automatic guidance corrections.

Bridges are commonly used to determine the change in resistance, and their indicators can be calibrated directly in terms of the quantity being measured. Potentiometer ar-

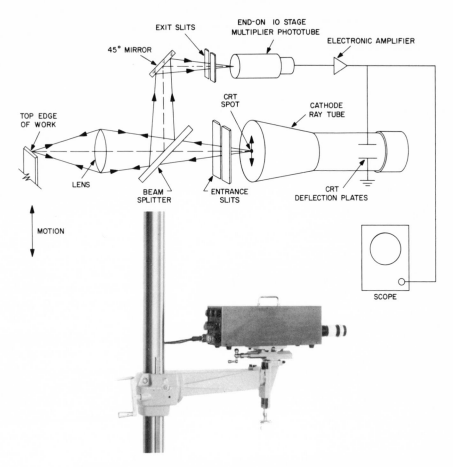

Fig. 9-9 Photoelectric pickup. (Courtesy, Optron Corporation.)

rangements can also be used for balancing and measuring purposes. (See Chapter 7 for both applications.)

It was stated previously that other electrical phenomena could be utilized for the design of shock and vibration pickups. The two types to be discussed here are those using crystals and light-sensitive elements.

Certain crystalline materials, when subjected to a mechanical force, generate an electric potential between opposite surfaces. These materials are called *piezoelectric crystals*, and include quartz, tourmaline, and Rochelle salt. These crystals are generally cut into rectangular wafers and mounted between two electrodes, as shown in Fig. 9-8, to form a crystal pickup; this device is actually a *generator* of electrical signals. Since the signals generated by a crystal pickup are very weak, the pickup is always followed by a sufficient number of amplifier stages.

All the foregoing pickup devices require that some mechanical movement or force be applied to an electrical circuit component so as to change the component value or cause it to generate an emf. Therefore, certain distortions are inherent because of the mass of the movable sensing elements themselves. In a photoelectric pickup, however, an almost instantly acting, weightless light beam serves as the sensing element. The light-sensitive element of the pickup responds to the radiant energy of the light beam.

Figure 9-9 shows the essential elements of such a system. A small spot of light (0.001 in. in diameter), generated by the cathode-ray tube, is focused on a sharp edge of any machined surface. The beam reflected from the work surface is passed to the phototube, amplified, and fed to the CRT deflection plates.

When the spot is focused on the target edge, 50% of the spot diameter is placed above the edge and 50% below the edge. This is shown in Fig. 9-10. The feedback control loop which is connected to the CRT deflection plates is adjusted so that the spot area above and below the target edge will always remain the same. Therefore, the spot "locks" on the target edge and follows it.

The waveform produced on the oscilloscope is an exact duplicate of the displacement which the target edge undergoes. By placing one or two integrating circuits between the pickup and the oscilloscope, the oscilloscope waveform can be made to represent the velocity or acceleration of the target edge.

CALIBRATION TECHNIQUES   The calibration of a vibration pickup consists of accurately determining the relationship between input motion and output signal amplitude. This relationship is known as the *displacement amplitude sensitivity* when applied to a displacement pickup. For velocity and acceleration pickups, the quantity is logically referred to as the *velocity* and *acceleration amplitude sensitivity*, respectively.

The device generally used to calibrate a vibration pickup is known as a *rectilinear electronic vibration pickup calibrator*, or, more commonly, a *shake table*. Figure 9-11 shows the essential components of this device as well as a photograph of a typical shake table.

The pickup being calibrated is mounted directly on a table which is movable in one direction. The extent of this motion is restrained by springs between the movable and fixed components. An exciting current (dc) is applied to the field coil within a fixed magnet. An alternating current is applied to the movable driving coil attached to the table. The interaction of these magnetic fields causes the table to undergo a sinusoidal motion in the axial direction.

Most shake tables are mounted on trunnions so that the axial motion of the table can be aligned in any desired direction.

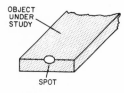

Fig. 9-10 Spot positioning for photoelectric pickup.

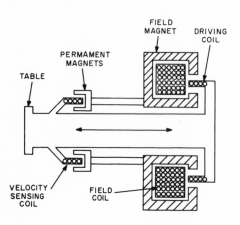

Fig. 9-11 Rectilinear electronic vibration pickup calibrator. (Photograph Courtesy, Optron Corporation.)

The motion of the table provides an input reference for the pickup being calibrated. Therefore, before a pickup can be accurately calibrated, the table itself must be calibrated.

The motion of the table is sensed by a coil attached to the table (see Fig. 9-11). The motion of the coil through the magnetic field of the permanent magnet, provides an output voltage, E_s, which is proportional to the *velocity* of the table.

The velocity of the table can be determined by monitoring the voltage E_s, since at a particular instant of time:

$$V_T = S_{V(T)}E_s$$

where $S_{V(T)}$ is the velocity amplitude sensitivity of the table. This factor can be computed from the physical parameters of the table, finally resulting in

$$S_{V(T)} = S_o + \frac{s\omega W}{g}$$

where W is the weight of the pickup which will be mounted on the table, g is the acceleration due to gravity (386 in./sec² if measurements are to be made in terms of inches), $\omega = 2\pi f$ (f is the frequency of mechanical vibration), and S_o and s are table constants (which can be found by determining the *transfer admittance* of the table). Since the sensitivity factor is dependent upon the weight and frequency involved, it must be recomputed each time a different pickup is to be calibrated, and each time the frequency of vibration is changed.

Figure 9-12 shows the circuit arangement for determining the transfer admittance of the table. This admittance also varies as the weight placed on the table varies. For calibration, the following procedure is first performed with no weight on the table, and then repeated with different values of weight on the table.

The procedure consists of applying a constant-frequency, alternating current to the table driver coil. After the table has gone through its transient vibration period and the

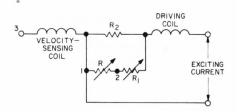

Fig. 9-12 Shake table calibration circuit.

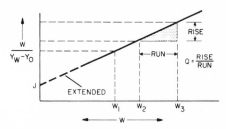

Fig. 9-13 Evaluation of J and Q for shake table calibration.

motion has settled between constant limits, R and R_1 are adjusted until the voltage across terminals 1 and 2 equals the voltage across terminals 1 and 3. When this voltage equality exists, the magnitude of the transfer admittance is given by

$$Y = \frac{R + R_1 + R_2}{RR_2}$$

After the transfer admittance is computed for several different weights, values for the following function are plotted against the values of weight, W

$$\frac{W}{Y_w - Y_0}$$

In this function, Y_w refers to the admittance at a given weight value, and Y_0 refers to the admittance with no weight on the table. Fig. 9-13 shows an example of this plot. By extending the straight line to the vertical axis, the intercept value J, can be determined by

$$J = \frac{W}{Y_w - Y_0}$$

The slope of the line (Q) can also be determined. The values of J and Q will be used later.

The table must next be reconnected as shown in Fig. 9-14. An external vibrational motion of the same frequency, f, as the previously applied driver current is applied to the table. However, the driver coil now acts as a generator. *No current is supplied to it.* The value of R_1 in this circuit should be several hundred thousand ohms. Resistor R is adjusted until the voltage between terminals 1 and 2 equals the voltage between terminals 1 and 3. When this equality exists, a constant, K, can be determined by

$$K = \frac{R}{R + R_1}$$

This completes the measurements which must be made to evaluate $S_{V(T)}$. Using the information obtained, the constant S_0 can be evaluated from

$$S_0 = 0.01711\sqrt{\omega JK}$$

and s can be computed from

$$s = 6.601 Q\sqrt{K/\omega J}$$

These are the two quantities needed for the equation

$$S_{V(T)} = S_0 + \frac{s\omega W}{g}$$

The foregoing value for $S_{V(T)}$ will be valid only at the calibrating frequency used.

The displacement to which a pickup device is subjected is determined from

$$D = S_{D(P)} E_P$$

where E_P is the amplitude of the output signal from the pickup, and $S_{D(P)}$ is the dis-

placement amplitude sensitivity. Similarly, the velocity (V) or the acceleration (A) to which a pickup is subjected is found by multiplying the voltage E_P from a velocity or acceleration pickup by the velocity amplitude sensitivity ($S_{V(P)}$) or the acceleration amplitude sensitivity ($S_{A(P)}$).

Calibrating each of the three types of pickups, then, becomes a matter of evaluating their appropriate sensitivity factors. These are given by

$$S_{D(P)} = \frac{Y_{D(P)}}{Y_{D(P)}'}\, \omega S_{V(T)}$$

$$S_{V(P)} = \frac{Y_{V(P)}}{Y_{V(P)}'}\, S_{V(T)}$$

$$S_{A(P)} = \frac{Y_{A(P)}}{Y_{A(P)}'}\, \frac{S_{V(T)}}{\omega}$$

where the Y terms represent transfer admittances under different conditions.

The first step for calibrating a pickup consists of evaluating $S_{V(T)}$ for the weight of the pickup involved and for the particular frequency of vibration desired.

Next, the pickup is placed on the vibration table, and the table set into vibration by applying an alternating current to the driving coil. One transfer admittance, $Y_{X(P)}$, is given by

$$Y_{X(P)} = \frac{\text{driving current}}{\text{velocity-sensing coil voltage}}$$

The other transfer admittance, $Y_{X(P)}'$, is given by

$$Y_{X(P)}' = \frac{\text{driving current}}{\text{pickup output voltage}}$$

Substituting these values in one of the previous equations will give the required sensitivity factor. This factor is valid only at the calibrating frequency.

RESISTANCE THERMOMETRY

As stated in the preceding section, the resistance of a conductor is subject to change as the surrounding temperature changes. This is true, to one degree or another, for all ma-

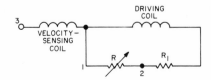

Fig. 9-14 Shake table calibration circuit.

terials. Usually, the hotter the material, the greater its resistance. There are a few materials, however, whose resistance decreases with increase in temperature.

The resistance of a conductor at some temperature above or below a specified reference temperature is given by

$$R = R_t + \alpha_t (T - t)$$

where R_t is the resistance of the conductor at reference temperature t, α_t is the temperature coefficient of resistance for reference temperature t, and T is the final temperature value for which the new resistance value is determined. The reference temperatures commonly used are 0°C and 20°C. A table of values for the α of common metals at 20°C is given in Appendix C-7. To use such a table, T must also be in °C. A *positive* temperature coefficient indicates that resistance will *increase* as temperature *increases*. A negative temperature coefficient indicates that resistance will *decrease* as temperature *increases*.

Thermistors (see Chapter 11) can also be used in resistance thermometry. These devices display a large negative temperature coefficient. In general, the resistance of a thermistor at some temperature, T, is computed from

$$R = \text{antilog}_{10} \left[\frac{A + B}{T + C} \right]$$

CIRCUITS The sensitivity of bridge circuits makes these circuits ideal for temperature measurements. The ordinary Wheatstone bridge and Kelvin bridge (see Table 7-1) can be used. The primary sources of error in these arrangements include switch contact resistances and thermal emf's generated at the junctions of the different metals. However, these errors can be kept to a minimum by the manufacturer. When the resistance bridges in Table 7-1 are for temperature measurements, resistor R_x becomes the temperature-sensing element, located in a probe connected to the rest of the bridge by long

leads. The scale on the variable resistor can be graduated directly in terms of temperature. This is true because

$$R_s = \frac{R_B}{R_A} R_X$$

and, consequently,

$$T = \left[\frac{R_A \alpha}{R_B} \right] R_S$$

The foregoing conditions exist when the bridge is balanced. T is the measured temperature. The quantity in brackets may be termed the *temperature sensitivity* of the bridge.

CALIBRATION TECHNIQUES The scale of a resistance thermometer can be calibrated by placing the probe in the various standard temperature baths.

An error which exists, but has not been mentioned previously, is produced by the current which must be supplied to the probe. This current produces heat in the resistance element, in addition to the heat provided by the source whose temperature is being measured. The temperature error is expressed by

$$t_e = \frac{I^2 R}{3.413 K} \text{ °F}$$

where I is the thermometer current and R is the thermometer resistance. The factor K is the over-all heat transferred from the probe to its surroundings by convention, conduction, and radiation (see Chapter 5).

THERMOELECTRIC THERMOMETERS

This type of electromechanical device utilizes the Seebeck effect discussed in Chapter 7. Since the net emf produced by a thermocouple-type arrangement is a function of the *difference* between the temperatures of two dissimilar metals, these devices can be usefully employed to measure *temperature changes*. They can also be utilized in exact temperature measurements.

One of the metals used in this device must be kept at a "cold" reference temperature while the other junction is "hot." For measurements above zero degrees, the cold junction is usually placed in an ice bath. For measurements below zero degrees, the hot junction is kept at room temperature, to serve as a reference, while the cold junction is placed in the area being measured.

The relationship between the emf generated by the thermocouple and the temperature difference is provided by manufacturers' calibration curves. The calibration can be checked by the usual temperature-bath methods.

RADIATION PYROMETERS

The temperature-measuring devices discussed thus far are limited to measurements below a few thousand degrees Fahrenheit, since the materials employed would melt at higher temperatures.

However, the high radiant heat emitted by bodies at temperatures above 2000 to

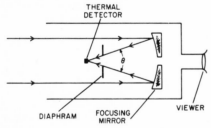

Fig. 9-15 Total radiation pyrometer.

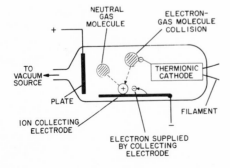

Fig. 9-16 Ionization gauge principles.

3000 degrees can be utilized to make temperature measurements. The theory involved is discussed in Chapter 5. Devices which utilize this phenomenon are called *radiation pyrometers*.

Figure 9-15 shows the essential elements of a radiation pyrometer which measures the *total radiation* emitted by a hot body. The source of radiation must entirely fill the viewing field (θ) and be focused on the thermal detector. Incoming radiation heats the thermal detector which may be any suitable temperature-sensitive device.

Since the temperature of a pyrometer is negligible with respect to the temperature of the hot body being measured, the hot body temperature is given by

$$T = K \sqrt[4]{\frac{\Delta T}{\epsilon A}}$$

where ϵ is the emissivity (see Appendix C-4) of the hot body, A is the area of the hot body, and ΔT is the change in temperature of the thermal element from its normal temperature. The constant K represents the sensitivity of the instrument, which is determined by calibration.

The instrument is calibrated by using a standard temperature (for instance, the melting point of tungsten or platinum) and measuring ΔT. The emissivity and radiant area of the standard must be found; the value of K can then be computed from the equation above.

The construction of this device makes the measurement independent of the distance between the pyrometer and the hot body.

The optical pyrometer makes a direct comparison of the radiation from a hot body with the image of a standard source of illumination. The standard source (a tungsten lamp) is built in. The image from the hot body and standard can be made to coincide by adjusting a mirror arrangement. The filament current to the standard is varied until the two images are of equal brilliance.

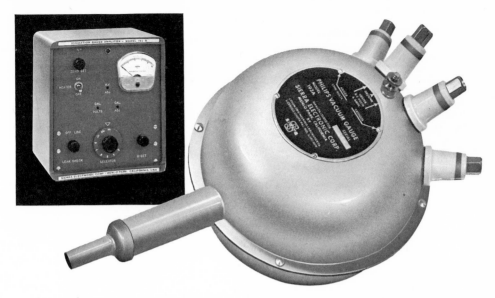

Fig. 9-17 Commercial ionization gage and amplifier. (Courtesy, Sierra Electronic Corp.)

The human eye can determine equal brilliancy to a high degree of accuracy, so that measurements made with this device have a high degree of accuracy. The measurements, however, are limited to temperatures below the filament burn-out temperature of the standard source.

IONIZATION PRESSURE GAGE

In a normal vacuum tube, electrons emitted by the cathode material are collected at the plate because of the plate's high positive potential. Any gas molecules present in the tube will be struck by the electrons, resulting in the formation of positive ions. If a negative electrode is inserted in the tube, this electrode will collect the ions, supply them with their missing electrons, and return them to their normal state. This is shown in Fig. 9-16. The gas molecules can then be re-ionized to repeat the process and provide a continuous current through the negative electrode circuit.

The current produced is proportional to the number of gas molecules present. Since the pressure in a confined space is also a measure of the number of molecules present, this *ionization gage* can be used to measure very low pressures by providing a connection between the tube and the vacuum container.

Several variations of this design have been produced commercially. The one shown in Fig. 9-17 is capable of measuring pressures between 10^{-4} and 10^{-7} mm of mercury. The current flow through such a device is minute. It can, however, be amplified by electronic means.

In some commercial devices, a radioactive source of beta particles (see Chapter 13) is utilized in place of the thermionic cathode. Such a device is useful at high pressures as well as low pressures.

QUESTIONS

1 What is generally used as a standard for the calibration of radiation pyrometers?

2 What determines the low temperature limit of an optical pyrometer?

3 If the electrode current of a vacuum gage is increasing, is the vacuum becoming greater or weaker? Explain.

4 Describe the "tracking" action of a photoelectric pickup.

5 What are the three major parts of an electromechanical measuring system?

EXERCISE Calibration of a Vibration Meter*

MATERIAL REQUIRED

1 Vibration meter, General Radio 1553A   2 Vibration calibrator, General Radio 1557-A

PROCEDURE

1 With the 1553A POWER switch set to OFF, zero the meter, if necessary, with the screw adjustment on the meter face.

2 Set following controls on the 1553A:

Control	Setting
POWER	2–20,000 c
METER READS	BAT 1

3 The meter should read within the CAL or BAT area.

4 Set METER READS switch to BAT 2. The meter should read within CAL or BAT area.

5 Set METER READS switch to BAT 3. The meter should read within CAL or BAT area.

6 If any battery checks low, refer to manufacturer's handbook for battery replacement procedure.

7 Set the METER READS switch to PK TP PK, and the FUNCTION switch to ACCEL.

8 Adjust the SCALE SELECTOR for a window reading of 10,000.

9 If necessary, adjust the ZERO thumbset control for a zero meter reading.

10 Set SCALE SELECTOR switch to CAL.

* Based on manufacturer's calibration procedure. (Courtesy of General Radio Company.)

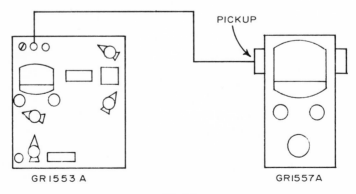

GR1553 A   GR1557A

Fig. 9-18

11 Allow 1 min for the amplifier gain to build up.

12 If necessary, adjust CAL thumbset control for a meter reading in the CAL or BAT area.

13 Set SCALE SELECTOR for a window reading of 3000.

14 Connect the equipment as shown in Fig. 9-18.

15 Set OFF-ON-BAT switch on the 1557-A to ON.

16 After several seconds have elapsed, adjust LEVEL control for a reading of 100 on the 1557-A meter.

17 Adjust CAL control on the 1553A for a reading of 1090m/sec^2 (1.0–1.2 on the lower scale) on the 1553A meter.

Electrical Power Equipment and Calibration Techniques 10

Electrical power delivered to a load at any instant is equal to the product of the voltage across the load and the current passing through it

$$P = EI \text{ watts}$$

or, in alternate forms,

$$P = I^2 R = \frac{E^2}{R} \text{ watts}$$

Under stable d-c conditions, this definition of power is also the *average power*.

In a-c circuits, inductive and/or capacitive elements temporarily store electrical energy and later return it to the source. For this reason, the definition foregoing applied to a-c measurements is termed *apparent power* when E and I are r-m-s values. The true average power for this situation is

$$P = EI \cos \theta \text{ watts}$$

where θ is the phase angle between the voltage and the current at the load ($\cos \theta$ is called the *power factor*). The energy stored by the reactive elements of the load, or *reactive power*, is given by

$$P_x = EI \sin \theta$$

The preceding equations are extended to nonsinusoidal periodic voltages by representing these arbitrary waveforms by their equivalent harmonic sinusoids (see Appendix D). For this representation, the power of each harmonic is computed separately and the total power is given by

$$P = E_o I_o + \Sigma E_n I_n \cos \theta^*$$

* Sigma (Σ) means "the sum of"; hence:
$\Sigma E_n I_n \cos \theta_n = E_1 I_1 \cos \theta_1 + E_2 I_2 \cos \theta_2 + \ldots + E_n I_n \cos \theta_n$

where $E_o I_o$ is a d-c component and E_n, I_n, and θ_n are values of each harmonic that is present. A more practical determination of power in the case of complex waveforms is the measurement of *peak power*. This method is dependent upon the width and repetition rate of the waveform and upon a *waveform correction factor* (see Appendix D).

Since a-c power measurements vary according to the reactive elements of the load, it is frequently desirable to deliver a *maximum* amount of power to the load for a given condition. If the phase angle of the load is not variable (the power factor is constant), the greatest output will be delivered to the load when the magnitude of the power-delivery network impedance, looking back from the network terminals, is equal to the magnitude of the load. This is shown diagrammatically in Fig. 10-1.

When $Z = Z_L$, the network and load are said to be *matched*. Certain coupling networks can be used between the load and network terminals to insure that a match is obtained. Simple resistance coupling networks (known as *attenuator* or *matching pads*) are given in Appendix A-2.

In Chapter 6 it was shown that voltage and current measuring techniques must be adapted to the particular frequency range in question. Since power is directly related to both these quantities, different methods and equipment must also be used to measure power as the frequency changes. The frequency ranges listed in Table 6-2 will be observed in the discussion of power measurements.

D-C AND LOW-FREQUENCY MEASUREMENTS

Power measurements in this range are generally made directly with wattmeters—instruments whose deflections are proportional to power as defined by the equations given previously. Electrodynamometer wattmeters are most widely used for power-line frequencies—DC to 800 cps. Electrostatic, thermocouple, and vacuum-tube wattmeters are used over the entire range (to 30 kc).

The basic electrodynamometer movement discussed in Chapter 7 can be modified to indicate power directly in watts by placing the fixed and movable coils in parallel, as shown in Fig. 10-2. The current in the fixed coil, is, of course, the load current. The current in the movable coil is proportional to the load voltage. Thus, the torque produced is proportional to the product of the two—the average power.

Inherent sources of error in this wattmeter include the self-inductance of the moving coil, the mutual inductance between the two coils, eddy currents in surrounding structures, stray fields, and resonance vibration at a frequency equal to twice the applied voltage frequency. The mutual inductance effect is negligible in well-designed instruments. Laminated iron shields and *astatic coils* are used to overcome the effects of stray fields. Various sets of removable *balancing weights* can be used to provide a resonance frequency well outside the frequency range being measured. A correction factor for self-inductance and eddy currents is given by

$$F = \frac{1 + \tan^2 A}{1 + \tan A \tan \theta}$$

where θ is the load power factor angle and A is the angle between the voltage and current in the movable coil. As can be seen from the circuit in Fig. 10-2, corrections must also be made for power absorbed by the coil cir-

cuitry. Well-designed instruments employ a stationary *compensating coil* in series with the movable coil to produce a countertorque just large enough to correct the error due to losses.

The maximum current which these instruments are designed to handle is about 20 amp. Current transformers are utilized for measurements of larger currents. Maximum power and voltage ratings are also applicable to this type of meter. These ratings should be determined and adhered to.

Laboratory wattmeters of this type may have an accuracy of 0.1%; portable wattmeters having an accuracy of 0.2 to 2.5% are available.

ELECTROSTATIC WATTMETER An instrument which is well suited for low power-factor measurements is the electrostatic wattmeter—a variation of the movement used in electrostatic voltmeters. This instrument will

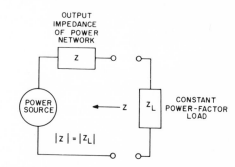

Fig. 10-1 Condition for maximum power transfer. The internal impedance of the power source is included as part of Z.

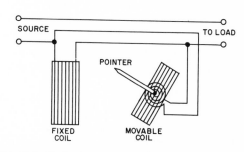

Fig. 10-2 Electrodynamometer wattmeter.

handle very high voltages and it has a frequency limit well above the audio range.

The basic movement consists of a metal drum divided into four sections by a good insulating material. A light metal disk is suspended inside the drum by a fine wire, to which a pointer is attached.

Figure 10-3 shows a compensated electrostatic wattmeter circuit which indicates only the load power—independent of circuit losses. The voltage drop across R_1 is proportional to the load current, and the voltage on the suspended disk is proportional to the load voltage. The electrostatic forces between the drum and disk produce a torque proportional to the average power in the load.

Measurements must be made on uncompensated wattmeters to determine the power lost in R. For these meters, the voltage-divider network, R_2, and the compensating resistor $\left[\dfrac{(n-2)}{2}\right] R_1$, are not used. The disk is connected directly to the top side of the load.

THERMOCOUPLE WATTMETER   The thermocouple ammeter arrangement discussed in Chapter 7 and illustrated in Fig. 7-4 can be utilized to measure power if two thermal converter units are arranged as in Fig. 10-4. This arrangement will indicate the average

power delivered to the load if the values of R_2 and R_3 are such that

$$R_2 + r_1 = R_3 + r_2$$

and

$$R_4 = \frac{r_1 + R_2}{r_2}\, R_1$$

where r_1 and r_2 are the resistances of the heater coils of thermal converters 1 and 2, respectively.

When calibrated under d-c power conditions, this instrument can be used for d-c and a-c measurements alike with a precision of 0.1%.

ELECTRONIC WATTMETERS   A commonly employed vacuum-tube wattmeter is shown in Fig. 10-5. As shown, the power must go from the source through the wattmeter divider network and then to the load. In other words, this instrument is placed in series with the load, whereas the instruments described previously were placed in parallel.

The two divider-network resistors, R_2, are made small enough to keep the drop across them from reducing the load voltage appreciably. In contrast, resistor R_1 is made very large so that its power consumption is negligible. These restrictions make the voltage across R_1 equal to the load voltage, and the voltage across either series resistor proportional to the load current. By inspection of the figure, it can be seen that the voltage

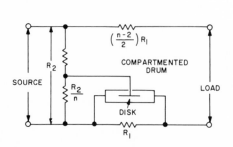

Fig. 10-3 Compensated electrostatic wattmeter.

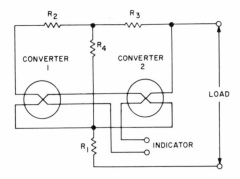

Fig. 10-4 Thermocouple wattmeter.

across the grid circuit of the upper tube is E_1 plus E_2. In the output circuit, the resistances in the plate circuits of the tube are equal. This provision makes the difference of potential between the plates proportional to the difference in the output currents of the tubes. The average value of the difference is indicated by the d-c meter connected to the plates. For the circuit to function as a wattmeter, the tubes must be operated over the parabolic region of their characteristics. This operation causes the difference current to consist of a number of components. The components proportional to either E_1 or E_2 make no contribution to the reading, as the average value of a sine wave is zero (it should be remembered that E_1 and E_2 are the r-m-s values of sinewave voltages). The only other appreciable component is the one proportional to the product of E_1 and E_2—in other words, proportional to the product of the load voltage and current. The average value of such a component is proportional to the product of E_1 and E_2 multiplied by the cosine of their phase difference. Consequently, the meter reading will be proportional to the power consumed by the load, and the scale can therefore be calibrated in watts. Nonlinearity of the scale may be minimized by applying only small inputs to the tubes.

Modifications of this basic circuit make possible the design of electronic wattmeters capable of measuring power over a range from DC to as high as 1 mc with varying

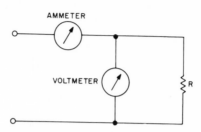

Fig. 10-6 Ammeter-voltmeter method.

degrees of accuracy.[*] Indications for positive and negative power, peak or average power, and complex waveforms as well as sinusoids are obtainable.

STANDARDIZED D-C MEASUREMENTS

A common method for making an absolute determination of d-c power for a standardized measurement, or for comparison with a wattmeter reading for calibration purposes, is to measure separately the values of E, I, and R and calculate the power. This simple volt-ammeter method is shown in Fig. 10-6A. The ammeter may also be placed between the voltmeter connection and the load. In either case, corrections must be made for the power consumed by the measuring devices. If the voltmeter is nearer the load (as shown), the true load power is

$$P = EI - \frac{E^2}{R_M}$$

where R_M is the resistance of the voltmeter circuit. If the ammeter is closer to the load, the true power is

$$P = EI - I^2 R_M$$

where R_M is the ammeter resistance.

The simplest approach to d-c calibration is to excite the current element and the voltage element of the wattmeter by separate power supplies. A calibrated voltmeter is used to

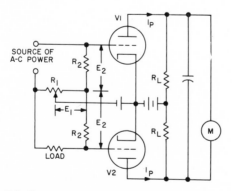

Fig. 10-5 Vacuum-tube wattmeter.

[*] D. E. Garett and F. G. Cole, "A General Purpose Electronic Wattmeter," *Proceedings of the I.R.E.*, Vol. 37 (September, 1949), 1003–1015.

monitor the voltage, and a calibrated ammeter to monitor the current. The product of these two magnitudes is calculated and compared to the wattmeter reading. For compensated electrodynamometer wattmeters, the voltage should not be applied across the compensating coil. Separate a-c sources may also be used in this manner to make low-frequency a-c calibrations. Errors introduced in the separate-source method of calibration are those associated with normal voltmeter and ammeter measurements (see Chapter 7).

To simplify d-c power calibration, the potentiometer circuits used for voltmeter and ammeter calibration (Fig. 7-1 and 7-2) can be modified so that the voltage and current measurements can be made simultaneously. Part of Fig. 7-14B is used in Fig. 10-7 to show how the Leeds and Northrup K-3 can be used for d-c power calibrations without the inconvenience of changing leads or using two potentiometers. The terminals marked "monitored quantity" should be connected across the voltage applied to the wattmeter (through a volt box, if necessary). The terminals marked "measured quantity" should be connected in series with the current coils of the wattmeter. A current shunt should also be used if necessary.

At least two readings should be made at

each calibration check point—one reading for one polarity and one for the opposite polarity. This reversal of polarity will eliminate the effects of any stray magnetic fields (DC) and any residual magnetism stored in the instrument structure.

AUDIO-FREQUENCY POWER COMPARISONS

The human ear responds more readily to ratio changes in power than to absolute changes. For this reason, and because of the need for a unit which expresses the relationship between output and input power in communication systems, a unit known as the *bel* was originated. In the audio range of frequencies, however, power measurements are expressed in terms of the *decibel* (*db*)—one-tenth of a bel. The expression is given by

$$db = 10 \log \frac{P_2}{P_1}$$

Since this system of units represents a ratio, it is particularly suited as a measure of how any electronic device affects the transmission of energy through itself. The gains (+ db) and losses (—db) in a complicated circuit can be added algebraically to determine the over-all effect of the circuit since the units are logarithmic in nature. An increase (or decrease) of 3 db doubles (or halves) the power being measured, resulting in the familiar half-power (down 3 db) level associated with electronic equipment. A measurement of 0 db indicates no power change. Measurements of 10 db, 20 db, 30 db, etc., represent power changes of 10, 10^2, 10^3, etc.

An expression of power in decibels is meaningless unless reference power is indicated for P_1 in the formula. This reference power may be any convenient value, depending upon the measurements being made. However, the reference must be indicated for future interpretation of the data. A standard of 1 milliwatt is frequently used. When this reference is used, the decibel is abbreviated *dbm*. A reading of 0 *dbm* indicates 1 milli-

NOTE: SWITCHES USED SHOULD BE BREAK-BEFORE-MAKE TYPE

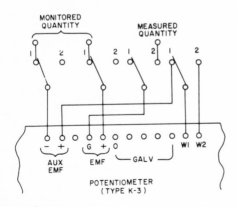

Fig. 10-7 D-c calibration with K-3 potentiometer. (Courtesy, Leeds and Northrup.)

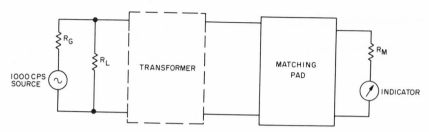

Fig. 10-8 Calibration of power-ratio meters. The basic circuitry is for a 600-ohm line. The transformer must be used for VU-meter calibration when a 150-ohm line is used. R_G and R_M are the source and meter resistances, respectively.

watt of power; $+$ 3 *dbm* indicates 2 milliwatts; 10 *dbm*, 10 milliwatts, etc.

It is also possible to compute voltage and current ratios in decibels. Unless the impedances across which the two powers are measured are equal, however, certain complications develop. A complete discussion of decibel measurements is given in Apendix A-1.

DB METER   Usually a db meter is a copper-oxide rectifier type a-c voltmeter (Fig. 7-6) or an a-c VTVM (see Chapter 7) with a scale graduated in db's. When calibrating the graduations, a specific power or voltage must be chosen as a reference point to represent 0 db. Based on this reference, various readings are made on the low scale and converted to decibels by the appropriate formula. Multiple-range instruments have a definite voltage ratio existing between each scale and the low reference scale. These ratios are usually indicated on the panel face as numbers ($+$db) to be added algebraically to each successive range reading in order to provide the correct value.

VU METER   The VU (Volume Unit) meter is rapidly replacing the db meter where standardized indications of power levels are involved. This unit was created because of the ambiguity involved in expressing power levels in decibels, since the decibel reference level may be any convenient power value. The American Standards Association and the Institute of Radio Engineers have defined the

volume unit with reference to 1 milliwatt of power feeding a 600-ohm resistive load.

The instruments and formulas associated with the db meter hold for the VU meter except that the scale graduations are calibrated with $P_1 = 1$ milliwatt.

A change in 1 VU is equal to a change in 1 db. Thus, a VU meter can always be used as a db meter, but a db meter can be used as a VU meter only if the 0-db level represents 1 milliwatt feeding a 600-ohm load.

The response time of VU meters is relatively low so that they are ideally suited for monitoring the amplitude modulation in a communication system.

The instrument should be calibrated on a sine-wave voltage of 1000 cps in terms of the r-m-s value of the voltage across a 600-ohm load. Since the load and meter must be matched at 600 ohms, it is necessary to insert an attenuator pad or matching pad (discussed in the introduction to this chapter) between the load and the meter, as shown in Fig. 10-8.

The establishment of the 600-ohm reference came about because of the commonly used 600-ohm transmission lines. More recently 150-ohm lines have come into common use. If a VU meter having a built-in attenuator pad for 600 ohms is to be used to make power measurements in a 150-ohm line, an appropriate low-loss transformer must be used between the line and the meter. The turns ratio for this transformer should be

$$\frac{N_1}{N_2} = \frac{1}{2}$$

A second method for calibrating a mismatched meter (although not as accurate as the foregoing procedure) is to compute a:

$$\text{correction factor (db)} = 10 \log_{10} \frac{\text{meter } Z}{\text{circuit } Z}$$

When the circuit Z is *greater* than the meter Z, *subtract* the correction factor. When meter Z exceeds circuit Z, add the correction factor.

RADIO-FREQUENCY MEASUREMENTS

At all but the microwave frequencies, it is usually possible to measure the effects of power directly. The basic procedure utilizing the thermocouple ammeter is virtually standard practice for frequencies up to 60 mc. The vacuum-tube wattmeter already discussed can also be used throughout the r-f range. Other instruments and methods will be discussed in detail in this section.

The minimum detectable radio signal is on the order of 10^{-13} watt. Detecting this signal is extremely difficult and requires a receiver bandwidth of about 1 mc. Radio-frequency power measurements are generally termed *low power* from 10^{-8} to 10^{-2} watts, *medium power* from 10^{-2} to 1 watt, and *high power* above 1 watt.

For all r-f power measurements at the higher frequencies, the coaxial line delivering the power must be properly terminated. This demands the use of attenuator or matching pads (Appendix A-2).

Many varied and often unpredictable factors enter into the accuracy of r-f power measurements. For this reason, accuracy is classified as excellent if it is within 2% or better of the actual value, good for 2 to 5%, and moderate for 5 to 10%.[*]

R-F POWER METERS   The instruments to be considered in the following discussion depend upon the power in a given load, or upon sampling a portion of the power delivered to a given load, for their operation.

If a lossless transmission line is terminated in its purely resistive characteristic impedence, the power delivered to the load is given by

$$P = I^2 R_o$$

where R_o is the characteristic impedance of the line and I is the r-m-s current value. An instrument which utilizes this principle is the thermocouple ammeter graduated in terms of power as previously discussed.

The power in the lossless transmission line is also given by

$$P = \frac{V^2}{R_o}$$

where V is the r-m-s voltage on the line. Several commercial power meters utilize this principle. A typical inexpensive unit of this kind, useful between 3 and 300 mc, is shown in Fig. 10-9. Notice the load resistor shunted directly across the input terminals. Unless this resistor is capable of dissipating the full amount of r-f power delivered to it, the heat generated will open the resistor and possibly cause other damage to the instrument. For low-power meters, as shown in Fig. 10-9, carbon piles are often employed; that is, disks of carbon are mounted, or "piled," on a suitable rod in sufficient quantity to form a resistance. When the transmission line is

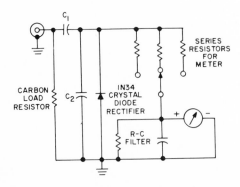

Fig. 10-9 Circuit of typical r-f power meter.

[*] R. A. Schrack, "Radio-Frequency Power Measurements," *NBS Circular 536*, March, 1953.

properly terminated by the carbon pile, the full power of the transmitter will be delivered to the r-f meter. The meter can also be used at lower frequencies when the output impedance of the transmitter is substantially equal to the value of the loading resistor in the meter.

In the circuit of Fig. 10-9, capacitors C_1 and C_2 form a voltage divider. C_1 is made small, about 5 $\mu\mu$f, in order to sustain a high percentage of the voltage developed across the loading resistor. It also keeps the capacitive reactance shunted across the load high, so that there is little effect on the standing-wave ratio. Only a relatively small voltage drop appears across C_2, which is about 0.25 μf. The crystal diode in parallel with C_2 provides a direct path to ground when the polarity of the incoming signal is negative, causing the average voltage developed across C_2 to be positive. This voltage produces a certain deflection of the meter, which is calibrated to read directly in watts. According to the amount of power involved, a suitable resistance is switched in series with the meter movement. An r-f filter is shunted across the meter.

Low amounts of power can be applied continuously to the meter, but higher amounts can be applied only long enough to obtain a reading. The upper frequency limit of the device is determined by the action of the capacitive voltage divider. Eventually, a frequency will be reached such that the reactance across the loading resistor causes a mismatch in the termination of the transmission line.

TEMPERATURE-LIMITED DIODE WATTMETER Vacuum diodes operated in their temperature-limited region offer a very sensitive method of measuring r-f power in the medium-power range. In the temperature-limited region the plate current is given by

$$I_p = AT^2\epsilon^{-B/T}$$

where T is the absolute temperature of the

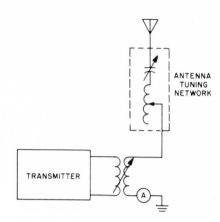

Fig. 10-10 Measurement of antenna input power.

cathode and A and B are characteristic constants depending upon the cathode material. A milliammeter placed in the plate circuit can be graduated in watts. Commercial instruments with an accuracy of 2% are available.

TRANSMITTER POWER MEASUREMENTS Thermocouple ammeters are well suited for measuring the r-f current delivered to a transmitting antenna. Power is then computed from the equation:

$$P = I^2R$$

where R is the effective resistance of the antenna.

A circuit arrangement similar to that of Fig. 10-10 is used extensively. The ammeter can be graduated in values of I^2. This part of the direct procedure for measuring r-f power is standard practice, but to be useful it must be preceded by an accurate determination of the effective antenna resistance. The three basic techniques devised for the measurement of antenna resistance are called the *variation*, the *substitution*, and the *bridge* methods. The necessary apparatus for the variation and substitution methods are as follows: an r-f generator that covers the desired frequency range, with an output-power rating of 50 watts approximately; a wavemeter or heterodyne frequency meter covering the desired frequency range and accurate to within at least 0.25%; a thermocouple ammeter or alternative type acceptable for the frequency range being measured, with an accuracy of 2.0% or better; a tuning capacitor and an inductor with values suitable for the frequency range being measured; and a decade resistor or suitable noninductive resistor with an accuracy equal to, or better than, 1.0%. The requirements of the bridge method will be stated later. Regardless of the method chosen, a series of measurements at different frequencies centered on the stipulated transmission frequency should be made if a high order of accuracy is desired. From these data, a graph of resistance versus frequency should be plotted, with the frequency appearing on the X axis. If the transmission is to be in the broadcast band, 10 to 12 measurements extending over a band 40 to 60 kc wide are recommended. The resistance indicated at the assigned frequency specifies the antenna resistance to be used in the power calculation. It is considered advisable to restrict the maximum dissipation of power in the antenna during the measurement to 10% of the power obtainable from the r-f generator in use. Although a broadcast transmitter is not ordinarily employed for measurement, it can be, provided that the output of a low-power stage is used.

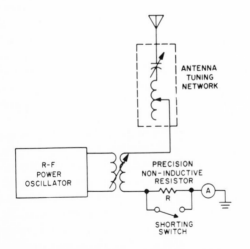

Fig. 10-11 Variation method of measuring antenna resistance.

In the variation method of measuring antenna resistance, a standard or known value of noninductive resistance is placed in series with the antenna and ground, as shown in Fig. 10-11. A wavemeter should be used to measure the frequency of the signal applied to the antenna circuit. By means of the tuning inductor and capacitor, it is possible to vary the resonant frequency above and below the fundamental frequency of the antenna and thus secure sufficient data for a graph. The tuning inductor is often omitted.

As a rule, the procedure for measuring antenna resistance based on Fig. 10-11 conforms with the steps given below.

1. The first antenna resistance measurement is taken at the natural frequency of the antenna system. First, connect the antenna to the ground or counterpoise through the coupling coil in which the signal is introduced. Be sure that the antenna circuit is energized only through the coupling coil. This requires careful shielding of the oscillator and the reduction of stray capacitances between the coupling link and other points in the antenna circuit.

2. Tune the r-f oscillator. Eventually there should be a noticeable dip in the grid-circuit miliammeter of the driver stage. This dip will occur at the resonant frequency of the antenna system. At the instant of the lowest grid-current reading, the deflection of the antenna milliammeter should be maximum. Be sure that the indication of the grid milliameter changes gradually as resonance is approached in either direction. An abrupt dip followed by a quick return to the original indication means that too much coupling exists between the driver and the antenna circuit. In this event, it is necessary to loosen the coupling until reaction between the two circuits is negligible. When accuracy is desired, a powerful driver, located several feet from the antenna, should be used.

3. Record the current flowing in the antenna circuit at the resonant frequency. After the known resistance has been connected in the antenna circuit, read the antenna current

again. Be sure to leave the oscillator undisturbed once the first antenna current reading has been taken. The following formula then gives the antenna resistance in ohms:

$$R_A = \frac{I_s}{I_A - I_s} R_s$$

where R_A is the value of antenna resistance, I_s is the current measured when the standard resistance is in the circuit, I_A is the current measured when the standard resistance is out of the circuit, and R_s is the value of the standard resistance.

The procedure of the foregoing steps evaluates the antenna resistance at its *fundamental frequency*.

4. It is now necessary to determine the resistance of the antenna at the frequency of transmission. Therefore, connect the tuning network, which should be shielded in order to eliminate any stray coupling paths. Refer to the network enclosed by the dotted line in Fig. 10-11. In accordance with the previous discussion, tune the circuit to resonance at the frequency of transmission, and read the antenna current once again. The standard resistor should remain in the circuit. Repeat this procedure for a number of additional frequencies, and plot a resistance-versus-frequency graph. The value of antenna resistance at the transmitting frequency obtained from the graph should agree with the measured value within reasonable limits.

Frequently, the circuit in Fig. 10-12 is helpful in disclosing the existence of stray capacitive paths to ground. Although an L-C tuning network is shown, a calibrated capacitor is ordinarily used alone. Note that in this circuit a standard resistor is present on the antenna side of the tuning network, as well as on the shielded side. The procedure described in the following steps should be observed for each frequency at which a resistance measurement is made.

1. With both standard resistors shorted out, adjust the tuning network of the antenna circuit to resonance, as indicated by maxi-

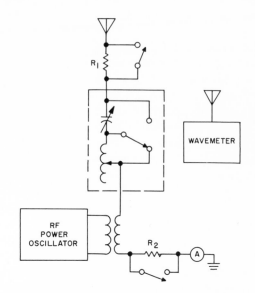

Fig. 10-12 Two-resistor variation method of measuring antenna resistance.

mum antenna current. Then adjust the output of the oscillator for a convenient deflection of the meter. Once this adjustment is made, it must be left untouched throughout the remaining procedure. Record the antenna current with the standard resistors out of the circuit.

2. Insert a known value of R_1 in the circuit, and measure the antenna current again. Then compute the antenna resistance by means of the formula given in the discussion of the basic variation method.

3. Short out R_1 and insert a known value of R_2. With R_2 in the circuit, make another measurement of the antenna resistance. The two measurements will agree only if there is no appreciable stray capacitance between the measuring circuit and ground. Assuming that the shielding is satisfactory, the amount of residual capacitance is dependent on the geometry of the surfaces presented by the various items of equipment. Naturally, the geometry of the setup is different for each physical arrangement of the parts. In the event of contradictory results, therefore, it will be necessary to relocate the components and to repeat the measurements. This pro-

cedure must be continued until there is a setup for which capacitive effects are acceptably small, as indicated by reasonable agreements between the two measurements. Of the two values, the resistance obtained by using R_1 is the more accurate, and it should be used to obtain the final measurement. Care is especially important when measuring the resistance of high-impedance antennas, particularly near a frequency corresponding to a half wavelength.

4. The reactance of the antenna at the frequency of the measurement is easily determined if such information is required. If a precision tuning capacitor is used in place of the tuning network, the reactance of the capacitor at the resonant setting ($X_C = 1/2\pi fC$) is equal to the reactance of the antenna. If a tuning network is employed, the impedance of the network at resonance is equal to the antenna reactance. These statements are based on the assumption that it is safe to ignore the reactance of the coupling coil and the standard resistors, and stray effects due to wiring.

The substitution method of measuring antenna resistance involves the replacement of the antenna by equivalent amounts of resistance and reactance, either inductive or capacitive according to the property of the antenna. Figure 10-13 shows a circuit arrangement in which capacitance is used to

help simulate the antenna. The substitution method is usually performed at the frequency to which the antenna circuit has been made resonant, and ordinarily this will be the operating frequency. If the frequency is already known, it is necessary only to place the switch in position 1 and to set the r-f oscillator at the resonant frequency by means of its calibration or preferably with the aid of the wavemeter. If the antenna system has not been made resonant to the operating frequency, it should be adjusted by means of its tuning elements before the resistance measurement is begun. This is accomplished by using the wavemeter to set the oscillator at the operating frequency, followed by an adjustment of the antenna tuning elements for maximum antenna current. As pointed out previously, if the coupling between the two circuits is sufficiently loose, the grid current meter in the driver should indicate a gradual dip as the antenna circuit approaches resonance.

Certain pitfalls must be avoided for accurate determinations. Primarily, there must be no stray transfer of energy into the antenna circuit. In this regard, it is essential for the oscillator to be well shielded, so that energy absorbed directly by the antenna is small compared to the energy induced in the coupling coil. If the oscillator cannot be shielded adequately, the antenna energizing current must be as high as the oscillator in use will permit. Even when the shielding is satisfactory, a high antenna energizing current helps to improve accuracy. The r-f generator should therefore be capable of delivering substantial power—at least 50 watts in the broadcast band.

The procedure for determining antenna resistance by the substitution method is as follows:

1. With the switch in position 1, measure and record the antenna circuit current. It is assumed that the oscillator has been set at the operating frequency by means of the wavemeter.

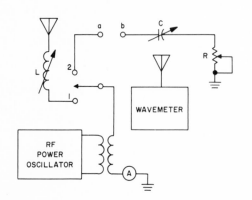

Fig. 10-13 Substitution method of measuring antenna resistance.

2. Place the switch in position 2, so that the antenna is disconnected. If an inductor, such as L in Fig. 10-13, has been used to resonate the antenna to the operating frequency, a resistor and a tuning capacitor, shown as R and C in the figure, should be employed. On the other hand, if a capacitor has been used to tune the antenna, a precision inductor must be used with the resistor.

3. Connect the antenna tuning element to points a and b as indicated in Fig. 10-13. Then tune capacitor C (or the inductor, if used) until resonance of the second circuit is indicated by maximum deflection of the milliammeter. Refer to the wavemeter in order to maintain a constant frequency. Then vary the resistance of R until the meter reading is the same as the value recorded when the antenna was connected. Under this condition, the resistance of R is equal to the antenna resistance, and the reactance of the tuning capacitor is equal to the reactance of the antenna circuit at the resonant frequency. The tuning capacitor and resistor are often referred to as a *dummy antenna*, since they are also used during test procedures when it is necessary to load transmitting equipment properly without allowing radiation of the signal.

4. Using the wavemeter, adjust the oscillator to various other frequencies, above and below resonance, and repeat the procedure of the foregoing steps at each frequency.

If connections are made properly and adequate shielding is provided, the bridge method is perhaps the most rapid and accurate means of determining antenna impedance. Several r-f impedance bridges are available for this purpose.

In addition to the bridge, a well-shielded signal generator providing an output of 1 to 10 volts and a well-shielded receiver having a sensitivity between 1 to 10 microvolts are necessary. The receiver serves as an indicating device for the bridge, so that a dependable balance can be attained. In this application, the avc of the receiver must be disabled, and, if possible, a beat-frequency oscillator should be included so that an audio output will be heard even if an unmodulated r-f signal is used. The usual communications receiver satisfies these requirements.

The equipment should be connected with considerable care, since measurements at radio frequencies are vastly more difficult than at audio frequencies. One especially important practice is to make all ground connections at a single ground point with 1-in. copper strips. If the bridge is properly grounded, its balance will not be affected by touching the panel. It is necessary, of course, to use suitable connectors to connect the r-f generator and the receiver serving as the balance detector. If these equipments are grounded properly, touching their panels will not affect the balance of the bridge. In extreme situations, it may be necessary to connect separate grounds from each piece of equipment to the bridge, and from the bridge to a ground. To check the shielding of the generator, remove the detector (receiver) cable from the panel jack of the bridge. If there is adequate shielding, the pickup of the receiver will be negligibly small. Finally, it should be possible to touch the shield connection of the cable against the ground terminal of the bridge without materially increasing the output of the receiver. If the output of the receiver is considerable when disconnected from the bridge, coupling through the power line and poor shielding are possible causes.

OTHER MEASUREMENT DEVICES   There are several additional methods and devices utilized to measure r-f power, such as the *bolometer mount* and the *calorimetry system*. The former device offers no particular advantage at normal radio frequencies; however, it is used extensively for microwave power measurements and will be discussed in Chapter 11. The use of a calorimeter is a fundamental approach to power measurement and provides an accurate system for r-f power calibration. For this reason, it is discussed in connection with r-f calibration systems.

A number of indirect procedures have been developed for power measurement at the higher end of the r-f spectrum where the direct approach begins to fail in accuracy and reliability. Invariably, these methods convert the r-f power under measurement to another form of energy, such as light or heat, which can be evaluated more readily. The amount of secondary energy produced must be related to the r-f energy. In one way or another, it is necessary to take the associated time interval into proper account in order to determine the r-f power.

For all r-f power measurements, at the high frequencies, the coaxial line delivering the power must be terminated properly. As an illustration, suppose that the termination of a 50-ohm line is required, and that conventional 28-volt, 4-watt lamps are to comprise the load. These conditions characterize the TS-78/W. Since the hot resistance of these lamps is 196 ohms, three lamps can be connected in parallel to provide approximately a 65-ohm, 12-watt termination. As a rule, the slight mismatch that results is trivial. It is interesting to note that as the lamps are dimmed, their resistance decreases and further minimizes the small mismatch. As the

parallel resistance falls below 50 ohms, however, the mismatch becomes increasingly worse. Attenuator or matching pads may also be used.

As indicated by the graph of Fig. 10-14, the light intensity of incandescent lamps can be correlated to power. If the human eye were capable of accurately determining light intensity, this graph would be a direct means of power evaluation. It is possible, of course, to measure light intensity by appropriate instrumentation and then to refer to a graph like the one in Fig. 10-14, but ordinarily this procedure is not utilized. Instead, recourse is made to a pair of identical lamp combinations, such as the two TS-78/U equipments shown in Fig. 10-15. One lamp load is energized by the r-f source, and the second by a 28-volt, d-c power source. If the two banks of lamps are adjacent and the potentiometer across the d-c source is adjusted, it is possible to judge rather accurately when the lamps are equally brilliant. This method is feasible because the eye is reasonably sensitive to relative brillance, in contrast to its fallibility when estimating absolute intensity. When the two sets of lamps appear equally bright, the product of the voltmeter and ammeter readings is equal to the r-f power.

When greater accuracy is desired, the uncertainties of visual observation can be avoided by the technique shown in Fig. 10-16. By means of a tunable matching network, a lamp load is matched to an r-f transmission line, as evidenced by maximum brightness. The light emitted is directed upon a photoelectric cell, which then passes a current on to a meter graduated in watts. This graduation is often recorded on a chart. If multiple ranges of power are desired, there must be lamp banks of suitable ratings. An instrument of this type is the TS-70/AP, which is accurate to 10% or better in the frequency range of 200 to 750 mc. It must be connected to a 50-ohm line. An accuracy of 2% or better is possible.

In measuring power by the lamp method, there are two main considerations: (1) the

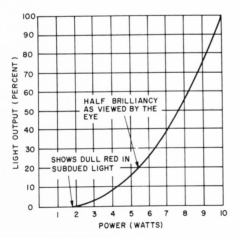

Fig. 10-14 Graph of light output versus power for a typical incandescent lamp.

wattage rating of the total lamp load should be greater than the power being measured; (2) the net resistance of the load should approximately match the impedance of the r-f source. Two examples of common lamps and their hot resistances are as follows: the No. 47 dial lamp, 42 ohms; and the 40-watt, 115-volt lamp, 330 ohms.

Another effective method of measuring power indirectly is to measure the temperature rise of, or the heat generated by, a noninductive resistor acting as a load for the r-f power source. A matching network is necessary only if the loading resistance does not correctly terminate the transmission line from the r-f source. A typical procedure for measuring the heating effect of the resistor consists of passing a stream of air around the resistor and determining the temperature rise of the air by means of thermocouples, as shown in Fig. 10-17. To evaluate the r-f power dissipated in the resistance, it is necessary to know the rate of air flow as well as the temperature rise. A refinement of this method is the insertion of the load resistor in an airtight box containing an inert gas. This provision enables the resistor to be operated at high temperatures indefinitely without undergoing changes in its characteristics. A power meter of this type is the TS-206/AR, which is accurate to within 10%, up to 1 kw in the 60-mc range, if used with a 50-ohm line.

Another way of determining the power dissipated in a resistance load has already been discussed. The method consists of rectifying the r-f voltage and applying the d-c output to a meter graduated in watts. Sometimes a vacuum-tube voltmeter is used to indicate peak power, which can be converted to average power by multiplying it by the duty cycle (see Appendix D). In this category is the TS-226A/AP, which is intended for frequencies between 400 and 500 mc. It is accurate to within 15%. Another way of measuring r-f power is to use a sampling method. One application of this method is the Model 185A series of termination wattmeters (page 230). The power dissipating resistor in the built-in

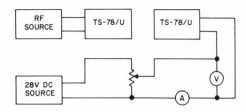

Fig. 10-15 Lamp-load calibration setup.

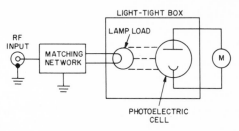

Fig. 10-16 Photoelectric-type lamp-load power meter.

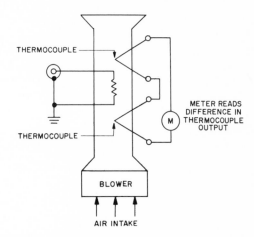

Fig. 10-17 Resistor-air-flow power meter.

dummy load is tapped at a suitable point. The sampled r-f from this point is fed through an isolating resistor to a rectifier diode and the rectified output applied to a meter calibrated in watts. An accuracy of ±5% is obtained with this method.

Another example of sampling is the directional coupler with a known coupling factor. The directional coupler output may be rectified and applied directly to a meter calibrated in watts or it may be measured with a vacuum tube voltmeter. Model 164 Bi-Directional Power Monitor uses the direct meter method with ±5% accuracy, while the 194A-A and the 400A peak power monitors use a vacuum tube voltmeter with an accuracy of ±10%.

R-F CALIBRATION SYSTEMS

Where a large number of power measuring equipments are in use, it is desirable to set up a power calibration standard to provide an accurate periodic check for the test equipment. Each individual test set may be checked against the standard, and any calibration errors may be noted and taken into account during measurement. If a certain test

set suddenly shows a large calibration error, it should be overhauled before being returned to service.

One type of power calibration standard is known as the water load calorimeter. A photograph of the Sierra Model 430A calorimeter and water loads with a block diagram of this system are illustrated in Fig. 10-18. The water load provides a nonreflecting termination for the r-f transmission line. The r-f power, which is completely absorbed by the liquid coolant, produces an increase in the coolant temperature. The 430A calorimeter operates on the principle that in a constant flow, liquid coolant system temperature rise across the load is directly proportional to the power introduced into the system. This temperature

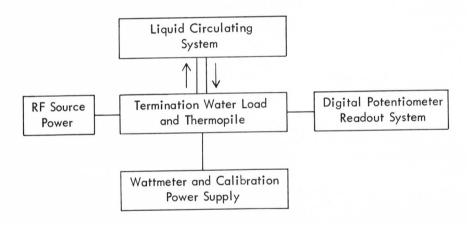

Fig. 10-18 Model 430A water load calorimeter. (Courtesy, Sierra Electronic Division, Philco Corporation.)

change is then measured and read out in terms of watts. The complete calorimeter is made up of four sub-systems: a liquid circulating system, a digital potentiometer readout system, a water load and thermopile, and a precision wattmeter and a-c calibration power supply. The liquid circulating system provides an extremely constant coolant flow which transfers the heat generated from the r-f termination water load to the thermopile. Temperature rise due to the r-f source power, or a-c calibration power, fed into the water load is sensed by the thermopile. The output of the thermopile is interpreted in terms of watts by the digital potentiometer readout system. The precision wattmeter is the power calibration standard of the instrument. The a-c calibration power supply and the wattmeter are used for routine calibration, and may be used for direct substitution power measurement. The units come filled with coolant and the proper water load is quickly connected to the calorimeter by means of quick disconnect, self-sealing hose connectors and an electrical cable and plug. The system is entirely self-contained. To make measurements requires only that it be connected to the r-f power source and to an a-c supply.

A second calorimetric system, the Model 290C (shown in Fig. 10-19) provides the closest available approach to the absolute measurement of average r-f power in the 30–1500 watt range. Measurement accuracies of 1% or better are possible over this range and 2–3% in the range 10–30 watts. Rapid response and readout are obtained through the use of high flow rates and the excellent heat-transfer characteristics of the r-f terminations. Operational versatility is obtained through the use of a a balanced measurement configuration, and the linear readout characteristics of a differential thermopile and associated galvanometer. Three specific measurement methods are available: null-balance method (for maximum accuracy), direct-reading method (for maximum speed), and the differential method (for expanded-scale readings). The functional diagram (included in

Fig. 10-19) shows the basic configuration of the instrument. Two identical r-f terminations are mounted in an isothermal enclosure, and are cooled with equal flows of coolant from a heat exchanger via an inlet manifold. Each termination heats the water in proportion to the applied powers. The difference in temperature between the termination water outlets is sensed by the differential thermopile and indicated on a galvanometer.

Initial calibration is accomplished by applying equal a-c powers, as measured by the precision a-c wattmeter, to each termination, A and B, and adjusting the water metering valves for zero voltage output of the thermopile. When a power measurement is made the unknown r-f power is applied to termination B. The known a-c power that is applied to termination A is adjusted so that the galvanometer indicates zero temperature difference between the waterflows through both terminations. Since the water flow through both terminations is set equal in the initial calibration, when the galvanometer indicates zero temperature difference the power being put into each of the terminations must also be equal.

The 290C Calorimetric Test Set, shown in Fig. 10-19, consists of four functional units: the AC Calibration Wattmeter (Electrodynamometer Wattmeter), the Calorimetric Wattmeter, the Heat Exchanger, and a Model 286 or 287 Dual Water Load. The particular water load to be used depends on the frequency of the power to be measured. The water loads may be easily changed as necessary.

The Calorimetric Wattmeter contains the a-c calibration power supply, the galvanometer, the waterflow rate control, and the majority of the test set operating controls. The controls and galvanometer are located on the front panel and the water load connections are in the rear.

The AC Calibration Wattmeter is a laboratory-standard type, 60 cycle dynamometer wattmeter. There are two current scales, 5 and 10 amperes, and four voltage scales, 25,

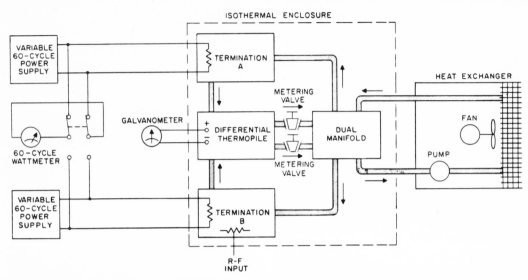

Fig. 10-19 Model 290C calorimetric test set. The colorimetric wattmeter contains the calibration power supplies and most of the test set controls. The electrodynamometer wattmeter has an accuracy of 0.25%. The heat exchanger circulates water through the dual water load (inset) and the colorimetric wattmeter. (Courtesy, Sierra Electronic Division, Philco Corp.)

75, 150 and 300 volts. Various combinations of these current and voltage scales provide six power ranges: 50, 100, 125, 250, 500, and 1000 watts. Wattmeter accuracy is 0.25% of full scale. Due to the wide range of powers encountered when making measurements, use of several of the wattmeter scales requires application of a maximum duty cycle. The wattmeter will maintain its rated full scale accuracy provided that operation on any red numbered power setting of the Wattmeter Scale dial is limited to a maximum of 1 minute followed by a minimum cooling off period of 4 minutes. Also, the 100 watt scale should never be used to measure power greater than 62.5 watts with the 50 ohm Coaxial Water Load. This duty cycle limitation prevents overheating the wattmeter, which would tend to adversely affect its specified 0.25% full scale accuracy.

The Heat Exchanger circulates the water

through the Water Load and Calorimetric Wattmeter, cools it, and regulates the pressure to approximately 40 psig. The water is cooled through the use of a fan-radiator heat exchanger. The front panel contains an input-water-temperature indicator, a water-pressure indicator, a flow-rate gage and a power control.

The Dual Water Load converts a power difference to a water-temperature difference. This temperature difference is converted to a voltage by the differential thermopile. Direct measurement of this voltage provides a precise power difference indication. Each Water Load contains two identical r-f terminations, coaxial or waveguide, symmetrically mounted on heat-insulating sections inside a specially designed enclosure. The enclosure has a metal liner which is in thermal contact with an aluminum casting that forms the inlet and the outlet water manifolds. This configuration insures that the interior of the enclosure is maintained at a temperature close to the average of the inlet and outlet water temperatures. The individual twin terminations were designed with emphasis on good heat insulation to the exterior surfaces, rapid heat transfer to the water, high r-f efficiency and very low r-f reflection. In the coaxial termination, the same film-resistor is used to dissipate r-f or a-c power. In the waveguide terminations, the cooling water flows

through a teflon tube positioned within the waveguide section and the water itself is the dissipating element for the r-f power. The a-c power is dissipated in a resistor mounted within the teflon water tube in the same area where the r-f power is dissipated.

The Test Set is entirely self-contained and requires no external instrumentation.

Although the instruments discussed so far have been for calibrations in the high-power range, calorimetric systems can also be used for low- and medium-power calibrations. In these ranges, the primary detriment to accuracy and over-all design is the low heating rate of the smaller power values.

MAGNETIC CORE LOSS MEASUREMENTS

Almost all electrical machinery and many electronic devices are dependent upon the magnetic properties of a ferromagnetic material for their operation. These properties are, in turn, dependent upon the energy losses of the material.

The most important characteristics can be obtained from a determination of the hysteresis loop described in Chapter 7. As shown in Fig. 7-23, this is a plot of flux density B versus field intensity (magnetizing force) H.

The energy lost due to hysteresis in the core during a complete cycle of applied cur-

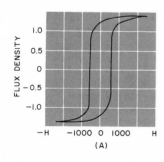
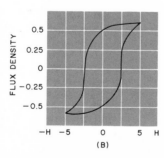
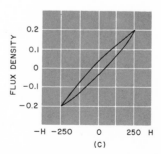

Fig. 10-20 Common hysteresis loops: (A) A large saturation current without excessive hysteresis loss—soft iron. (B) Large magnetization with very little magnetizing force and low hysteresis loss—Permalloy. (C) Very little hysteresis loss and a constant permeability—Perminvar.

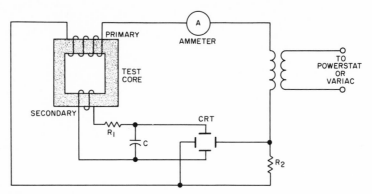

Fig. 10-21 Oscilloscope viewing of hysteresis loop. A low-frequency alternating current should be used. For accurate results the test specimen should be laminated. The current is controlled by an autotransformer as shown. The magnetizing force is calculated from the ammeter reading and the number of primary turns. The emf due to the magnetizing force is developed across R_2 and applied to the horizontal plates. R_2 should be a small resistance. A voltage proportional to the flux density is produced by the integrating circuit, $R_1 - C$, and applied to the vertical plates.

rent is the area enclosed by the hysteresis loop. The loop is usually plotted from experimental data and the area measured by a planimeter.

Along with the determination of core losses, a series of related hysteresis loops can be used to determine the normal magnetiza-tion curve for calculating permeability (Fig. 7-23).

Figure 10-20 shows the loops for three different materials and discusses their interpretation. These loops are easily obtained with an oscilloscope connected as shown in Fig. 10-21.

QUESTIONS

1 Describe the factors affecting power measurement in a-c circuits containing reactive components.

2 Discuss the technique of calibrating a water load calorimeter.

3 Explain the procedure of expressing audio power levels in terms of decibels (dbm).

Microwave Equipment: Measurements and Calibration Techniques   11

All the techniques considered before this chapter have involved the currents and voltages present within circuits rather than the electromagnetic fields which must always be present when a current flows. For d-c and for a-c frequencies up to the microwave region, the circuit parameters are "lumped" and the direct measurement of current and voltage is practicable because of the normal relationship between voltage, current, and impedance.

In the microwave frequency region, however, the electromagnetic fields are of primary importance. This is true because the circuit parameters are no longer lumped, but are variously distributed throughout the system. Voltage and current cease to exist in their familiar forms, and the concepts of electric and magnetic field strengths become all-important.

Electromagnetic waves which exist in free space are generally radiated by antennas in all directions or in specific directions, depending on the design of the antenna. The electromagnetic wave occurs at right angles to the disturbance, or excitation, which creates it. This is shown in Fig. 11-1A. The electromagnetic wave which is "created" then propagates through space in a direction which is perpendicular to both the original excitation and the plane of the resultant electromagnetic wave. This is also illustrated. If it were possible to view the electromagnetic wave at various points in space, it would appear as shown. The wave is "stopped" at specific distances, d_1, d_2, and d_3. Since electromagnetic waves are variable in space and time, they appear to be shifted with respect to the propagation axis. Thus, the wave starts out with a zero point at the propagation axis, and this zero point moves away from the axis as time passes. Figure 11-1B shows that the propagation is in all directions radially from the source, which may be assumed to be a vertical rod.

An electromagnetic wave consists of two components: a magnetic field and an electrical field. The planes of these two fields are perpendicular, as illustrated in Fig. 11-2. The fields pictured in Fig. 11-2A represent their magnitudes and locations at one particular instant of time; for another time, these would be different, as shown in Fig. 11-2B.

The discussion in this chapter will not be concerned with the transmission of electromagnetic waves through space. It will, rather, consider the measurements which can be made when the waves are *guided* from one point to another within a given electronic system. Some discussion of measurements on *broadcast* waves is included in the next chapter, which considers the evaluation of radar systems.

The boundaries used to confine and guide an electromagnetic wave are metallic in nature and are arranged so as to form either a two-conductor or a one-conductor system. The two-conductor system includes parallel-wire and coaxial transmission lines. Waveguides constitute the one-conductor system. Waveguides are hollow pipes of various cross-sectional configurations. Rectangular

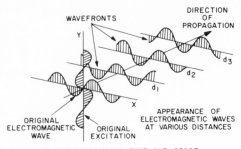

A. PROPAGATION IN TIME AND SPACE

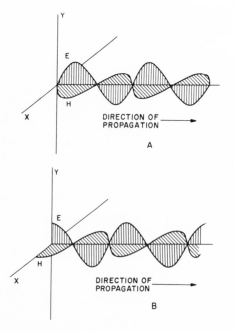

B. RADIAL PROPAGATION ABOUT Y-AXIS

Fig. 11-1. Creation and propagation of electromagnetic waves.

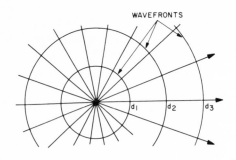

Fig. 11-2 Electromagnetic wave components.

and circular cross sections are the most common configurations, the rectangular guide being the more useful of the two.

There is no definite frequency point between the r-f and microwave regions which determines the use of transmission line or waveguide. The choice of which to use depends upon the application and the results desired.

Because electromagnetic waves vary with time at various points in space, it would be impracticable to determine the absolute electric and magnetic field intensities at every point. It is possible, however, to describe the electromagnetic fields in relative terms. The *absolute measurements* in the area of microwaves are confined to determinations of frequency, wavelength, and power.

WAVE PROPAGATION

Propagation of electromagnetic waves may occur along a waveguide or transmission line in various *modes*, or wave patterns. The pattern illustrated previously in Fig. 11-2 comprises one mode—the *transverse electromagnetic* (TEM) mode. For this mode both the electric and magnetic fields are perpendicular (transverse) to the direction of propagation. It is possible for components of the electric and magnetic fields to exist in any of the three spatial reference planes. *However, en electric and magnetic component cannot both exist in the same plane simultaneously.* This leads to two other propagation modes: (1) transverse magnetic (TM), and (2) transverse electric (TE). Both are shown in Fig. 11-3. In A there is an electric component in the y and z (propagation) direction. These components add to produce the resultant electric field which is not perpendicular to the direction of propagation. The only magnetic component which can exist must be H_X, so that the magnetic field is transverse to the direction of propagation. Similar reasoning may be applied to Fig.

11-3B, where only the electric field is perpendicular to the propagation direction.

Transmission lines are capable of propagating any of the three modes, although the TEM is most commonly employed. Waveguides can only support the TE and TM modes. The two modes are commonly followed by two numerical subscripts, $TE_{m,n}$ and $TM_{m,n}$. In rectangular waveguides, m refers to the number of half-waves which exist for the transverse field across the width (larger dimension) of the guide, and n refers to the number of transverse half-waves across the height of the guide. For circular guides, m indicates the number of whole waves around the circumference, and n refers to the half-waves along a diameter. A half-wave variation of the field consists of an increase in magnitude from zero to a peak value and back to zero, with the direction of the field remaining constant. Examples are shown in Fig. 11-4.

The mode which will be propagated in a waveguide is dependent upon the relationship of the waveguide to the wavelength of the electromagnetic wave. This can be seen from the preceding definitions of the mode numbers. For example, if the $TE_{1,0}$ mode is desired in a rectangular waveguide, the width of the guide must be greater than one-half wavelength but less than one wavelength, and the height must be less than one-half wavelength. Similarly, if the $TM_{1,1}$ mode is desired in a circular guide, the circumference must be greater than one wavelength but less than two wavelengths, whereas the diameter must be less than one-half wavelength.

Since wavelength and frequency are related, for each propagation mode there is a specific *cutoff frequency*—the frequency below which the waveguide or line cannot support electromagnetic waves. For transmission lines, the cutoff frequency is zero. For waveguides, the lower limit is dependent upon the physical dimensions of the

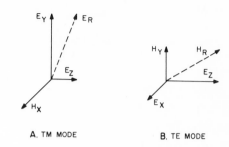

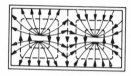

A. TM MODE   B. TE MODE

Fig. 11-3 Wave modes—vector representation.

A. RECTANGULAR—$TM_{2,1}$

B. CIRCULAR—$TM_{0,1}$

Fig. 11-4 Mode support in waveguides. For part A, m = 2 and n = 1. Across the width of the guide there are two half-waves, as shown by the reversal of the field direction. Across the height of the rectangular guide there is only one half-wave (the field occurs in only one direction). In part B, m = 0 because a whole wave does not exist around the circumference of the guide (the field must change direction once to form a whole wave). The field does not change direction along the diameter, showing that one half-wave exists (n = 1).

guide. In the case of the rectangular waveguide,

$$f_c = \frac{v}{2a}$$

where v is the propagation velocity and a is the width of the guide. This equation assumes that the height of the guide will be kept below one-half wavelength, which is usually true in practical applications.

When the electromagnetic wave strikes the load at the end of the transmission medium, this load may absorb all of the power transmitted, it may absorb only part of the power, or it may absorb none of the power. In the last two instances, the power that is not absorbed will be repropagated in a direction opposite to the original direction of propagation. As a result, the components of the *transmitted wave* and the *reflected wave* add together to produce a *standing wave* along the length of the transmission medium. This is illustrated in Fig. 11-5. This figure shows the complete reflection of the transmitted wave. Standing waves are usually considered in terms of magnitude only, without regard to direction. Two values are of major importance—the peak value and

the node, or zero value. The distance between successive peaks (or nodes) is one-half wavelength. Since the transmitted wave varies with time, the reflected wave must vary in a similar manner. As a result, the magnitude of the standing wave is different at different time intervals. The peaks and the nodes will always occur at the same points and the standing wave may be thought of as pulsating along fixed points, as shown in Fig. 11-6.

If only a part of the transmitted energy is reflected, standing waves similar to those shown in Fig. 11-7 will be produced. The specific form will depend upon the amount of energy reflected.

If there is no reflection (i.e., if all the transmitted power is absorbed by the load), the standing wave will be at the same level throughout the length of the transmission medium, as shown in Fig. 11-8. The magnitude of this level will, however, still pulsate with varying time.

The amount of reflection which is present can be determined by introducing a concept known as the *characteristic wave impedance* of the transmission medium. This impedance is defined as the ratio of the electric field intensity to the magnetic field intensity, or

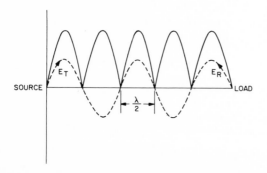

Fig. 11-5 Standing wave formation. The transmitted wave (E_T) and reflected wave (E_R) add to produce the standing wave, which is shown in magnitude only.

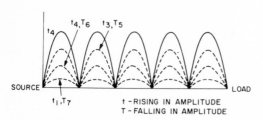

Fig. 11-6 Variation of standing wave with time. The pattern "pulsates," with its peak value varying sinusoidally with time. This value starts at zero and grows larger until it reaches a maximum value at T_4. The value then decreases to zero. In reality, the value then increases and decreases in the negative direction. For convenience, however, magnitude only is considered so that the pattern peak varies only between zero and some maximum value.

$$Z_0 = \frac{E_T}{H_T} = \frac{E_R}{H_R} \text{ ohms}$$

The T subscripts refer to the transmitted wave, and the R subscripts refer to the reflected wave. The characteristic impedance can be related to the fundamental physical properties of the transmission medium by the equation:

$$Z_0 = \sqrt{\frac{j\omega\epsilon}{\sigma + j\omega\epsilon}} \text{ ohms}$$

where $\omega = 2\pi f$, μ and ϵ are the permeability and permittivity of the medium, and σ is the conductivity of the medium. For waveguides filled with a good dielectric material (such as air), the foregoing equation reduces to

$$\text{r-m-s value} = \sqrt{I_2{}^2 + I_3{}^2 + I_4{}^2 + \ \cdots}$$

This will yield a purely resistive characteristic impedance; i.e., theoretically there are no power losses within the waveguide. The characteristic impedance of an air-filled waveguide is 376.6 ohms.

If the load is matched to the characteristic impedance ($Z_L = Z_o$), 100% of the transmitted power will be absorbed by the load. If the two impedances are not matched, however, a certain portion of the transmitted power will be reflected as previously described. The ratio of reflected to transmitted values is the *reflection coefficient*:

$$K = \frac{E_R}{E_T} = \frac{H_R}{H_T}$$

or, related to the impedances,

$$K = \frac{Z_L - Z_o}{Z_L + Z_o}$$

Transmission lines contain a certain inherent amount of inductance and capacitance, so that Z_o for these mediums is not a pure resistance. Thus, there will be losses along the line. These losses are usually expressed by an attenuation constant, α, which is expressed as the number of nepers or decibels lost per meter of line length. The presence of the reactive components will also produce a phase shift in the magnetic and electric field components, which is usually specified by the phase constant, β, in radians/meter of line length. These two constants are generally expressed as parts of the *propagation constant*:

$$\gamma = \alpha + j\beta$$

The characteristic impedance of the transmission medium can be related to the propagation constant by

$$Z_o = \frac{\gamma}{\sigma + j\omega\mu} \text{ ohms/meter of line length}$$

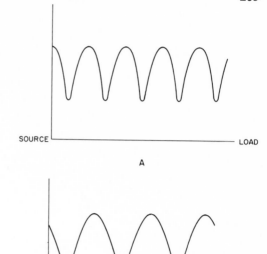

SOURCE   LOAD

A

SOURCE   LOAD

B

Fig. 11-7 Standing wave phase shift.

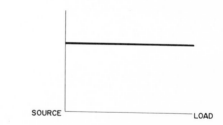

SOURCE   LOAD

Fig. 11-8 Standing wave with no reflection.

The existence of a cutoff frequency in waveguides has been previously mentioned, although a solution for frequency value was limited to modes with $n = 0$. Actually, the cutoff is not abrupt; the electromagnetic waves are not attenuated instantaneously to zero at one specific frequency. They are attenuated gradually, a fact that can best be explained by introducing a propagation constant for waveguides, which is similar to the transmission-line constant just given. This factor depends upon the mode and guide dimensions, and is given for a rectangular guide by

$$\gamma_{m,n} = \sqrt{\left(\frac{m\pi}{a}\right)^2 + \left(\frac{n\pi}{b}\right)^2 - \omega^2 \mu \epsilon}$$

where a and b are the width and height of the guide, respectively.

$$\lambda_c = \lambda_{m,n} = \frac{2}{\sqrt{\left(\frac{m}{a}\right)^2 + \left(\frac{n}{b}\right)^2}}$$

$$f_c = f_{m,n} = \frac{1}{2\pi\sqrt{\mu\epsilon}} \sqrt{\left(\frac{m\pi}{a}\right)^2 + \left(\frac{n\pi}{b}\right)^2}$$

Another power loss in waveguides is the loss due to the metal guide walls. For the rectangular waveguide this loss in power for a particular frequency, f, in the TM mode is given by

$$\alpha = \sqrt{\frac{\pi\mu}{\sigma}} \frac{v^2 \sqrt{f}}{2Z_o f_c^2} \frac{(n^2/b^3 + m^2/a^3)}{\sqrt{1 - f_c^2/f^2}} \text{neper/m}$$

and in the TE mode by

$$\alpha = \sqrt{\frac{\pi\mu}{\sigma}} \frac{2\sqrt{f}}{bZ_o \sqrt{1 - f_c^2/f^2}}$$

$$\left\{ \begin{matrix} \left[1 - \left(\frac{f_c}{f}\right)^2\right] \frac{bm^2/an^2 + 1}{bm^2/an^2 + a/b} \\ + \left(1 + \frac{b}{a}\right)\left(\frac{fc}{f}\right)^2 \end{matrix} \right\} \text{neper/m}$$

In these last equations, μ and σ refer to the metal material and f is the frequency of the propagated wave.

Because of waveguide geometry and the high velocities of propagation[*] involved, the wavelength of the electromagnetic waves inside the waveguide is not the same as it would be if the waves were not confined. Therefore, there exists, within the guide, an apparent wavelength:

[*] A complete discussion of wave propagation can be found in John D. Ryder's *Networks, Lines, and Fields*, Englewood Cliffs, N. J., Prentice Hall, Inc., 1960.

$$\lambda_a = \frac{\lambda}{\sqrt{1 - \left(\frac{\lambda}{\lambda_c}\right)^2}}$$

where λ is the actual wavelength.

MICROWAVE POWER SUPPLIES

Just as it was necessary to have standard, or calibrated, d-c and a-c voltage sources for previous electrical measurements and calibrations, it is necessary to have microwave sources with a high degree of stability and which can be readily and reliably calibrated. These are new problems associated with the design and use of this equipment—problems that are not encountered at the lower r-f frequencies.

As the frequency in a circuit increases, effects that are negligible at the lower frequencies become more prominent. One well-known example is *skin effect*, a condition which restricts the electron flow in a conductor to the surfaces. At very high frequencies the inner regions of the conductor contribute nothing to its effective conductivity. Furthermore, when adjacent conductors are carrying current, the magnetic flux surrounding one conductor adversely affects the current distribution in the other conductors. This influence, termed *proximity effect*, increases the actual resistance to a value greater than that attributable to skin effect.

Serious deterrents to the operation of vacuum tubes at high frequencies arise because a finite time, called *transit time*, is required for the electron to travel from the cathode to the plate of the tube. A few of the effects of transit time are "back-heating" of the cathode, increased losses in the grid circuit, distortion of the plate current, and increased losses at the screen and suppressor grids in the case of pentodes.

The actual transit time of an electron is determined by the distance between the plate and the cathode, and the potential difference between these elements. At the lower frequencies, since transit time is very short relative to the period of the signal, the electrode voltages are virtually constant during the brief time an electron is in motion; no detrimental effects occur. The following conditions will prevail: (1) all the electrons leaving the cathode will proceed to the plate, (2) the current induced in an electrode such as the grid while the electron is approaching is canceled by the current induced as the electron recedes, and (3) the current induced in the plate circuit depends only on the number of electrons striking the plate.

If the signal frequency is sufficiently high, the voltage present on the tube electrodes will change significantly during the transit time of an electron. One possible condition is that of electrons suspended near the cathode during a period when the tube would be nonconducting if the frequency were low. Such electrons are usually repelled back to the cathode by the negative electric field in the region. The energy released by the returning electrons may be enough to heat the cathode considerably. Filament current, which normally supplies all the heat required for cathode operation, must then be reduced by an amount dependent on the conditions within the tube. Continued bombardment of the cathode can eventually destroy the emitting surface.

Another phenomenon is the absorption of power by the grid structure. Since the velocity of an electron is both increased and decreased during various junctures of the transit time interval, the currents induced in an intermediate electrode will not be entirely canceled. Energy absorbed by the grid in this manner is furnished to other electrons. A portion is used for back-heating effects, and does not contribute to the useful output power. The remainder helps determine the velocity of the electrons impinging on the anode. Under favorable conditions, a substantial amount of such energy can appear in the useful output of the tube. It may be

regarded as energy transferred from the grid to the output circuit without amplification.

At high frequencies, the influences of stray inductances, losses due to wiring, and interelectrode capacitance become decisive. To begin with, the product of L–C producing resonance is decreased as the frequency becomes greater. As a result, the inductance associated with a short length of wire may be sufficient to resonate with the interelectrode capacitance of a tube. This condition establishes the highest frequency to which a given circuit can be tuned. Another important condition at high frequencies is the increased feedback between the plate and grid circuits. Even pentodes at such frequencies may require neutralization. Certain tubes have therefore been constructed to minimize lead inductance and interelectrode capacitance. Examples of such tubes are the lighthouse tube, the acorn tube, and the doorknob tube. In the lighthouse tube, the coaxial construction and general electrode arrangement not only minimize capacitive effects, but also act as electrically continuous extensions of associated concentric transmission lines.

DETECTORS

Since voltage and current do not exist in the same sense at high frequencies as they do at low frequencies, certain power-sensitive devices have been developed for microwave applications. These power detectors include *bolometers* (loading devices which undergo resistive changes) and standard crystal detectors.

There are two chief types of bolometers: the *barretter* and the *thermistor*. The barretter is characterized by an increase in resistance as the dissipated power rises, but the thermistor decreases in resistance as the power increases. In the case of either device, resistance is measured before and after signal power is applied. If the same change in resistance is then produced by a variable d-c source of power, the signal power is equal to the measured d-c power. This relationship makes possible the calibration of a bridge circuit directly in units of power. In other words, there is one condition of balance when no signal is applied, but in the presence of power there is a second condition of balance owing to the resistance change of the bolometer. It is this change of resistance that is calibrated in units of power or voltage.

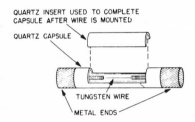

Fig. 11-9 Typical barretter.

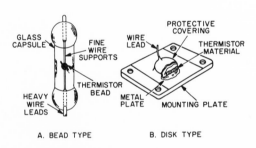

Fig. 11-10 Typical thermistors.

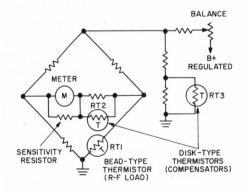

Fig. 11-11 Thermistor bridge circuit.

Figure 11-9 shows the structure of a typical barretter. The fine wire shown, usually made of tungsten, is extremely small in diameter, so that r-f current can penetrate to the center and thereby nullify skin effect. It is supported in an insulating capsule between two metallic ends, which also act as connectors, giving the barretter an appearance resembling a cartridge fuse. The enclosure is a quartz capsule made in two parts, the second of which is an insert cemented in place after the tungsten wire has been mounted. In operation, the barretter is matched to the transmission medium after the signal is applied. An interesting property of the device is the square-law relation characterizing its resistance-versus-power curve at low levels of power.

The *thermistor* is a resistance element with a negative temperature coefficient of resistance. When current is passed through a thermistor, heat is generated and the resistance is lowered. The change in resistance may be measured and converted to indicate the heat, in watts, required to produce the change. In microwave measurements, a thermistor is used to terminate a transmission line so that all the power flowing down the line is absorbed in the thermistor, which serves as the load. The amount of power absorbed by the thermistor is indicated by a resistance change. Figure 11-10 shows two types of thermistors in wide use. The disk type is used for temperature compensation, and the bead type is used for measurements. In the bead-type thermistor, the active material is in the form of a very small bead, which is supported by two fine wires held in place by heavy pigtail leads imbedded in the glass capsule. The entire capsule is supported by means of the heavy pigtail leads, which also serve as electrical connections. The fine inner wires, which support the bead inside the capsule, are made very small to prevent heat from being carried away from the bead by thermal conduction. To prevent high-frequency skin effect from causing resistance errors, the bead is made small

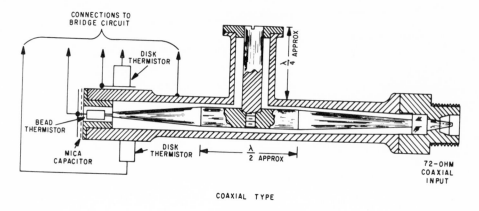

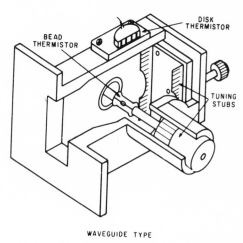

Fig. 11-12 Typical thermistor mounts, showing construction.

enough that the r-f current flow penetrates to the center of the bead. Bead resistance will vary from about 10 ohms, hot, to about 1000 ohms, cold.

Complicated procedures were found necessary in early thermistor applications because of the effect of ambient temperature changes causing changes in thermistor resistance. This difficulty has been corrected by the development of the compensated thermistor bridge circuit, shown in Fig. 11-11. This circuit incorporates a Wheatstone bridge circuit, which is made up of three resistors and a bead-type thermistor. The bead thermistor acts as a matched load for the r-f line when the bridge is balanced. Two disk-type thermistors are used for tem-

perature compensation and are in thermal contact with the section of r-f line containing the bead thermistor. Figure 11-12 shows the construction of two typical thermistor mounts.

The resistance of the bead thermistor may be varied by means of the balance rheostat. The bridge is balanced by electrically adjusting the circuit to a point where one milliwatt of power will produce zero meter current. A zero-centered type of meter is used, and the value of the sensitivity resistor (Fig. 11-11) is factory adjusted so that, with a full-scale meter reading, 1 milliwatt of power is required to restore the reading to midscale.

Temperature compensation of the bridge

is necessary for two reasons: first, bridge balance must be maintained; second, sensitivity must remain constant under varying temperature conditions. In Fig. 11-11, thermistor #3, with its associated resistors, compensates for any unbalance due to temperature variation, as follows: As the ambient temperature rises, the resistance of the bead thermistor drops, so that if no compensation were provided, an unbalanced condition would occur. At the same time, however, the resistance of thermistor #3 decreases, causing a reduction in the d-c voltage applied to the bridge. The resulting reduction in d-c bridge power allows the resistance of the bead thermistor to return to normal, with the result that the bridge balance is maintained. Since microwave

energy is applied only to the bead thermistor, compensation does not depend upon power.

At high ambient temperatures, the value of DC applied to the bridge is low. This condition results in reduced bridge sensitivity, and if uncompensated, would result in errors in measurements. Compensation is provided by thermistor #2, which is effectively in series with the indicating meter. At high temperatures, where bridge sensitivity is reduced, this thermistor presents a lower series resistance to the meter, and, therefore, increases the meter sensitivity in the same proportion as the loss of bridge sensitivity. Thus, the over-all sensitivity is maintained essentially constant at different temperatures. In practice, most bridge cir-

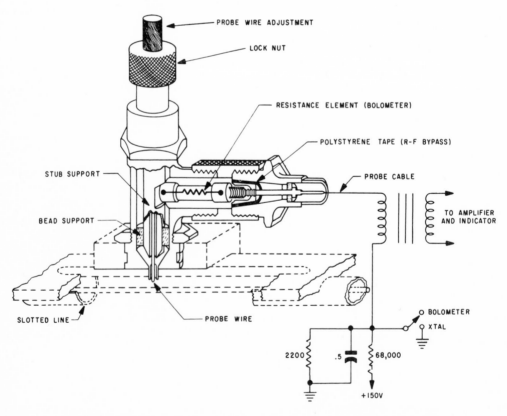

Fig. 11-13 Typical r-f probe, showing construction and associated circuit. The bolometer element shown above may be replaced by a crystal rectifier. The Bolometer switch position allows bias current to flow; the XTAL position does not.

cuits are designed to give exact readings at 0°, 30°, and 60°C. At other temperatures, a slight error exists.

A crystal rectifier, such as the 1N21 or 1N23, may be used in place of the barretter, in which case no d-c bias current is necessary.

Bolometers and crystal rectifiers are used in conjunction with an r-f probe and a slotted line. The slotted line is a coaxial or waveguide section of transmission medium, with a longitudinal slot cut into its outer wall to permit the insertion of a probe. The slot is generally at least one wavelength long, and is narrow enough to cause very little loss due to radiation leakage. Through this slot a probe can be placed in the electromagnetic field inside the section, and can be moved up and down the section to explore the voltage field. The probe feeds directly to the detector unit and the rectified output operates a meter that indicates the relative voltage or current magnitude.

Figure 11-13 shows the construction of a typical r-f probe. The probe wire is adjustable for depth of penetration (coupling), so that the amount of r-f pickup can be controlled. In practice, the coupling is kept at a minimum to reduce distortion of the fields inside the transmission medium.

The indicating meter may be a microammeter located directly in the probe cable circuit, or it may be an ammeter preceded by a d-c amplifier to which the probe voltage is fed. Usually, if amplification (greater sensitivity) is desired, the microwave source is amplitude-modulated with an audio-frequency square wave, so that the detector output can, in turn, be amplified by normal audio circuitry. Low-frequency modulation is desirable, as shown by the curve in Fig. 11-14.

DETECTOR RESPONSE DETERMINATION   The response characteristic for a barretter is shown in Fig. 11-15. This curve displays a linear response over the region from I_1 to I_2, and

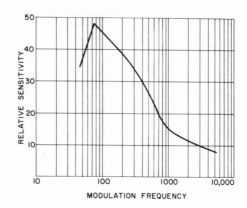

Fig. 11-14   Sensitivity characteristic for square-wave amplitude-modulated detection system.

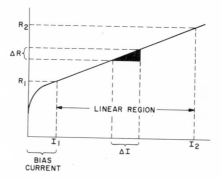

Fig. 11-15   Barretter response characteristic.

illustrates the necessity of providing a bias current for normal barretter operation. The thermistor is also a linear device over a specific portion of its operating characteristic. Crystal response is very nonlinear.

It is not safe to assume that the power response of the detector is proportional to the square of the current (or voltage) output. The detectors produce accurate square-law response over only a limited portion of their operating characteristic. In general, the power response will be given by

$$P = K_1 I^{2/n} = K_2 V^{2/n}$$

where K_1 and K_2 are proportionality constants, and n is the exponent which specifies the actual *law of response*.

The response law curve is a function of

λ_a and the distance between half-power points (D) in the slotted section standing-wave pattern, as shown by the curve in Fig. 11-16. λ_a, remember, will vary as frequency varies. The value of n for a particular *measurement system* (slotted section-probe-indicator combination) varies as the power to the system changes. It is possible to obtain a *response calibration curve* for any particular measurement system with the test setup shown in Fig. 11-17. The procedure is as follows:

1. Tune the test setup until the desired frequency is indicated on the wavemeter.

2. The measurement system is designed to operate over some specified power range. Adjust the attenuator until the test setup is receiving power equal to the minimum value of this range.

3. Locate a position along the slotted section which gives a maximum reading on the indicator. Compute the half-power value:

$$0.707 \times \text{maximum reading}$$

4. Determine a value for D by measuring the distance between two successive half-power readings.

5. Determine a value for λ_a by measuring the distance between two points on the slotted section which give a minimum reading on the indicator, and computing:

$$\lambda_a = 2(D_2 - D_1)$$

6. Find the value for n from Fig. 11-16, corresponding to the measured value of D/λ_a.

7. Adjust the attenuator so that the test setup receives a larger power value. Do this in incremental steps until the upper limit of the measurement system range is reached. At each increment, repeat Steps 3 through 5.

8. Plot the values of n versus power level to obtain the response calibration curve over the specified power range.

The value of n will vary only slightly for barretter and thermistor detectors. A crystal

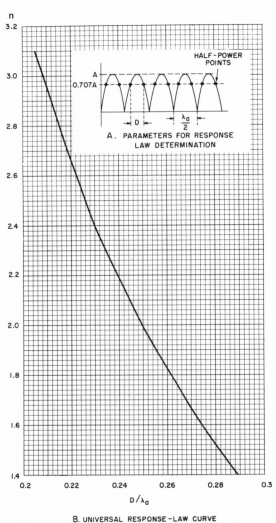

B. UNIVERSAL RESPONSE-LAW CURVE

Fig. 11-16 Reference data for calibrating detectors.

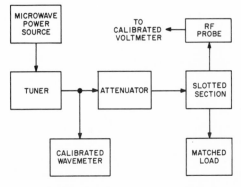

Fig. 11-17 Detector response-law determination.

varies greatly, as mentioned previously. The curve previously established is valid only in the region of the frequency used for the measurements.

VOLTAGE MEASUREMENTS

The statement has been made that voltage and current do not exist, in the normal sense, at microwave frequencies. This is true; however, it is not meant to imply that voltage and current measurements cannot be made at these frequencies. The measurement of these quantities is accomplished by thermal elements which are more readily associated with power measurement. The indicators used with the bolometer and crystal rectifier discussed previously may be calibrated to read voltage or current directly, as well as voltage and current ratios. The two devices to be discussed in this section can also be used to measure voltage and current. They are, however, meant to be standards, most commonly used to calibrate other meters within their frequency ranges.

ATTENUATOR-THERMOELEMENT VOLTMETER
The A-T voltmeter, pictured in Fig. 11-18, was developed by the National Bureau of Standards for calibration in the r-f and lower microwave regions, and is produced by Ballantine Laboratories. Its accuracy is ±1%, which is maintained for at least one year. This device, itself, is calibrated by NBS. The d-c output is measured with a 0–200 micro-ampere, 5-ohm meter having a mirror-backed scale and minimum pivot friction. This meter must accompany the A-T voltmeter when submitted to NBS for recalibration.

The device consists of an adjustable below cutoff attenuator (described in a following section) and a specially adapted thermocouple. The attenuator is adjusted until a standard d-c current value is obtained, and the input signal voltage is then determined from a calibration chart. This chart shows the input voltage for a particular micrometer setting at the frequency of measurement.

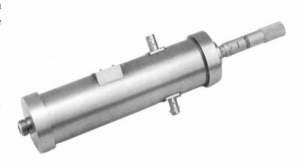

Fig. 11-18 A-T voltmeter. (Courtesy, Ballantine Laboratories, Inc.)

Fig. 11-19 Standard micropotentiometer. (Courtesy, Ballantine Laboratories, Inc.)

The frequency range of this device is 10 mc to 1 kmc, and the voltage range is 0.5 to 300 volts.

MICROPOTENTIOMETER   The NBS micropotentiometer, pictured in Fig. 11-19, is also produced by Ballantine Laboratories. This device accomplishes the same purpose as the A-T voltmeter over a range of 40 microvolts to 0.33 volt; however, it may be used from dc to 900 mc. An accuracy better than 0.25% can be obtained below 10 mc, and an accuracy better than 1% can be obtained at 100 mc. The NBS certified accuracy is ±3%.

To use the micropotentiometer as an absolute voltage standard, the output must be calibrated at dc. The device, in effect, is a transfer instrument—transferring a d-c calibration to the frequency under test.

Several thermocouple-resistor combinations are available in order to adapt the device to a specific requirement.

STANDING WAVE RATIO MEASUREMENTS

As discussed previously, standing waves created along the length of a transmission medium are caused by a mismatch between the characteristic and terminating impedances. Standing waves can, therefore, be related to the parameters of the line or waveguide, as well as to the load characteristics and power. As a matter of fact, standing waves provide a fundamental and absolute method of determining these quantities.

The basic definition of *voltage standing wave ratio (VSWR)* is given by

$$VSWR = \frac{E_{max}}{E_{min}}$$

Since the values of E_{max} and E_{min} along the transmission medium are dependent upon the peak transmitted voltage and the peak reflected voltage, $VSWR$ can be related to these quantities, or, more specifically, to the reflection coefficient K, which then provides a relationship to Z_o and Z_L:

$$VSWR = \frac{1 + |K|}{1 - |K|} = \frac{|Z_L|}{|Z_o|}$$

The vertical lines around K and the impedances indicate that only the magnitudes of these quantities are to be used. Since $VSWR$ must always be 1 or greater, if Z_L in the preceding equation is less than Z_o, the position of the two quantities should be reversed. In fundamental $VSWR$ determinations, Z_L and Z_o should be purely resistive; when this condition must exist, the symbols R_L and R_o will be used throughout this manual. The use of various matching devices permits this condition to exist (see Appendix D-4).

Although power measurements will be discussed in a later section of this chapter, a second concept of standing waves known as *power standing wave ratio (PSWR)* will be introduced here. Since power is proportional

to voltage squared, the basic definition for $PSWR$ is

$$PSWR = \frac{E_{max}^2}{E_{min}^2} = \frac{P_{max}}{P_{min}} = (VSWR)^2$$

A more detailed discussion of $PSWR$ will be included as the need arises.

SLOTTED SECTION METHOD   Standing wave ratio measurements are made with one of the detection systems discussed previously, in a circuit arrangement similar to that shown in Fig. 11-17. The $PSWR$ can be determined from

$$PSWR = \left[\frac{\text{maximum reading}}{\text{minimum reading}} \right]^{2/n}$$

and

$$VSWR = \sqrt{PSWR}$$

where n is the response law value discussed in the previous section. The indicator face on most commercial standing wave devices is calibrated to read $PSWR$ or $VSWR$ directly. Unless otherwise indicated by the manufacturer, commercial instruments operated within their specified power range operate as square-law detectors, so that $n = 2$. In this case the $PSWR$ is directly proportional to the ratio of maximum to minimum readings.

At the discretion of the manufacturer, the indicator readings may be marked so that they are *directly proportional to the voltage* on the line. In this event,

$$VSWR = \frac{\text{maximum reading}}{\text{minimum reading}}$$

and

$$PSWR = (VSWR)^2$$

This does not contradict the previous relationships when it is remembered that direct proportionality constitutes linear detection ($n = 1$) rather than square-law detection.

SLOTTED-SECTION CALIBRATION   The insertion of a slotted section and an r-f probe into a microwave transmission system invariably introduces some distortion to the actual standing wave pattern. In order to make precise standing wave measurements, it is necessary to determine appropriate correction factors for a particular slotted-section and r-f probe combination. The first step in this determination is the plotting of a *slotted-section calibration curve.*

The test setup for obtaining this curve is the same as that used for normal standing wave measurements, shown in Fig. 11-17. The slotted section indicated in the figure should be the one which is to be calibrated. *The frequency of the oscillator source must remain stable.* If a waveguide, rather than a coaxial line, is used, the apparent wavelength for the particular waveguide and test frequency must be computed from

$$\lambda_a = \frac{\lambda}{\sqrt{1 - \left(\dfrac{\lambda}{2a}\right)^2}}$$

The unconfined (free-space) wavelength is found from,

$$\lambda = \frac{c}{f}$$

where c is the speed of light in a vacuum (very nearly the same as in air). The slotted section should then be terminated in a short circuit rather than a matched load, and λ_a measured with the slotted section undergoing calibration.

Again, this procedure is not necessary for a slotted coaxial line section because coaxial lines do not have any relative effects on the impressed wavelength.

For the precision determination of voltage minimums along a transmission medium, the procedure shown in Fig. 11-20 is recommended. The scale on the slotted section provides an arbitrary zero reference for locating the r-f probe. The distance from the arbitrary zero to the end of the slotted section or to the end of the waveguide termination must be determined by external measurements. The x_1 and x_2 measurements

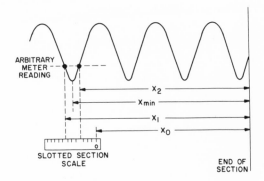

Fig. 11-20 Prefered method for locating standing wave voltage minimum.

represent the locations of two equal indicator readings for standing wave amplitude—one on either side of the minimum. The location of the minimum can be determined from

$$x_{\text{min}} = \frac{x_1 + x_2}{2}$$

The distance between two successive minimums represents λ_{as}. (The s in the subscript denotes the slotted section, as will be true throughout this discussion.)

The remainder of this procedure applies to the calibration of waveguide and coaxial slotted sections. The slotted section should be terminated with a variable short with dimensions identical to those of the slotted section, and the scale reading (distance) D_{s1} for the first minimum should be determined. This is illustrated in Fig. 11-21A.

Move the sliding short 1, 2, 3, etc., half wavelengths from the end of the slotted section, reading D_{s1} at each location. At this point, the distance from the slotted section to the variable short, D_{t1}, is determined.

The final procedure for obtaining the calibration data consists of moving the variable short back toward the slotted section by incremental distances, Δd_t. Each Δd_t will shift the standing wave pattern so that the scale reading for the minimum on the slotted section will shift by the amount, Δd_s. This is illustrated in Fig. 11-21B. The procedure is repeated until Δd_s traverses the length of the slotted-section scale.

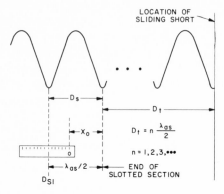

A. DETERMINATION OF FIRST MINIMUM

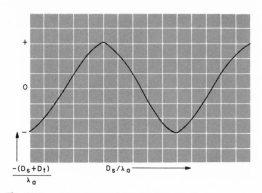

Fig. 11-22 Slotted-section calibration curve.

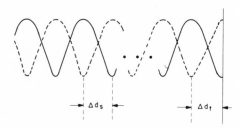

B. WAVE SHIFT AS SHORT LOCATION IS VARIED

Fig. 11-21 Slotted-section calibration measurements.

Using the data obtained, it will be possible to determine the distance from the minimum to the end of the slotted section for each shift in the standing wave pattern:

$$D_s = \Delta d_s + \frac{\lambda_a}{2}$$

It will also be possible to determine the distance from the end of the slotted section to the variable short for each shift:

$$D_t = \frac{n\lambda_a}{2} - \Delta d_t$$

A plot of the quantity $-(D_s + D_t)$ versus D_s yields the desired calibration curve. As a rule, both quantities are divided by λ_a so that the plot will be in terms of wavelength. Such a curve is sinusoidal in shape, as shown in Fig. 11-22. The value of $-(D_s + D_t)/\lambda_a$ is the correction factor which must be added to scale readings at particular settings to ob-

tain distance values for a standing wave pattern not distorted by the presence of the slotted section and r-f probe.

Although the foregoing calibration curve was obtained for a short-circuit termination, the values can be computed for any load by

$$\frac{-(D_s + D_t)}{\lambda_a}\,(\text{any load}) =$$

$$\frac{-(D_s + D_t)}{\lambda_a}\left[\frac{(VSWR)^2 + 1}{(VSWR)^2 - 1}\right]$$

where the value of $VSWR$ is obtained with the slotted section under short-circuit conditions.

The value of $VSWR$ as computed previously must also be corrected because of slot and probe effects. This correction is given by

$$VSWR = 4\pi(VSWR)_m\left[\frac{-(D_s + D_t)}{\lambda_a}\right]$$

which may be either positive or negative. The quantity $(VSWR)_m$ is the value obtained without any corrections.

HIGH-VOLTAGE VSWR MEASUREMENTS The r-f probes used in $VSWR$ and $PSWR$ measurements are low-voltage devices. In order to determine $VSWR$ when $E_{\max}$ is above the range of the probe, a reading should be taken at some intermediate point between $E_{\min}$ and $E_{\max}$ to determine the constant:

$$K^2 = \frac{(\text{intermediate reading})^2}{(\text{minimum reading})^2}$$

This equation is valid for a detector which produces an output that is proportional to the square of the standing wave voltage.

The $VSWR$ can be computed from

$$VSWR = \frac{K^2 - \cos^2 (\pi D/\lambda_a)}{\sin (\pi D/\lambda_a)}$$

where D is the distance between two successive intermediate readings of the same value.

FREQUENCY AND WAVELENGTH

The direct relationship between frequency, wavelength, and the velocity of propagation of an electromagnetic wave in any medium was discussed in Chapter 8. The formulas are repeated here for convenience:

$$f\lambda = v \quad \text{and} \quad v = \frac{1}{\sqrt{\mu \epsilon}}$$

where f is the frequency in cps, λ is the wavelength in units of length, v is the velocity, and μ and ϵ are the permeability and permittivity of the propagation medium. The units of λ, v, μ, and ϵ must be compatible.

WAVELENGTH MEASUREMENTS From a study of the section on standing wave measurements, the reader should be led to the conclusion that the slotted section is an excellent instrument for determining wavelength. All the procedures outlined in that section can be used over almost the entire microwave range (300 mc to 40 kmc) with 0.05% accuracy. This is possible, of course, because of the fact that the distance between standing wave minimums is $\lambda_a/2$. Since λ_a is not the true value desired, the unconfined wavelength must be determined from λ_a by computing λ, using the formula previously given.

FREQUENCY-MEASURING DEVICES AND TECHNIQUES Frequency measurements in the microwave region depend upon the comparison

of an unknown frequency with a known frequency. Either the latter is adjusted until it produces the same effects as the unknown, or the two frequencies are heterodyned to simplify the measurement process.

Table 11-1 lists the four types of frequency devices, along with their range and accuracy:

Table 11-1 Microwave Frequency Devices

Device	Frequency range	Accuracy (%)
Lecher wire	Few mc–3 kmc	0.1–3
L-C meter	300 mc–1.5 kmc	0.1–3
Cavity meter	450 mc–40 kmc	0.005–1
Heterodyne meter	300 mc–10 kmc	0.002–0.01

The *Lecher wire* procedure is applicable only to transmission lines, as is the L-C meter. Figure 11-23 represents a system which determines either current peaks or current nodes along the Lecher system. The length of the Lecher wire is not important, provided it is at least 1 wavelength. There should be loose coupling between the line and the current source, so that the normal frequency of the source is unchanged during the measurement. Since standing waves are pronounced when the far end of a line is open- or short-circuited, either of these possible terminations may be used. By sliding a current-indicating device (preferably a thermocouple ammeter) along the Lecher wire frame, points of maximum current will be indicated by maximum deflection of the instrument, and points of minimum current (nodes) will be indicated by minimum deflection. The distance between successive

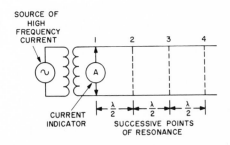

Fig. 11-23 Frequency measurement with Lecher wires, current method.

maximums, or between successive minimums, is always equal to a half-wavelength. This distance can be readily measured with a suitably calibrated scale. If the measurement is in meters, the frequency in megacycles will be $f = 150/$distance in meters. Similarly, a measurement in inches is related to frequency by $f = 5905 \cdot 5/$distance in inches. A voltage indicator, such as a neon lamp, can

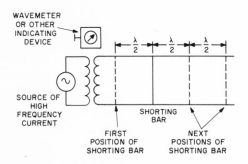

Fig. 11-24 Frequency measurement with Lecher wires, shorting-bar method.

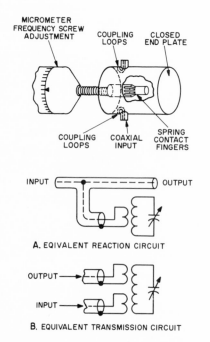

Fig. 11-25 Resonant-coaxial-line frequency meter and equivalent circuits.

also be used to make the measurement. The distance between successive voltage maximums, or minimums is also equal to a half-wavelength.

There are a number of precautions to observe. Primarily, the measurement itself must be made with extreme care, as the accuracy of the result is limited by the physical measurement. The looser the coupling, the sharper will be the indications of maximums or minimums. It is desirable for air to be the dielectric separating the conductors of the line. These conductors should be made of copper tubing or of wires stretched tautly between convenient supports. Satisfactory spacing between the conductors is from approximately 1 to 1½ in. The contacts of the indicator should be maintained at right angles to the line. A system can be employed more conveniently and accurately if it is built solidly and permanently. Experience shows that somewhat greater accuracy is possible by measuring the distance between nodes rather than between peaks. If the foregoing precautions are taken, an accuracy as high as 0.1% is possible.

The resonant properties of the short-circuited transmission line can be utilized somewhat differently to measure wavelength, as illustrated in Fig. 11-24. Here the current loops are found by moving a "shorting bar" (simply a metal strip or knife edge) along the length of the Lecher wires. Once again, the coupling between the source and the line must be as loose as possible. Also coupled loosely to the source is some convenient indicating device, such as a wavemeter or even a flashlight lamp connected to a loop of wire. As the shorting bar is slid toward the far end of the line, it will reach a resonance point at which a pronounced dip in the meter indication, or a glow of the lamp, will take place. With the shorting bar in such a position, the line is tuned to the frequency of the source, and thus absorbs maximum energy from it. At a half-wavelength beyond the first resonant point, the line will exhibit the same characteristics. The distance between these points must be measured carefully, as explained previously.

The *L-C meter* mentioned in Table 11-1 is simply a resonant circuit with variable inductance or capacitance, as discussed in connection with wavemeters in Chapter 8. This meter must be very lightly coupled to the test signal—*otherwise, inaccuracies will mount, and burnout may occur.*

Figure 11-25 shows a typical *resonant coaxial line frequency meter,* which employs a section of coaxial line, shorted at one end, and tuned to resonance by its distributed capacitance and inductance. Energy is coupled into the line by means of a small inductive coupling loop, and, in most cases, another coupling loop is provided so that an output is available to operate some form of indicator. In addition, the coupling loops may be made adjustable to provide control over the degree of coupling. The resonant frequency is varied by changing the length of the sliding center conductor, thus varying the distributed capacitance of the line, and, therefore, the frequency. The length of the conductor is adjusted by means of a micrometer screw attached to the conductor, and making connection to it through spring contact fingers. The micrometer screw may be calibrated for frequency by means of a chart, or it may drive a dial which indicates frequency directly.

Resonant-coaxial-line frequency meters operate as either transmission or reaction-type indicators, as shown in Fig. 11-25A and B. When used as the transmission type, energy is fed into one coupling loop, and the indicating device is connected to the other loop. When the circuit is resonant, the greatest energy transfer takes place; therefore, the indicator shows the greatest output signal. When used as the reaction type, the resonant circuit functions as an absorption device, so that at resonance the indicator shows a dip in the reading. Since no energy is coupled from the line, only one coupling loop is used, as shown.

The resonant-cavity frequency meter, a

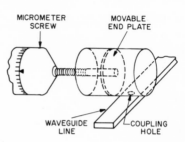

Fig. 11-26 Resonant-cavity frequency meter, showing construction.

common type of which is shown in Fig. 11-26, consists essentially of a hollow metal cylinder coupled to a waveguide by means of a small hole or a coupling loop and coaxial connector. The cavity within the cylinder is resonant by virtue of its volume. The two end plates may be thought of as the capacitance elements, and the adjoining walls as the inductance. The frequency is varied by adjusting the position of one of the end plates with a micrometer screw (as in the coaxial frequency meter), which is calibrated to indicate frequency. The results obtained with a resonant-cavity frequency meter are comparable to those obtained with a resonant-coaxial-line frequency meter.

The *heterodyne* process consists of a variable frequency oscillator, an audio amplifier, a reference standard oscillator, and a zero-beat indicator, just as for the lower-frequency techniques discussed in Chapter 8. The equipment setup, test procedure, and interpolation methods are also the same. If the approximate value of the test frequency is not known, it is possible to avoid confusion with higher harmonics by using the values of two successive zero-beat readings of consecutive harmonics, and solving for the frequency:

$$f = \frac{f_1 f_2}{f_2 - f_1}$$

In this equation, f_1 is the lower heterodyne oscillator frequency and f_2 is the higher.

MICROWAVE FREQUENCY STANDARDS There is no standard oscillator at frequencies above

300 mc. There is, however, an *MIT microwave frequency standard,* shown in block form in Fig. 11-27, which derives its frequency by using the harmonics of low-frequency primary or secondary oscillators. The comparison oscilloscope has three functions: (1) to check the division accuracy of each stage, (2) to compare the signal from the tunable oscillator, (3) to check the audio

oscillator. The output of any of the multipliers on the left may be used as a standard.

Commercial multipliers of this type, as well as klystron multipliers, are used where large quantities of harmonic power are required.

CALIBRATION AT MICROWAVE FREQUENCIES
Temperature, relative humidity, and atmospheric pressure have an appreciable effect upon the accuracy of a frequency meter. This effect is minimized by constructing the resonant sections of materials that minimize or compensate for changes of temperature, and by hermetically sealing the units against moisture; sufficient accuracy can be obtained for most applications. Where greater accuracy is necessary, the correction charts for varying atmospheric conditions (furnished with the equipment) must be used.

Factory calibration of frequency meters is usually carried out at 25°C and 60% relative humidity. Atmospheric pressure variations, under normal conditions, are not great enough to require compensation; however, the effect of the reduced pressure at high altitudes may be appreciable. It should be emphasized that the conditions mentioned are the conditions *inside the frequency meter,* rather than the external conditions.

Most of the early frequency meters were tuned by means of a micrometer screw, and the readings were converted into frequency with the aid of a calibration chart. The newer meters employ a dial, geared to the screw, which indicates frequency directly. Thus dial readings are greatly simplified, but the gear mechanism associated with the dial introduces a certain amount of backlash, which affects the accuracy of the indication. The backlash effect may be minimized by always approaching the final dial setting from the same direction. This direction should be the same as was used during factory calibration, and should be specified by the manufacturer.

Three commonly used methods for cali-

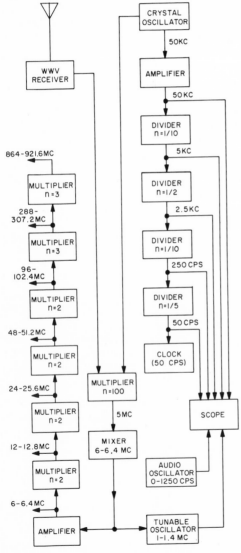

Fig. 11-27 MIT microwave frequency standard.

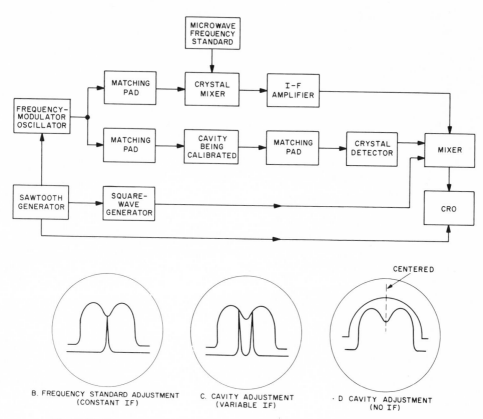

Fig. 11-28 Resonant-cavity frequency meter calibration, visual display method.

brating frequency meters are as follows: (1) the standard frequency and the test meter frequency are compared on an oscilloscope; (2) the test meter is tuned to the various outputs of the MIT microwave frequency standard; (3) the frequency of a continuous-wave or square-wave amplitude-modulated signal is set by a calibrated heterodyne frequency meter or calibrated cavity, and then compared with the test meter reading.

The equipment for the first method as applied to a cavity frequency meter, is arranged as in Fig. 11-28A. After sufficient warmup time has been allowed, adjust the FM oscillator frequency, amplifiers, tuners, etc., to obtain the desired oscilloscope presentation. *While these adjustments are being made, remove the test cavity if it is a transmission-type cavity.*

Set the frequency standard to the desired frequency so as to obtain an oscilloscope presentation similar to that shown in part B or C of Fig. 11-28. This may require that the FM oscillator be readjusted. Resonate the test cavity and remove the i-f amplifier from the circuit. An oscilloscope presentation similar to that shown in part D of the figure should result. Adjust the cavity until the zero beat signal is centered on the resonance-curve peak, as shown.

The same procedure is followed for a transmission- or absorption-type cavity. The oscilloscope patterns in Fig. 11-28 are for the latter type. The transmission-type cavity has a single-peaked resonance curve similar to a typical tuned-circuit response curve.

Test setups for the other cavity calibration methods are shown in Fig. 11-29. In these arrangements, the calibrated heterodyne frequency meter and the calibrated cavity serve as secondary standards.

PHASE MEASUREMENTS

The slotted section can be used in the circuit arrangement shown in Fig. 11-30 to determine phase differences in the microwave region. The network under test must be terminated in its characteristic impedance. The two attenuators should be adjusted so that the two signals entering the slotted section are equal in amplitude, in order to produce a high value of standing wave. If a reference position is first established by not using the test network and shifted slot input, the movement of the combined standing wave pattern will yield the relative phase shift:

$$\theta^o = 180n \pm \frac{369D}{\lambda_a}$$

In this equation, D represents the distance between the reference minimum and the *nearest* minimum value when both signals

combine in the slotted section. The factor n, which may be 0, 1, 2, 3, etc., introduces an ambiguity which necessitates prior knowledge of the *quadrant* within which θ lies. The apparent wavelength can be determined by the methods already described. The units of λ_a and D must be the same.

INSERTION LOSSES

Insertion losses are a measure of the power lost because of the insertion of a specific device into a microwave transmission system. Although this could be measured in terms of absolute power units, it is universally expressed in terms of power-ratio units (decibels, etc.). For attenuation (insertion-loss) measurements, the decibel is defined by

$$db = 10 \log \frac{P_1}{P_2}$$

where P_1 is the power absorbed at the load *without* the device in the line, and P_2 is the power absorbed *with* the device in the line.

ATTENUATION MEASUREMENTS

Attenuation measurements are usually accomplished by using an r-f probe in conjunction with a calibrated indicator—usually a

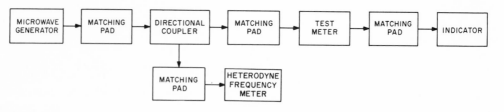

A. HETERODYNE FREQUENCY METER COMPARISON

B. MODIFICATION FOR RESONANT CAVITY COMPARISON

Fig. 11-29 Resonant-cavity frequency meter calibration, heterodyne meter and cavity comparison methods.

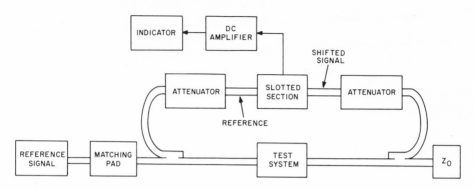

Fig. 11-30 Component arrangement for phase determination.

voltmeter. Amplifiers may or may not be used between the probe and the indicator. The voltmeter scale may be calibrated directly in power-ratio decibels. In such an instance, the graduations will be established in terms of r-m-s voltage squared—because of the square-law characteristic of the detector. It is also possible, however, that the voltmeter will be calibrated in terms of the r-m-s voltage itself. In this case the power-ratio decibel will be given by

$$db = 20 \log \frac{V_1}{V_2}$$

where the subscripts 1 and 2 carry the same descriptions as given previously for P_1 and P_2.

When using commercial instruments graduated directly in decibels, it should be ascertained whether the response is proportional to the voltage or the voltage squared (power).

Regardless of the instruments used, the definition of attenuation requires that the transmission medium be terminated in a load equal to its own characteristic impedance. The source impedance must also equal the characteristic impedance of the transmission system.

A second system for measuring attenuation depends upon the substitution of attenuation standards for the device in question. This method, of course, provides a basis for calibrating the indicator in the probe-indicator method, and will be discussed later.

ATTENUATION STANDARDS There are two types of attenuators—below-cutoff attenuators and resistive attenuators. The below-cutoff attenuator provides a primary standard since its attenuation can be calculated from its fundamental dimensions and the propagation mode. The resistive attenuator is a secondary standard, and must be calibrated by using a below-cutoff attenuator.

CALIBRATION BY AUDIO SUBSTITUTION METHOD There are three substitution methods available for calibrating (or measuring) attenuation. These include the r-f substitution method, the i-f substitution method, and the audio substitution method. The first two methods require linear amplifiers and calibrated monitoring meters. For this reason, the audio method—requiring only an audio attenuation standard—will be the only method discussed.

The circuit arrangement is shown in Fig. 11-31. The buffers provide isolation of components. Number 1 isolates the oscillator. Number 2 (variable) isolates the frequency meter. The tuners provide matching between the oscillator and the line, and between the load and the line.

Initially, the standard is set at some particular value, A_1 db. This is done with the empty line section (test device not in circuit). The test device is then placed in the circuit and the standard adjusted to a second setting, A_2 db, necessary to produce the same indication of the terminating amplifier and

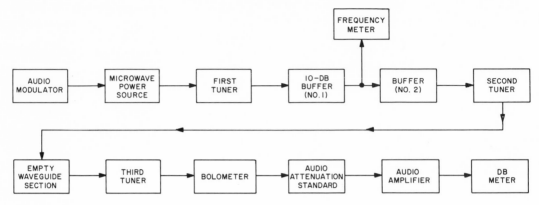

Fig. 11-31 Attenuation calibration by audio substitution.

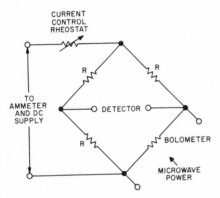

Fig. 11-32 Modified Wheatstone bridge providing for bolometer bias current.

meter. The average of A_1 and A_2 gives the attenuation due to the test device.

Remember that bolometers are low-power devices. Five milliwatts is the maximum power to which they should subjected. *Bolometers must be operated at a d-c bias level.*

The calibration error for audio attenuation standard is on the order of 0.05 db, and the general error for this procedure is a few tenths of a db.

DIRECTIONAL COUPLERS

Directional couplers serve as stable, accurate and relatively broad-band coupling devices, which can be inserted into a transmission line so as to measure either incident or reflected power. A measure of the coupling of

a directional coupler is simply a ratio of power into the main-line terminal to the power out of the side-line terminal:

$$\text{coupling db} = 10 \log \frac{P_{\text{in}}}{P_{\text{out}}}$$

Insertion loss is a measure of attenuation introduced into the main transmission line and can be determined by the same circuitry and procedure described previously for attenuation measurements.

MICROWAVE POWER MEASUREMENTS

At frequencies above 300 mc, absolute power measurements must be made with heat-sensitive detectors such as the three discussed at the beginning of this chapter. Thermocouples are also used. Power measurements will be classed as low-power (up to 10 milliwatts), medium-power (10 milliwatts to 1 watt), and high-power (above 1 watt). The methods discussed will pertain to average power. Peak-power measurements are discussed in Chapter 12.

The relationship between power standing wave ratio and voltage standing wave ratio has already been discussed. The reflected power, P_r, and the transmitted power, P_t, can be related to the reflection coefficient by

$$\frac{P_r}{P_t} = |K|^2$$

The vertical lines indicate that only the magnitude of K is to be used. The reflection coefficient can be determined by measuring the $VSWR$ or $PSWR$ on the line, since

$$K = \frac{VSWR - 1}{VSWR + 1} = \frac{\sqrt{PSWR - 1}}{\sqrt{PSWR + 1}}$$

LOW-POWER TECHNIQUE Low-power microwave measurements are best accomplished with a bolometer-mount device. Crystals are less accurate absolute power indicators.

The impedance of the bolometer mount itself will have an effect on the error produced by the use of this device. The insertion loss due to the introduction of the mount can be determined, or the actual power absorbed by the mount (P_M) can be determined by

$$P_M = P_I \left[\frac{1}{(1 - |K_M|)^2} - 1 \right]$$

where P_I is the indicated power shown on the detector meter, and K_M is the reflection coefficient determined with the mount in the system. The error introduced by the mount is then given by

$$\% \text{ error} = \frac{P_M}{P_I + P_M} \times 100\%$$

The power source must be matched to the transmission medium.

The balanced-bridge method utilizes the bolometer mount as one arm of a Wheatstone bridge, while the resistance values of the other arms are kept constant. The basic bridge must be modified so that the d-c bias current necessary for bolometer operation can be obtained. This is shown in Fig. 11-32. The bridge is initially balanced by adjusting the d-c current when R_A is equal to the bolometer resistance. Microwave energy is then fed to the bolometer mount, and the d-c current is changed by some amount ΔI to obtain a new balance. If $R = R_A = R_B = R_C = R_D$, the power is determined by

$$P = \Delta I \, (2I - \Delta I) \, \frac{R}{4}$$

The current, I, is the initial balance current. The d-c current source must be stable.

With the thermistor bolometer, it is possible to use a temperature-compensated bridge, such as the one shown in Fig. 11-11.

SLOTTED-SECTION TECHNIQUE The use of a slotted section allows the power delivered to the load to be determined in terms of the voltage along the transmission medium:

$$P_L = \frac{V_{max}^2}{(VSWR) \, Z_0} = \frac{(VSWR) \, V_{min}^2}{Z_0}$$

If, however, a calibrated voltmeter can be used to measure the voltage across the load (V_L) directly, and the slotted section can be used to determine $VSWR$, then

$$P_L = \frac{V_L^2}{(VSWR) \, Z_0 \left\{ 1 + \left[\frac{1}{(VSWR)^2} - 1 \right] \sin\left(\frac{2\pi x}{\lambda} \right) \right\}}$$

where x is the distance from the load to the first voltage minimum. This particular method is time-consuming, since measurement of V_L, $VSWR$, and x must be made and there must be a knowledge of Z_0 and λ.

Both of these slotted-section measurements relate the power delivered to the load to the more fundamental properties of the transmission medium. They are, therefore, particularly suited to calibration measurements and efficiency determinations.

EXTENSION OF LOW-POWER TECHNIQUES The bolometer mount may be used to measure medium power and high power by inserting a *power absorber* or a *power divider* of constant magnitude into the transmission system.

Power absorption devices include the below-cutoff and resistive attenuators mentioned previously. These devices absorb or dissipate a fixed amount of the incident power applied to them.

Special power divider junctions are available. The directional coupler, however, may be used as an excellent power divider.

SPECIAL DEVICES FOR HIGH-POWER MEASUREMENTS The lamp-load technique, discussed

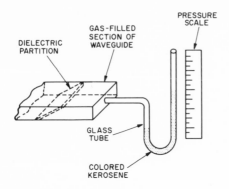

Fig. 11-33 Gas load arrangement for high power applications.

Fig. 11-34 Microwave power meter with built-in dummy load. (Courtesy, Sierra Electronic Division, Philco Corporation.)

transfer. As the temperature of the gas increases, the pressure increases. This pressure is measured by a manometer tube, the scale of which is calibrated directly in power units.

COMMERCIAL POWER METERS Several commercial power meters and associated dummy loads are available. A model which has a "built-in" dummy load is shown in Fig. 11-34. Three models are available to cover the range from 0 to 1000 watts with an accuracy of ±5%. Another type of power meter, with an accuracy of ±5%, is the Bi-Directional Power Monitor which is connected into a coaxial line between the source and the load. This instrument, the Sierra model 164, with the Models 180A, 181A and 270A insert units, measures r-f power from 1 watt to 1000 watts and covers a frequency range of 2 to 1000 megacycles. Reflected power from the load (antenna or dummy load) is measured by rotating the insert 180 degrees.

Peak power may be read directly by either of two similar in-line bi-directional instruments. Model 194A-A measures peak power from 0 to 30 kilowatts in the frequency range 200 to 1215 megacycles. Model 400A covers a power range of 0 to 5000 watts over a frequency range of 960 to 1215 mc and in addition reads VSWR directly, in the power range 500 to 5000 watts. Accuracy of both these instruments is ±10%.

CALIBRATION METHODS The calorimetric methods discussed in Chapter 10 are also commonly used in making microwave power calibrations.

A calorimeter or water load can be calibrated by placing a heating coil between the water flow line and the thermocouples. Direct current or commercial 60-cycle power is then applied to the coil, and a calibrated meter is used to measure the applied power. The power indicated by the calorimetric device can be plotted against the applied power. This curve will provide correction values between actual power and indicated power.

in Chapter 10, can also be used to measure microwave power. Lamp-load devices, however, can seldom be matched to the transmission system at the higher microwave frequencies. The photoelectric sensing element may be replaced by an optical pyrometer to measure the filament brightness.

The gas load, illustrated in Fig. 11-33, may also be used. The gas (usually ammonia) is held in a waveguide section by a dielectric window, which is slanted to minimize reflections. This section is matched to the transmission system to provide maximum power

When microwave power is applied, some of it will be absorbed by the water load device. This power loss can be determined by comparing the indicated power when microwave energy is applied to the indicated power of the previously mentioned curve.

MICROWAVE SYSTEM PARAMETERS

The fundamental parameters of microwave systems—dielectric constant, characteristic impedance, propagation constant, attenuation constant, and phase constant—have been introduced throughout this chapter. Precision measurement of these quantities is important to design and performance considerations. A complete discussion for the step-by-step measurement of these parameters, as well as system C and noise figure, is included in *Handbook of Microwave Measurements* (Polytechnic Press, Polytechnic Institute of Brooklyn). The following section is limited to a discussion of Q, impedance, and propagation constant determination.

DETERMINATION OF Q In microwave systems the determination of Q can be quickly and simply determined by measuring the system bandwidth based on the circuit resonance curve. The system bandwidth Q is then computed from

$$Q = \frac{F_0}{\Delta F}$$

with the parameters of this equation defined as shown in Fig. 11-35.

Q, remember, is related to the stored energy and the dissipated energy by the relation:

$$Q = 2\pi \, \frac{\text{power dissipated/cycle}}{\text{power stored/cycle}}$$

For values of Q equal to, or greater than, 10 this definition of Q and the definition of bandwidth Q are equivalent.

The bandwidth of a microwave system can be readily determined by plotting a curve of output power (or voltage) against frequency. From this curve, F_0 and the half-power points (limits on ΔF) can be found. These determinations must be made under matched-impedance conditions.

TERMINATING IMPEDANCE DETERMINATION   The impedance of a transmission-medium termination can be measured by the system shown in Fig. 11-36 if the medium is supporting only its dominant propagation mode. This is essentially a measurement of *VSWR* with a modulated signal source. The apparent half-wavelength, $\lambda_a/2$, must be determined.

The first step in the procedure is to establish a reference point on the slotted-section

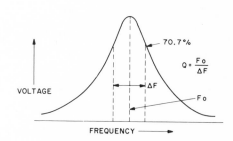

Fig. 11-35   Microwave circuit response curve.

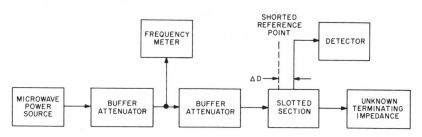

Fig. 11-36   Impedance measurement for transmission-medium termination.

scale. This is accomplished by shorting the slotted-section output and locating the voltage minimum nearest the load.

The short is then replaced by the test ter-

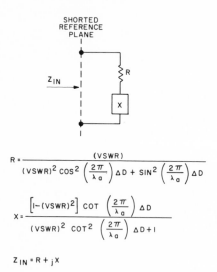

$$R = \frac{(VSWR)}{(VSWR)^2 \cos^2\left(\frac{2\pi}{\lambda_a}\right)\Delta D + \sin^2\left(\frac{2\pi}{\lambda_a}\right)\Delta D}$$

$$X = \frac{\left[1-(VSWR)^2\right]\cot\left(\frac{2\pi}{\lambda_a}\right)\Delta D}{(VSWR)^2 \cot^2\left(\frac{2\pi}{\lambda_a}\right)\Delta D + 1}$$

$$Z_{IN} = R + jX$$

Fig. 11-37 Evaluation of "lumped" terminating impedance components.

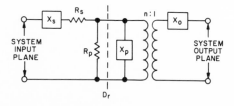

Fig. 11-38 Weissfloch equivalent network for lossy microwave system impedance measurement.

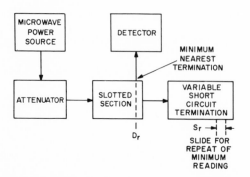

Fig. 11-39 Establishing reference points for microwave system impedance determination.

mination, and the shift in the location of the first minimum, ΔD, is noted.

The *VSWR* is then determined.

From the foregoing data the resistive and reactive components of the terminating structure are then computed. The necessary formulas are given in Fig. 11-37, along with the equivalent "lumped parameter" circuit.

TRANSMISSION SYSTEM IMPEDANCE DETERMINATION　The microwave transmission system is effectively a four-terminal network and can be represented by an equivalent-T "lumped parameter" network. The measurements required for a representation of such an equivalent would be simple if the system were *lossless*—contained no inherent power loss component—however, in practical applications, all structures contain some losses.

For microwave systems containing losses (dissipative elements), a very good method of representing the system is by the Weissfloch network shown in Fig. 11-38. If the equipment used is properly calibrated and the measurements are carefully made, the results may be considered as precision determinations.

1. Establish the reference points, D_r and S_r. D_r can be located by placing a variable short as near as possible to the output end of the slotted section and locating the voltage minimum nearest the output. The circuit setup is shown in Fig. 11-39. At this point also, it will be expedient to determine the input system wavelength, λ_{a1}. Slide the variable-short plunger away from the output end of the slotted section until the same voltage minimum reading obtained before is repeated. *The probe should be left at D_r.* The scale setting on the variable short establishes S_r. Measure the variable-short wavelength, λ_{as}, by moving the short through two minimum points ($\lambda_{as}/2$).

2. Replace the variable short in Fig. 11-39 with the system to be measured to produce the setup shown in Fig. 11-40. Use an arbitrary length of shorted transmission medium for the terminating impedance shown in the

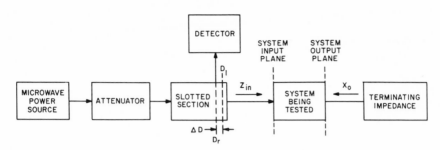

Fig. 11-40 Microwave system impedance determination.

figure. Compute the relative output reactance from

$$X_{1(out)} = \tan \frac{2\pi}{\lambda_{as}} L$$

where L is the length of the arbitrary terminating impedance.

3. Determine the $VSWR$ and the location of the voltage minimum, D_1, nearest the slotted-section output. Compute the relative input impedance, $Z_{1(in)}$, from the formulas given in Fig. 11-37. λ_a in the figure is now the value for λ_{a1} and ΔD is the distance between D_1 and D_r.

4. Repeat Steps 3 and 4 for at least three other shorted terminating sections of arbitrary (but different) lengths.

5. Plot the values of input impedance and draw a circle, as shown in Fig. 11-41, which best fits the data. The length of the diameter of the circle is equivalent to R_p in Fig. 11-38. The values for R_s and X_s are also shown in Fig. 11-41.

6. In Fig. 11-41, draw straight lines between each impedance point and the center of the circle. The intersection of each straight line and the arc of the circle establishes a new relative input impedance value, Z_n', as shown in Fig. 11-42. These new impedance values have resistive components, R_n', and reactive components, X_n', which can be determined directly from Fig. 11-42. R_2' and X_2' are shown for illustrative purposes.

7. Now establish a graph with parallel axes X' and X_{out}, as shown in Fig. 11-43. Values along both axes must be to the same

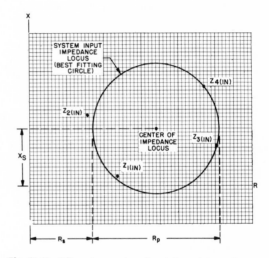

Fig. 11-41 Microwave system input impedance plane.

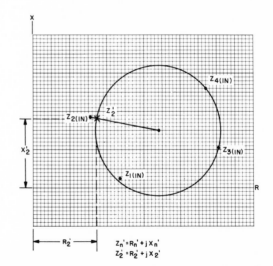

Fig. 11-42 Relative input impedance determination from system input impedance locus.

scale. Locate all the relative output reactances calculated in Step 2 along the X_{out} scale and all the relative input reactances X_n' (Step 6) along the X' scale. Draw an arbitrary reference axis perpendicular to the X' and X_{out} axes. Selecting any two points, P_1 and P_2, along the reference line, draw a line through P_1 and X_1' and another line though P_2

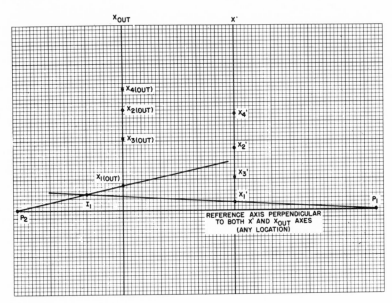

Fig. 11-43 Reactance transformation process.

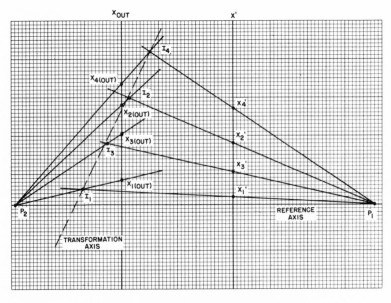

Fig. 11-44 Construction of transformation axis.

and $X_{1(\text{out})}$. Locate the intersection, I_1, between these two lines as shown in Fig. 11-43. Find an intersection for each corresponding $X_{\text{out}} - X_n'$ combination, always using P_1 and P_2 as before. The end result will appear as shown in Fig. 11-44.

8. The intersecting points, I_1, I_2, I_3, and I_4, in Fig. 11-44 should be in a straight line as shown by the dashed line in the figure. If they do not lie exactly in a straight line, center them about some straight line. The dashed line is called the transformation axis.

9. Draw a straight line between P_2 and $X_{\text{out}} = 0$, and denote the point of intersection with the transformation axis as I_1'. Draw a line from I_1' through P_1, and find the value X_{i1} where this line crosses the X' axis. This is shown in Fig. 11-45A.

10. Draw a straight line parallel to the X_{out}-axis through P_2. The intersection between this line and the transformation axis is marked I_2' in Fig. 11-45B. A line from I_2' to P_1 will intersect the X' axis at X_{i2} as shown.

11. Pick any arbitrary point, A, along the transformation axis. As shown in Fig. 11-45C, draw lines through A and P_1 and A and P_2. The intersection between the A-P_1 line and the X' axis gives the value X_{i3}. The intersection between the A-P_2 line and the X_{out} axis gives the value X_0'.

12. The values of the three remaining elements in Fig. 11-38 can now be computed from

$$X_p = X_{i2}$$

$$n = \frac{X_{i2}}{\sqrt{\dfrac{X_0'\,(X_{i2} - X_{i3})\,(X_{i2} - X_{i1})}{X_{i3} - X_{i1}}}}$$

$$X_0 = \frac{X_0'\,(X_{i2} - X_{i3})}{X_{i3} - X_{i1}} - \frac{1}{n}$$

With the use of the transformation axis, the input reactance for the particular system tested can be found for *any value of output reactance*. The output reactance, X_0, is located and a line drawn through P_2 and X_0. The intersection, I, between the P_2-X_0 line

and the transformation axis is found, and a line is drawn through I and P_1. The intersection of the I-P_1 line with the X_i axis yields the desired input reactance, as shown in Fig. 11-45D. This last construction works equally well in the reverse direction—the determination of X_0 from any X_i value.

The procedure just outlined uses four sets of data to establish the transformation axis. If a larger number of sets is used, the final equivalent circuit representation becomes more precise in its value.

ATTENUATION AND PHASE CONSTANT DETERMINATION Set up the equipment as shown in Fig. 11-46, and establish reference points S_r and D_r as outlined in the discussion on measurements for transmission system impedance. Also determine λ_a. Slide the shorting plunger to any arbitrary reading, S_1. Find the minimum point nearest the output of the slotted section and determine ΔD_1, the difference between D_1 and D_r. Determine the VSWR.

Find values of ΔD for three more arbitrary settings of the shorting plunger. Also find the VSWR for each setting.

For each of the preceding determinations compute the reflection coefficient from

$$K = \left|\frac{VSWR - 1}{VSWR + 1}\right| \Big/ 720\,\Delta D/\lambda_a$$

The first term provides the magnitude of K and the second term provides the phase angle. Remember that magnitudes do not carry any algebraic sign.

If none of the angles associated with K exceed $\pm 90°$, compute the attenuation from

$$\alpha = \frac{1}{2L}\,|1n|\ \frac{\sqrt{(1 + K_{\max})\,(1 - K_{\min})}}{\sqrt{(1 + K_{\max})\,(1 - K_{\min})}}$$

$$\frac{+\sqrt{(1 - K_{\max})\,(1 + K_{\min})}}{-\sqrt{(1 - K_{\max})\,(1 + K_{\min})}}\ \text{neper/}\atop\text{unit length}$$

If any of the angles associated with K exceed $\pm 90°$, compute the attenuation from the preceding formula with both signs posi-

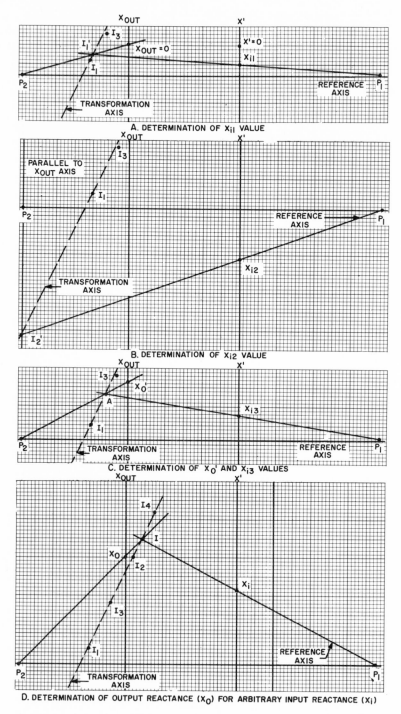

Fig. 11-45 Final constructions for determining the Weissfloch equivalent network.

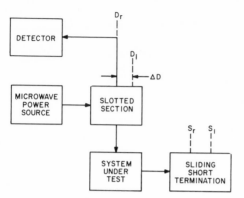

Fig. 11-46 Attenuation and phase constant determination.

tive under the first radical (numerator and denominator) and with both signs negative under the second radical (numerator and denominator).

Increasing the number of measurements in the foregoing procedure will result in greater accuracy.

The phase constant may be easily determined since it is given by

$$\beta = \frac{2\pi}{\lambda_a} \text{ radians}$$

This can be expressed in radians/unit length by dividing by L.

QUESTIONS

1 Discuss the characteristics of detectors used in microwave measurements.

2 Why is a d-c bias lead established for a barretter?

3 Explain the use of a resonant cavity in measuring the frequency of a microwave signal.

4 What relationship exists between VSWR and PSWR?

5 If the PSWR of a transmission line is known, how may the reflection coefficient be determined?

6 Why is the dielectric window in a gas load power meter mounted at an angle to the perpendicular?

EXERCISE 1   Standing Wave Ratio Measurements from 800–4000 mc.*

MATERIAL REQUIRED

1 Signal generator, HP 614A or equivalent

2 Function generator, HP 202A or equivalent

3 Slotted line, HP 805A or equivalent

4 Standing wave indicator, HP 415B or equivalent

5 50-ohm coaxial cable, N-type connectors

6 50-ohm coaxial cable, BNC-type connectors

7 50-ohm coaxial cable, BNC to dual banana plugs

8 Coaxial terminations, HP 908A

PROCEDURE

1 Set up equipment as shown in Fig. 11-47.

2 Set the following controls on the instruments:

* Based on Air Force calibration procedures.

Control	Instrument	Setting
	HP 202A	
FUNCTION		SQUARE
RANGE		X100
FREQUENCY		10
AMPLITUDE		CLOCKWISE (MAXIMUM)
	HP 614A	
FREQUENCY		1500 mc
FM-CW-OFF		OFF
	HP 415B	
RANGE		30
INPUT SELECTOR		CRYSTAL 200 K
GAIN		CLOCKWISE (MAXIMUM)
METER SCALE		NORMAL

3 Turn all equipment on and allow 15 min warmup.

4 Using the ZERO SET control on the HP 614A, zero the instrument meter.

5 Set the FM-CW-OFF switch to CW. Using the POWER SET control set the meter to read POWER SET.

6 Set the OUTPUT ATTEN control for a dial reading of −10 dbm.

7 Set the FM-CW-OFF switch to EXT−.

8 Set the RANGE switch on the HP 415B to obtain a meter indication.

9 Adjust the Function Generator FREQUENCY control for a maximum meter reflection on the HP 415B, adjusting the HP 415B RANGE switch as necessary.

10 Adjust the tuning knob on the HP 805A Slotted Line for a maximum deflection on the HP 415B, adjusting the HP 415B RANGE switch as necessary.

11 Connect the Coaxial Load HP 906A.

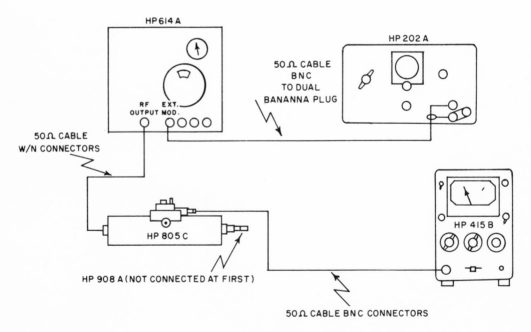

Fig. 11-47

12 Move the probe of the HP 805A along the slotted line for a maximum meter deflection on the HP 415B, adjusting the RANGE switch of the HP 415B as necessary.

13 With the HP 415B RANGE switch set to 30, METER SCALE switch to NORMAL, and GAIN to nearly maximum, adjust the probe insertion of the Slotted Line for a full-scale meter deflection ("1" on the SWR scale). The crystal in the HP 805A Slotted Line has the proper r-f power input when the HP 415B meter indicates full scale with the switches set as above. (After this adjustment has been completed, the HP 415B switches and the HP 805A probe may be moved to any position during the measurement without overloading the crystal.)

14 Move the probe along the Slotted Line for a minimum deflection on the Standing Wave Indicator. Read the SWR.

15 If the SWR is less than 1.3,* set the METER SCALE switch on the HP 415B to EXPAND, switching the RANGE switch to obtain an upscale deflection.

16 Move the probe along the Slotted Line to obtain a maximum deflection on the HP 415B, switching the RANGE switch as necessary. Adjust the GAIN control to obtain a full-scale deflection on the EXPANDED SWR scale.

17 Move the probe along the Slotted Line to obtain a minimum deflection on the HP 415B. Read the SWR.

18 Withdraw the probe on the Slotted Line by a slight amount and repeat the SWR measurement. Repeat until a difference of less than 1% is obtained between consecutive readings.

19 To meet certification requirements, the SWR of the coaxial load must be less than 1.05.

EXERCISE 2 Standing Wave Ratio Measurements from 8.2-12.4 GC†

MATERIAL REQUIRED

1 Klystron, Varian X-13

2 Klystron power supply, HP 715A or equivalent with HP 715A-16C cable

3 Variable attenuator, HP X 382A

4 Standing wave indicator, HP 415B

5 Probe carriage, HP 809B

6 X band slotted section, HP X 810B

7 Probe, HP 444A

8 Cooling fan for Klystron

9 Low-power termination, HP X 910B

PROCEDURE

1 Set up the equipment as shown in Fig. 11-48.

2 Set the following controls on the equipment:

Control	Instrument	Setting
	HP 715A	
REFLECTOR RANGE		600-900
MOD SELECTOR		OFF
BEAM VOLTS		380
REFLECTOR VOLTS		Clockwise
MOD VOLTS		Partially clockwise
	HP 415B	
BOLO-CRYSTAL		CRYSTAL 200Ω
RANGE		30
METER SCALE		NORMAL
GAIN		Maximum clockwise

* See Step 19.
† Based on Air Force calibration procedures.

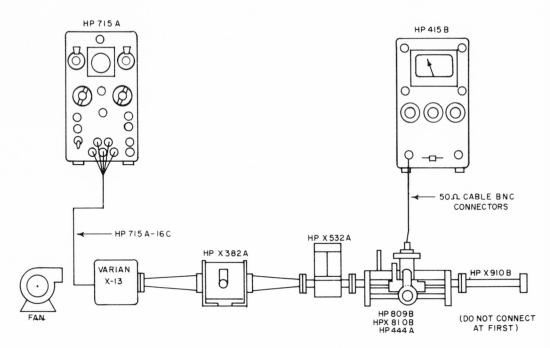

Fig. 11-48

3 Set the X 382A attenuator to 20 db.

4 Turn the Klystron cooling fan on.

5 Turn all equipment ON and allow 10 min for warmup.

6 Set the X-13 Klystron micrometer to 11.5 Gc.

7 Set the HP 715A MOD SELECTOR to 1000 cycles. Decrease the REFLECTOR VOLTS control until the Klystron starts to oscillate, as indicated by a jump in the cathode current.

8 If necessary, switch the RANGE switch on the HP 415B to obtain an upscale deflection.

9 Adjust the HP 715A MOD FREQ control for a maximum deflection on the HP 415B, switching the RANGE switch as necessary.

10 Adjust the HP 715A REFLECTOR VOLTS and MOD VOLTS controls for a maximum deflection on the HP 415B, switching the RANGE switch as necessary.

11 Check the Klystron frequency by adjusting the X 532A Frequency Meter until a dip occurs on the HP 415B. Read the frequency, then turn the frequency meter knob at least one-fourth turn from this point.

12 Connect the HP X 914B load to the end of the slotted section. Be sure the waveguide sections are accurately aligned.

13 Move the HP 444A probe along the slotted section to obtain a peak deflection on the HP 415B.

14 With the HP 415B GAIN control nearly maximum and the RANGE switch on 30, vary the r-f power level with the X 382A Attenuator to obtain a reading of "1" on the SWR scale.

The crystal in the slotted line probe now has the proper r-f power input. (After this adjustment has been completed, the HP 415B switches and the probe may be moved to any position during the course of the measurement without overloading the crystal.)

15 Move the probe along the slotted section to obtain a minimum deflection on the HP 415B. Read the SWR. If the SWR is greater than 3, switch the RANGE switch to the next position and read on the 3 to 10 SWR scale.

16 If the SWR in Step 15 is less than 1.3, then switch the METER SCALE switch to EXPAND.

17 Move the probe to obtain a maximum deflection on the HP 415B, switching the RANGE switch as necessary. Adjust the HP 415B GAIN control to obtain a full-scale deflection on the EXPANDED SWR scale.

18 Move the probe along the slotted section to obtain a minimum deflection on the HP 415B. Read the SWR.

19 Withdraw the probe slightly from the slotted section by loosening the LOCK and pulling the probe upward. Relock and repeat the SWR measurement. Keep withdrawing the probe and repeating until succeeding measurements are within 1% of each other. If necessary decrease the attenuation of the X 382A variable attenuator to provide more signal to the HP 415B.

EXERCISE 3 SWR Measurements of Adaptors*

MATERIAL REQUIRED

1 Standing wave indicator, HP 415B

2 Klystron power supply, HP 715A μf HP 715-16C cable

3 Klystron, Varian X-13

4 Variable attenuator, HP X 382A

5 Probe carriage, HP 809B

6 X-band slotted section, HP X 810B

7 Probe, HP 444A

8 Cooling fan for Klystron

9 Coaxial load, HP 906A

10 Waveguide-to-coax Adaptor, HP X 281A (2 required)

PROCEDURE

The relationship between SWR and the coefficient of reflection p (ratio of reflected voltage to incident voltage) is given by the formula:

$$SWR = \frac{1 + p}{1 - p}$$

In an ideal system, a slotted line or an adaptor should be terminated by a load having no reflection. Since loads have some reflection, however, one is chosen that has approximately the same amount as that of the adaptor or slotted line. In this measurement a moving load is used, so the phase of the reflected signal may be varied. SWR measurements are made with the reflections of the moving load and adaptor or slotted line adding and subtracting algebraically. The SWR of the adaptor or slotted line can then be calculated from the known relationships. (P_L = residual reflection on load; P_A = residual reflection of adaptor.)

1 Set up the equipment as shown in Fig. 11-49.

2 To find the SWR of the adaptor, adjust the moving load until the measured SWR is a

* Based on Air Force calibration procedures.

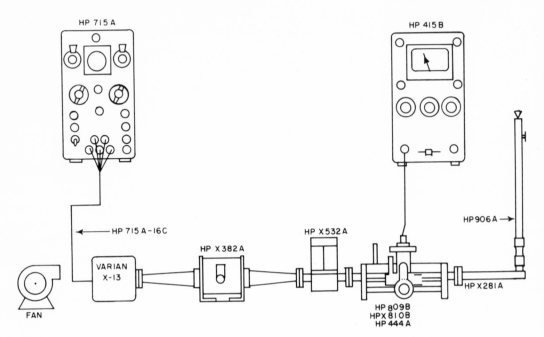

Fig. 11-49

maximum, using the SWR measuring technique of Exercise 2 of this chapter. This condition occurs when P_L and P_A are adding in phase.

3 Using the measured SWR, calculate P_{max} by the formula:

$$P_{max} = \frac{SWR_{max} - 1}{SWR_{max} + 1}$$

4 Adjust the moving load until the measured SWR is a minimum. This condition occurs when P_L and P_A add out of phase.

5 Using this minimum SWR value, calculate P_{min} by the formula:

$$P_{min} = \frac{SWR_{min} - 1}{SWR_{min} + 1}$$

6 Since P_A and P_L add **in** phase to give P_{max}, and add **out** of phase to give P_{min}, the following relationships are established:

$$P = \frac{P_{max} + P_{min}}{2}, \quad \text{and} \quad P = \frac{P_{max} - P_{min}}{2}$$

7 It must now be determined which value is P_L and which is P_A.

8 To determine which is P_A, the measurement is again made using a second adaptor. Since the same load is used for both measurements, one of the reflection coefficients found when measuring the second adaptor will be identical to one of those found when measuring the first adaptor. Hence, the reflection coefficient common to both is the reflection coefficient of the load, and the other two values are the reflection coefficients of the adaptors.

9 Using the coefficients of the adaptors, the SWR for each can be determined by

$$SWR_A = \frac{1 + P_A}{1 - P_A}$$

EXERCISE 4   Certification of a Microwave Frequency Meter*

MATERIAL REQUIRED

1 Klystron power supply, HP 715A w/HP 715A-16C cable

2 Klystron, Varian X-13

3 Attenuator, HP X 382A

4 Frequency meter, HP X 532A (2 required)

5 Directional coupler, HP X 752A

6 Waveguide-to-coax adaptor, HP X 281A

7 Detector mount with crystal, HP 485B

8 Transfer oscillator, HP 540B

9 Frequency counters, HP 524C

10 Frequency convertor, HP 525B

11 Oscilloscope, Tektronix 545A

12 High-gain, wide band preamp, Tektronix 53/54 B.

PROCEDURE

1 Set up the equipment as shown in Fig. 11-50.

2 Preset all controls as follows:

Control	Instrument	Setting
	HP X 382A	
ATTENUATION		10 db
	FAN	
ON-OFF		ON
	HP 715A	
MOD SELECTOR		OFF
REFLECTOR RANGE		OFF
BEAM VOLTS		380 V
REFLECTOR VOLTS		900
	TEK 545A	
VOLTS/CM		0.1 V/CM
AC/DC		AC
TRIGGERING MODE		LINE
TRIGGER SLOPE		+
TIME/CM (A)		0.5 ms/CM
	HP 524C	
FUNCTION		FREQUENCY
FREQUENCY UNIT		1 Sec
DISPLAY TIME		Full CCW
	HP 540B	
LOW FREQ		Full CW
GAIN		Full CW
HIGH FREQ		Full CW

3 Turn all equipments ON and allow 10 min for warmup.

4 Set the micrometer screw on the X-13 klystron for a test frequency of 8.2 gc. (See row 1, Table 11-2.)

5 Set the 540B Transfer Oscillator FREQUENCY dial to the value in Table 11-2, corresponding to the test frequency. The small corner number is the subharmonic number of the 540B frequency from the test frequency.

* Based on Air Force calibration procedures.

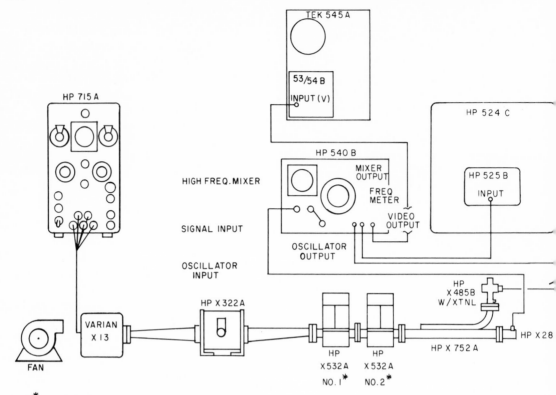

* FREQUENCY METER NO. I IS A CERTIFIED UNIT.

** FREQUENCY METER NO, 2 IS THE UNIT BEING CERTIFIED

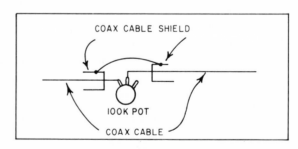

Fig. 11-50

6   Set the 525B MIXING FREQUENCY CONTROL to the listed value in Table 11-2.

7   Set the MIXER-DIRECT-WAVEMETER switch to MIXER.

8   Adjust the COARSE and FINE tuning controls on the HP 540B for a frequency counter reading as listed in Table 11-2.

9   Set the X 532A Frequency Meter No. 1 to the test frequency.

10   Set the HP 715B REFLECTOR RANGE control to 600–900. Set the MOD SELECTOR to 60 cycles.

11   Starting at the high end, adjust the HP 715A REFLECTOR VOLTS control to obtain a sweep mode on the oscilloscope.

Table 11-2

	X — 13	540 B	525 B (mc)	Counter reading limits (mc)	X532A #1	X532A #2
1.	8.2 gc	205 mc / 40	200	4.89750 to 5.10250	8.2 gc	At
2.	9.0 gc	180 mc / 50	170	9.910 to 10.090	9.0 gc	least one
3.	10.0 gc	200 mc / 50	190	9.90 to 10.10	10.0 gc	quarter turn
4.	11.0 gc	220 mc / 50	210	9.90 to 10.10	11.0 gc	off test
5.	12.0 gc	200 mc / 60	190	9.90 to 10.10	12.0 gc	frequency

12 Adjust the MOD VOLT control to its maximum clockwise position so that the best mode pattern is obtained. Adjust the 60 cycle PHASE control for the best display. If necessary, adjust the X 382A or the oscilloscope VOLTS/CM control to keep the trace on the screen.

13 Adjust the X-13 klystron micrometer screw so that the notch from the X 532A Frequency Meter appears on the mode resonance curve. A zero-beat pip representing the test frequency should also appear on the mode. When both appear on the mode resonance curve, the klystron is adjusted to the proper frequency.

14 Adjust the HP 715A REFLECTOR VOLTS, MOD VOLT, and 60 cycle PHASE controls, if necessary, to produce the beat oscilloscope trace. The trace should be similar to Fig. 11-51.

15 Adjust the HP 540B HIGH FREQ control counterclockwise to reduce the width of the zero beat to a fine line. The pip represents the calibration frequency.

16 Detune X 532A No. 1 by turning the knob. Position the zero beat on the mode resonance peak by adjusting the klystron micrometer screw.

17 Tune the HP X 485B Detector Mount for the maximum display on the oscilloscope. Reduce the height of the mode response curve for good presentation on the oscilloscope by increasing the 100K potentiometer attenuation. If necessary, increase the attenuation of the X 382A Variable Attenuator. The X 382A or the 540B GAIN control adjust the amplitude of both the pip and the mode curve. The potentiometer on the X 485B tuning control only adjusts the amplitude of the mode response curve.

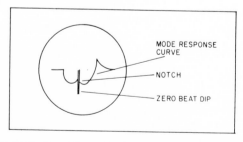

Fig. 11-51 Scope trace showing Klystron made response curve and test frequency pip.

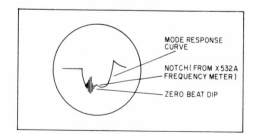

Fig. 11-52 Scope trace showing test instrument (X523A #2) adjusted to the calibration frequency.

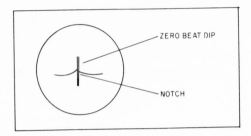

Fig. 11-53 Scope trace showing expanded notch and pips for precise frequency measurements.

18 Adjust the X 532A No. 2 knob to position the notch produced by the test instrument exactly on the zero beat pip. It is now set at the test frequency. The accuracy of the dial can now be certified. It should be within 0.05% of the test frequency. Fig. 11-52 shows the proper oscilloscope trace.

19 For better accuracy increase the oscilloscope sweep time (TIME/CM) to expand the trace and adjust the TRIGGERING LEVEL and HORIZONTAL POSITION controls to position the trace at the center of the screen. Move the notch by adjusting the X 532A No. 2 knob to coincide with the zero beat pip. Fig. 11-53 shows the oscilloscope presentation.

20 Repeat Steps 3 through 18 for the remaining test frequencies as listed in Table 11-2.

EXERCISE 5   Certifying a Variable Attenuator*

MATERIAL REQUIRED

1 Klystron power supply, HP 715A w/HP 715A-16C cable

2 Klystron, Varian X-13

3 Slide screw tuner, HP X 870A (2 required)

4 Variable attenuator, HP X 382A

5 Frequency meter, HP X 532A

6 Variable flap attenuator (instrument being certified) HP X 375A

7 Detector mount with barretter, HP X 485B

8 Microwave power meter, HP 430C

PROCEDURE

1 Set up the equipment as shown in Fig. 11-54.

2 Preset the following controls:

Control	Instrument	Setting
	HP X 382A	
ATTENUATION		35 db
	HP X 375A	
ATTENUATION		0 db
	HP 715A	
MOD SELECTOR		OFF
REFLECTOR RANGE		600–900
BEAM VOLTS		380
REFLECTOR VOLTS		Clockwise
	HP 430C	
POWER		OFF
COEFFICIENT		POS
RESISTANCE		200
BIAS CURRENT		OFF
ZERO SET		full CCW

* Based on Air Force calibration procedures.

CAUTION   Turn the BIAS CURRENT switch OFF when connecting a bolometer. The open circuit voltage developed across the input jack may be sufficient to burn out a barretter— even when the BIAS CURRENT is set to a safe current for the bolometer in use.

3   Turn on the klystron cooling fan.

4   Apply power to the instruments and allow 10 min for warmup.

5   Set the micrometer screw on the klystron to the proper point for 10 gc.

6   Set the HP 715A MOD SELECTOR to CW, and reduce the REFLECTOR VOLTS control until the klystron oscillates as indicated by a sharp rise in cathode current.

7   Set the HP 715A MOD SELECTOR to OFF.

8   Set the HP 430C BOLO BIAS CURRENT switch to 0–6 ma, and the RANGE switch to 1.0 mw.

9   Rotate the ZERO SET controls clockwise. If the pointer goes off scale at the high end or moves to a non-zero position on scale, zero set the meter with the ZERO SET control.

10   If the pointer rests off scale at the low end, return the ZERO SET controls to the full counterclockwise position. Increase the BIAS CURRENT switch setting, one step at a time, and attempt to zero the meter. Always return the ZERO SET controls to the full counterclockwise position (minimum bias) before advancing the BIAS CURRENT switch to the next higher position. Do not go beyond the setting which corresponds to the maximum current for the bolometer in use.

11   Turn the HP 715A MOD SELECTOR switch to CW.

12   If a power level is indicated on the meter, adjust the X 485B Detector Mount for a maximum reading.

13   Tune the X 870A Slide Screw Tuners for a maximum reading.

14   Adjust the X 382A Variable Attenuator for a DBM reading of 0.

15   If there was no initial meter indication in Step 12, decrease the HP X 382A until a reading is obtained on the 1.0 mw scale.

16   The X 870A's and X 485B are tuned for a maximum reading, while the X 382A is used to set the meter to 0 DBM.

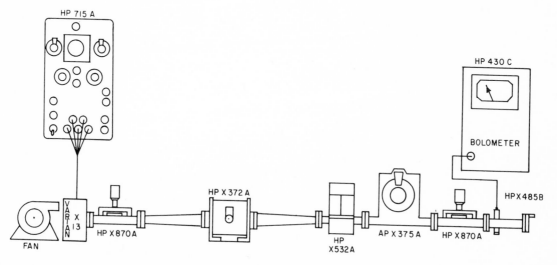

Fig. 11-54

17 Adjust the frequency meter X 532A for a minimum reading on the Power Meter. This will occur around 10 gc.

18 Readjust X 382A for 0 DBM.

19 Set the Flap Attenuator X 375A for a dial reading of 5.

20 The HP 430C should now read −5 DBM.

21 Set the Flap Attenuator for a reading of 20.

22 Set the RANGE switch on the HP 430C to 0.10 mw. The meter should now read −10 DBM.

Radar Equipment and Systems: Calibration and Measurement Techniques   12

The radar system, although complex in over-all design, utilizes timing, generating, transmitting, and receiving circuitry and techniques suitable for operation at microwave frequencies. Since operation is in the microwave region, all the microwave techniques discussed in Chapter 11 for the measurement of voltage, impedance, frequency, wavelength, system power, standing-wave ratio, and attenuation are applicable. For the most part, the same equipment is used. Voltage and impedance measurements are rarely, if ever, made on a radar system. Philco Training Manual AN-447—*Radar System Measurements*—contains detailed discussions of the principles specifically applied to radar systems.

PEAK POWER

Since radar transmissions are essentially pulse transmissions, the measurement of peak power is of more importance than the measurement of average power discussed previously. *Peak power* is defined as the peak value of power output from the radar set, and, in the case of pulsed equipment, it is the power output during the short burst of transmitted energy.

Since the resting time of a radar transmitter is long as compared to its operating time, the average power output is quite low as compared to the peak power. This is shown in Fig. 12-1. The average power value, which represents the actual heating value of the energy contained within the pulses, is

located at a point somewhere between zero and peak power. The actual transmitter output occurs at the peak level. Most modern power equipment, however, responds to the heating effects of this energy—the average power. Therefore, it is necessary to determine the peak power from the information given by the average power indication. This is accomplished by using the relation shown by the shaded areas in Fig. 12-1. The *pulse energy* (peak power $\times$ pulse width) must equal the *average energy* (average power $\times$ pulse repetition time). *Thus for the rectangular pulse shown*:

$$\text{peak power} \times \text{pulse width} =$$
$$\text{average power} \times \text{pulse repetition time}$$

Transposing,

$$\frac{\text{average power}}{\text{peak power}} = \frac{\text{pulse width}}{\text{pulse repetition time}}$$

The ratio of the pulse width to the pulse repetition time is called the *duty cycle*, or *duty factor*, since it represents the time that the transmitter is actually "working." For the rectangular pulse, if the pulse width were 0.5 microsecond and the PRF were 2000 pulses/second (pps), the pulse repetition time would be 1/2000, or 0.5 millisecond and the duty cycle would be 0.001 (0.1%). If the average power indicated by a thermistor bridge were 200 watts, the peak power associated with the transmission would be 200/0.001, or 200 kw.

In actual measurements, the two time intervals are determined by displaying the

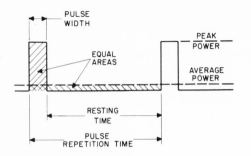

Fig. 12-1 Relationship between peak power and average power.

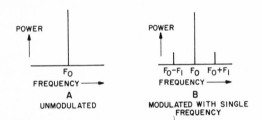

Fig. 12-2 Frequency spectrum for single-tone amplitude-modulated sinusoid.

transmitted pulses on a synchroscope or an oscilloscope which can be triggered by an external signal. The amplitude of the commercial synchroscope display gives the peak power measurements which are desired. The synchroscope was employed in an early power measurement method, but it is not used extensively at the present time.

SPECTRUM ANALYSIS

Analysis of a complex periodic wave on the basis of magnitude-versus-time plots has been discussed in Chapter 8. A second method of representing these waveforms is with a *magnitude-versus-frequency plot*, known as the *wave spectrum*. For the purposes of spectrum analysis, remember that complex periodic waveforms can be represented by a series of sinusoidal waveforms of a particular fundamental frequency and a large number (theoretically, an infinite number) of harmonics. The amplitudes of the various sinusoidal components are as-

sociated by a relationship known as the *Fourier* series, which is discussed in Appendix D-3.

Spectrum analysis has become an important measuring technique since it provides an exact description of an otherwise complicated phenomenon. In radio-frequency systems, the analysis of AM and FM transmitter performance is readily accomplished by the use of spectrum displays. A pure sine wave represents a single frequency. Its spectrum is shown in Fig. 12-2A as a single vertical line (F_0), the height of which represents the power contained in the single frequency. Fig. 12-2B shows the spectrum for a single sine-wave frequency, F_0, amplitude-modulated by a second sine wave, F_1. In this case, two sidebands are formed, one higher than and one lower than the frequency F_0. These sidebands correspond to the sum and difference frequencies as shown. If more than one modulating frequency is used (as in the case with practical broadcasts), two sidebands are added for each frequency.

The mathematical expression for a frequency-modulated transmission is long and complicated, involving a special mathematical operator known as the *Bessel function*. The spectrum representation of the FM wave is very straightforward, however, as shown in Fig. 12-3, and it gives all the information necessary for evaluating the system's performance.

In the microwave region, spectrum analysis has become an important aid in the design of magnetrons and other devices associated with radar systems. The increasing use of pulse time, pulse width, and pulse code modulation systems has also increased the applications of spectrum analysis techniques.

RECTANGUAR PULSE SPECTRA A perfect square wave is effectively made up of a fundamental sine wave plus an infinite number of odd-harmonic, in-phase sine waves which are progressively smaller in amplitude as the harmonic number increases. Theoretically, therefore, a 100-cps square wave contains frequencies of 100 cps, 300 cps, 500 cps, 700 cps, etc. In practice, however, it contains only a limited number of harmonics, because a perfect wave is impossible to obtain. It is the imperfect waveforms produced by practical limitations of electronic circuitry which limit the number of harmonics produced,

thereby making spectrum analysis a practical process. A good square wave, however, may contain frequencies up to the one hundredth harmonic.

The fundamental sine-wave component of a rectangular pulse is related to the width of the pulse, as can be seen by reference to Fig. 12-4. In this figure, the width of the pulse is T, and the period of the sine wave is

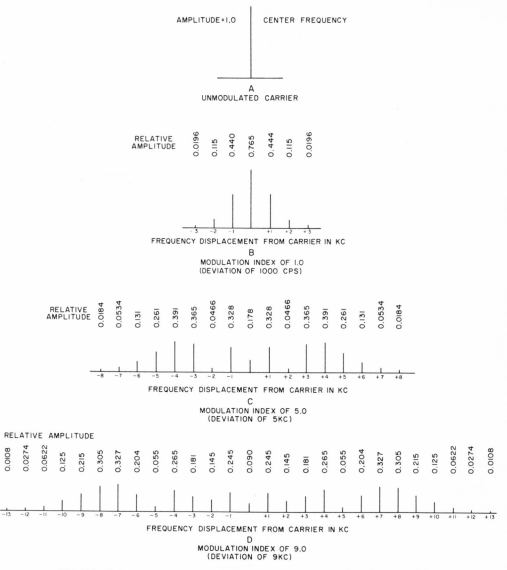

Fig. 12-3 Frequency spectrum for single-tone frequency-modulated sinusoid. The modulation index is given by $\Delta f/f_c$ where Δf is the maximum frequency deviation and f_c is the carrier (center) frequency. The single tone used for the spectrum plots above was a 1000-cps sine wave.

$2T$. Therefore, the fundamental sine-wave frequency, or the *fundamental pulse frequency* as it is usually called, is $\frac{1}{2}T$. Any harmonic can be determined, in terms of T, by multiplying the expression $\frac{1}{2}T$ by the number of the harmonic. For example, the second harmonic is $2 \times (\frac{1}{2}T)$, or $1/T$.

Since a radar transmission is modulated by short, rectangular pulses occurring at the PRF of the radar set, two distinct modulating components are present. One component consists of the PRF and its harmonics, and the other consists of the fundamental and odd-harmonic frequencies that make up the rectangular pulse. In Fig. 12-5, which shows an ideal spectrum of an r-f carrier modulated with a rectangular pulse, the vertical lines represent the modulation frequencies produced by the PRF and its harmonics, and the lobes represent the modulation frequencies produced by the fundamental pulse frequency and its harmonics. The vertical lines are separated by a frequency equal to the PRF. The amplitude of the main lobe falls off on either side of the carrier until it is zero at the points corresponding to the second harmonic of the fundamental pulse frequency. The first side lobe is produced by the third harmonic of the fundamental pulse frequency; the second zero point, by the fourth harmonic; and the second side lobe, by the fifth harmonic. In the ideal spectrum, each frequency above the carrier has as its counterpart another frequency equally spaced below the carrier, so that the pattern is symmetrical about the carrier.

In the ideal spectrum, the first side lobe represents 4.5% of the carrier amplitude, and the second side lobe, 1.6% of the carrier amplitude. The main lobe carries the major portion of the transmitted energy. The *pulse bandwidth* is the band of frequencies in-

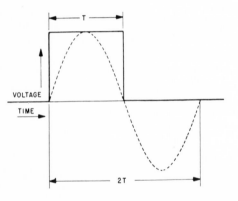

Fig. 12-4 Rectangular pulse and its fundamental sine-wave component.

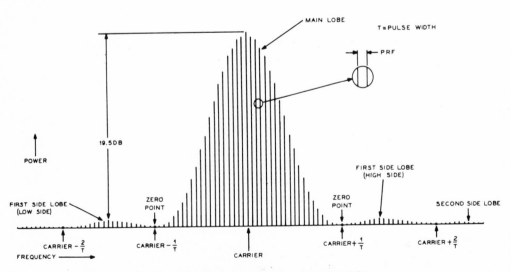

Fig. 12-5 Ideal spectrum for a rectangular pulse.

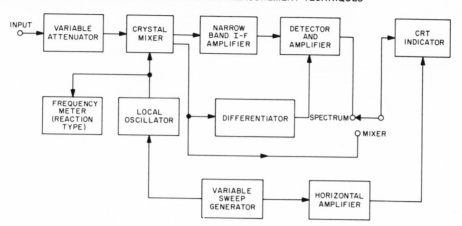

Fig. 12-6 Block diagram of a typical spectrum analyzer.

cluded by spectrum amplitudes of a specific value.

ANALYZER OPERATION   The conventional microwave spectrum plotter makes use of a form of panoramic receiver called a *spectrum analyzer*. In the spectrum analyzer, a narrow-band receiver is electrically tuned through a range of frequencies, and the output, in terms of power, is displayed vertically upon an oscilloscope whose horizontal sweep is synchronized with the frequency sweep of the receiver. A block diagram of a typical spectrum analyzer is shown in Fig. 12-6. The spectrum-analyzer receiver is of the superheterodyne type. The input, which usually consists of a coaxial-line termination, a broad-band attenuator, and a crystal mixer, is untuned and, therefore, responds equally well to all signals within the operating band. The local oscillator is usually of the reflex-klystron type, and is made accessible for ease of replacement. The i-f amplifier is a high-gain, narrow-band (50 kc or less) amplifier, usually operated above 20 mc. In some cases, double or triple superheterodyne action is used to obtain the narrow bandwidth required. The i-f section is followed by a detector and amplifier which feed the vertical plates of a crt. The sweep generator produces a variable-frequency sawtooth which sweeps the local-oscillator repeller (and therefore the receiver frequency) and the horizontal c-r-t plates simultaneously. A reaction-indicating frequency meter is included, and is designed to absorb local-oscillator power at resonance and, therefore, to indicate the local-oscillator frequency.

The indicator (crt) has a function switch labeled mixer-spectrum. In the spectrum position of this switch, the indicator displays the output of the receiver. In the mixer position, the indicator displays the crystal-mixer current flow, which is a function of the reflex-klystron local-oscillator output. Figure 12-7 shows a typical reflex-klystron chart. Note that the tube will oscillate only at certain voltages and that, as the voltage is varied, the power output varies. Each separate voltage range of oscillation is called a *mode*. The modes are relatively flat on top, and each succeeding mode becomes stronger as the repeller is made more negative. Within any given mode, the frequency is proportional to the negative voltage on the repeller and a frequency range of 60 mc is common in X-band tubes. The frequency of the top of each mode, however, is determined by the size of the resonant cavity in the tube; therefore, all the modes have the same center frequency.

In the spectrum analyzer, the sweep gen-

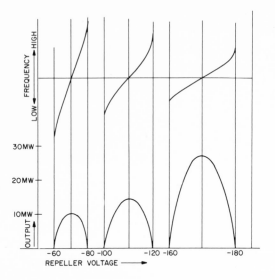

Fig. 12-7 Typical reflex-klystron chart.

Fig. 12-8 Klystron modes (spectrum analyzer in mixer function).

erator produces a sawtooth, which is adjustable in both amplitude and average voltage value. The sawtooth amplitude control, usually called the *spectrum width* control, has sufficient range to cover at least one mode and quite often two. The average voltage control of the sawtooth, usually called the *spectrum center* control, allows the operator to choose any klystron mode desired or to use any range within a particular mode. In normal use, only a limited section of one mode is utilized.

When the function switch is in the mixer position, the presentation is similar to that in Fig. 12-8, which shows one complete klystron mode and part of another. (The pip in the center of each mode is due to the frequency-

meter indication.) The mixer function of the analyzer allows the condition of the local oscillator to be checked, and, if desired, the oscillator frequency can be set to any specified value. Thus, the spectrum analyzer is an ideal klystron tube tester. The klystron to be tested may be substituted for the local oscillator in the spectrum analyzer and the mode pattern observed. The amplitude of the mode indicates power relative to that of the regular oscillator. The tuning range may be examined and any irregularities noted. Each mode should represent a smooth, regular curve. If desired, the tube under test may be pretuned to the approximate operating frequency before insertion into the radar, to simplify radar tune-up.

When the spectrum of a radar transmitter is to be observed, a small portion of the transmitter output is coupled into the signal input circuit of the spectrum analyzer. Care must be taken to keep the input low enough to prevent burnout of the attenuator. A directional coupler provides an ideal coupling system. As the spectrum-analyzer frequency is swept, the transmitter spectrum appears upon the c-r-t indicator in the form of a series of vertical pulses. These pulses are not to be confused with the vertical lines shown in Fig. 12-5, which are separated by a frequency equal to the *PRF*. The pip separation on the analyzer screen is a function of the local-oscillator sweep rate as well as the radar *PRF*, or:

$$N = F_R / F_S$$

where N is the number of pips, F_R is the radar *PRF*, and F_S is the sweep rate. For example, if the spectrum analyzer has a bandwith of 50 kc, a large number of *PRF* lines are included in each pulse, because the analyzer samples a 50-kc segment of the spectrum each time the transmitter fires. Thus each pulse in the spectrum represents the energy contained in a 50-kc band at the frequency of the analyzer at that instant. If the radar *PRF* is 200 pulses per second and the analyzer sweep rate is 10 cps, the observed spectrum will consist of 20 pulses across the face of the crt. (See Fig. 12-9.)

Since the analyzer produces a pip only when a pulse occurs, the period between pips equals the period between pulses.

To facilitate frequency measurements, the spectrum analyzer employs a unique system. (See Fig. 12-6.) A portion of the crystal-mixer current is applied to a differentiator, and the differentiated waveform is applied to the amplifier section of the spectrum analyzer. Figure 12-10 shows the result of differentiating and amplifying the mixer signal. Note that the frequency-meter pip now appears as an S curve and that the mode ends are marked by pips. This signal is applied to the indicator, along with the spectrum signal, and appears superimposed on the base line of the indication. (See Fig. 12-11.) The exact frequency is taken at the center of the S curve, where it crosses the base line. The pips, marking the mode end limits, should never be seen on the indicator since no spectrum indication may be obtained outside mode limits.

ACCURACY AND CALIBRATION The *resolving power* of a spectrum analyzer is a measure of its ability to discriminate between two adjacent frequencies of equal amplitude. This criterion is best established in terms of the response of the analyzer to a c-w signal. The response is largely a function of i-f bandwidth and local-oscillator sweep rate. Screen persistence introduces a lower limit on the sweep rate. Ideally, from a resolution standpoint, the i-f bandwidth should be very narrow. As the bandwidth is made narrower, however, the amplitude sensitivity of the analyzer is decreased by the factor $2.25T_D^2 (\Delta F)^2$, where T_D is the pulse duration and ΔF is the bandwidth. The maximum resolving power for a specific bandwidth is given by

$$R_{max} = 3.28 \ \Delta F$$

R_{max} will be an optimum value when

$$F = \frac{\Delta F_s}{2T_s}$$

where ΔF_s is the variation in local-oscillator frequency and T_s is the sweep period.

A test for optimum resolution consists of

Fig. 12-9 Typical magnetron spectrum.

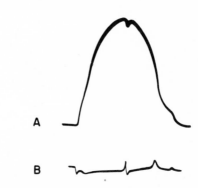

A

B

Fig. 12-10 Effect of differentiator upon mixer output. Part A shows the mixer function, and part B, the spectrum function.

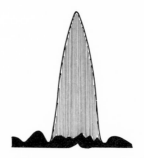

Fig. 12-11 Spectrum signal with output of differentiator superimposed on the base line.

applying a test frequency, F_0, which is amplitude-modulated by a single frequency, F_1. If optimum resolution exists, a display similar to that shown in Fig. 12-12 will result. A display, such as that illustrated in Fig. 12-13, indicates poor resolution.

The accuracy of the spectrum analyzer depends upon the accuracy of the individual components in the system. Calibration can be accomplished by calibrating these individual components.

Spectrum measurements may also be made with an *echo box*. As a rule, echo-box measurements will be more accurate than spectrum-analyzer measurements. This device will be discussed in a following section.

RANGE CALIBRATION

Since pulsed radar systems were developed primarily for the detection and ranging of various objects, accurate calibration of tim-

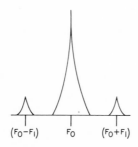

Fig. 12-12 AM spectrum (single tone) presentation with optimum analyzer resolution.

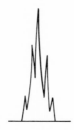

Fig. 12-13 AM spectrum (single tone) presentation with poor analyzer resolution.

ing circuits which produce the range indication is essential.

Figure 12-14 shows a typical method of precision range measurement. The system trigger, which is used to drive the modulator, also initiates the action of the range-marker generator. The range-marker generator produces an output pulse at some time after the occurrence of the trigger pulse, the exact time depending upon the time delay introduced. The time delay is adjusted by means of a control, with a dial marked in miles or yards of range. To determine range, the operator sets the control to a point where the range pulse coincides with the target to be measured. The range is then read from the dial. In the case of fire control or bombing, the dial may be mechanically coupled to a computer.

ZERO ERROR   In every radar, there is a series of time delays, within the equipment, between the time the system trigger occurs and the time the echo pulse arrives at the indicator. These delays are as follows:

1. A short delay between the application of the trigger input pulse and the development of the modulator output pulse.

2. A delay occurring because the r-f output from the transmitter takes time to build up after application of the modulator pulse.

3. A delay equal to the time required for the r-f pulse to travel to the antenna and then back to the receiver.

4. A delay equal to the time required for the r-f pulse to travel through the receiver. (This is the greatest delay.)

The combined delays may represent a range of 150 to 350 yd. This means that a target at zero range would be indicated at a range of 150 to 350 yd. This zero error affects the accuracy of all range indications. For example, a target at 1000 yd would be indicated at a range of 1150 to 1350 yd. Since the error is fixed by the equipment, it is the same at all ranges.

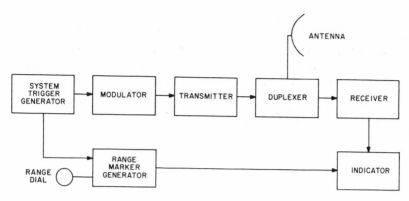

Fig. 12-14 Block diagram of typical precision radar ranging system.

Successful operation of a high-altitude bombing system requires accurate knowledge of the aircraft altitude. To determine the altitude, the radar system is used to range the ground return, and the information is fed to a computer, which also receives information concerning the bomb trajectory and ground speed. The computer output is in the form of a range marker which shows the theoretical impact point of the bomb on the radar indicator. The aircraft is then flown so that the target crosses the impact point on the indicator, at which time, the bombs are released. If the range marker is in error, bombing accuracy decreases for two reasons: The altitude information fed to the computer is wrong, and the impact point, indicated by the computer, is wrong.

DETERMINATION OF ZERO ERROR Before the effect of zero error can be corrected, it is necessary to determine how much time delay is present in a given system.

The most reliable measurement of zero error involves the use of a fixed target at some accurately known range. A natural target may be used, but a portable reflector will give more reliable results. In the case of an aircraft radar, a target is selected, and the distance is carefully measured to a certain point where the aircraft may be easily positioned. The target range indicated by the radar system is carefully read and compared to the measured range. The range indicated by the radar should be greater than the measured range, and the difference is the zero error.

This method has the main disadvantage that each aircraft must be located in a predetermined position, which means that the aircraft must be moved into position, the zero error checked, and the aircraft moved out of the way to make room for the next one.

A much simpler method for everyday use consists of measuring the apparent radar range of an object whose true range is known by other means. The object selected may be a feature of the surrounding landscape or a reflector on a mast set up specifically for this purpose.

The absolute altimeter may be used to check the zero error of a radar during a flight. In this way, the radar in each aircraft may be checked without using a fixed target, and the checks are independent. The check merely consists of ranging the radar ground return and reading the absolute altimeter dial. The radar reading should be greater, and the difference of the two is the zero error.

This method relies on the accuracy of the altimeter and presupposes that it is carefully calibrated. Furthermore, the aircraft must be in flight to make the check.

COMPENSATION After the zero error of a radar is measured, the range-marker circuit should be compensated. In most cases, calibration is carried out at two different points in the delay range. If a given radar has a 200-yd zero error and a 12,000-yd range-marker circuit, and the calibration points are at 1000 yd and 10,000 yd, the 1000-yd point should be set up at 800 yd and the 10,000-yd point should be set up at 9,800 yd. After compensation, the zero error should be measured again to make sure that it has been reduced to zero yards.

The value of the zero error should not change unless components are damaged or replaced. Therefore, the zero error of a radar need be measured only after such overhaul or repair job. It is common practice to label the equipment with the last measured value of zero error, to facilitate compensation during range-marker calibration.

The manual, *Radar System Measurements*, mentioned previously also contains a synchroscope method for determining zero error. This method, however, is less accurate than the methods just described. Nevertheless, it is a more convenient method since it does not require the use of fixed targets nor does it impose any conditions on the aircraft.

PICKUP ANTENNAS

The method of microwave (radar) measurements discussed up to this point have consisted of inserting the meter, or components of the meter circuitry, directly into the systems being studied. An alternative to this is the use of the directional coupler discussed in Chapter 11 to sample part of the microwave energy. It is also possible—and sometimes necessary—to sample the energy radiated from the antenna itself. This is accomplished by using a *pickup antenna*, as shown in Fig. 12-15.

This device consists of a directional antenna array which is broadly tuned to the radar band to be used. It is placed in the radiation field of the radar antenna, and picks up a certain percentage of the radiated signal. The test antenna may be made portable by mounting it on a tripod frame, or it may be fixed by means of a bracket installed as a part of the radar system. It is common practice to locate the pickup antenna at least one diameter of the radar antenna reflector away from the radar antenna (see Fig. 12-15), and to orient the two antennas for maximum pickup. With this procedure, the space attenuation is approximately 30 db. The exact loss either will be given for the particular installation or must be measured. Any subsequent measurements should be made with exactly the same antenna spacing. Another placement method is to clamp the pickup antenna to the edge of the radar reflector in such a manner that the pickup is directed toward the radar antenna feed array. In this position of the pickup, antenna leakage power is utilized rather than direct radiation. This method has the advantage of allowing operation of the test equipment at various radar antenna positions, and the radar antenna does not require careful orientation. The use of a pickup antenna has the important advantage of testing the entire radar system including the radome, if the

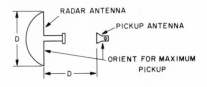

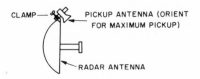

Fig. 12-15 Pickup-antenna placement.

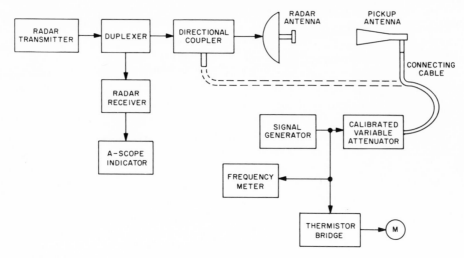

Fig. 12-16 Pickup-antenna calibration setup.

antenna is placed outside the radome. This enables the test procedure to show operating efficiency, with all controllable factors included.

Four primary disadvantages are associated with the pickup antenna:

1. The placement of the antenna is critical.

2. Antennas are sensitive to frequency changes.

3. It is difficult to make tests during radar scanning.

4. Near-by objects may modify the signal picked up by the antenna.

Near-by objects may cause reflections and result in large errors in signal pickup. The presence of these reflections may be detected as follows: While observing the signal picked up by the antenna, carefully move the pickup antenna closer to the radar antenna. A smooth increase in signal strength should be noted, and, if the pickup antenna is moved farther away, a smooth decrease in signal strength should be noted. Any sudden or erratic variations or minimum points indicate that near-by objects are influencing the pickup, and another pickup position must be chosen.

CALIBRATION TECHNIQUE   The space attenuation between the radar and pickup antenna is given by

$$A_s = 10 \log \frac{158 \; d^2}{G_1 \; G_2} \; \text{db}$$

where d is the spacing between antennas (centimeters), and G_1 and G_2 are the gains of the radar antenna and pickup antenna, respectively, in terms of power ratio. The formula is accurate only when the antennas are more than one reflector diameter apart.

Space attenuation can be calibrated by any one of several methods, as given in *Radar System Measurements*. The setup shown in Fig. 12-16 is the easiest to use, since the radar antenna feed system need not be disconnected. The trigger signal from the radar system can be used to trigger the signal generator, which may be of either the pulsed or FM type described in Chapter 11. The connecting cable and directional coupler must also be calibrated so that the space attenuation can be isolated. These calibrations can be accomplished by the methods described in Chapter 11. The space attenuation calibration itself is a substitution process for calibrating insertion loss.

After a 1-mw reference level is established

with the signal generator, the connecting cable is attached to the directional coupler, as shown by the dashed lines in Fig. 12-16. The calibrated variable attenuator is adjusted to give a pulse of about ½ in. on the A-scope, and the attenuator reading A_1 is noted. *Be certain that saturation does not occur*, as determined by inspection of the A-scope presentation. The connecting cable is then transferred to the pickup antenna, and the attenuator is readjusted for a ½-in. pulse. The difference between this reading A_2 and the previous A_1 *combined*, with the directional-coupler loss, A_D, is the space loss:

(1) $A_S = A_D$ (if $A_1 = A_2$)
(2) $A_S = A_D + A_1 + A_2$ (if $A_1 > A_2$)
(3) $A_S = A_D - (A_1 + A_2)$ (if $A_1 > A_2$)

If the measurement is repeated at several points in the operating-frequency band, a graph of space attenuation versus frequency can be constructed.

Errors associated with this procedure can be minimized by allowing sufficient warmup time (at least 30 min) for all equipment, by making certain that all connections are tight, and by repeating critical measurements several times to determine an average reading. The calibration should be made at the temperature, pressure, relative humidity, and other operating conditions specified in the equipment specifications. Corrections must be made in accordance with the manufacturer's specifications if any of these factors change.

RECEIVER SENSITIVITY

Radar receiver faults are the most common causes of loss of maximum-range performance. This fact is mainly due to the greater number of adjustments and components associated with the receiver. Loss of receiver sensitivity has the same effect on range as a decrease in transmitter power. For example, a 6-db loss of receiver sensitivity would shorten the effective range of a radar just as much as a 6-db decrease in transmitter power. Such a drop in transmitter power is very evident in meter indications and, therefore, is easy to detect. On the other hand, a loss in receiver sensitivity, which can easily result from a slight misadjustment in the receiver (a quarter turn of the TR adjustment in some radars causes a change of 10 to 12 db), is very difficult to detect unless accurate measurements are made.

Receiver sensitivity determines the ability of the radar to pick up weak signals. The greater the sensitivity, the weaker the signal that can be picked up. Sensitivity is measured by determining the power level of the minimum discernible signal (MDS). MDS denotes the weakest signal that produces a visible receiver output, and its value is determined by the receiver output noise level, which tends to obscure weak signals. For example, a noisy receiver will be less sensitive than a quiet receiver. It follows, therefore, that an MDS measurement is dependent upon the receiver noise level, and that measuring either one will give an indication of receiver sensitivity. If it can be established that the specified MDS level is correct, the noise figure will also be correct.

MDS MEASUREMENT   The most reliable MDS measurement can be made with an FM signal generator adjusted to give an appropriate artificial echo, as discussed previously. If special-function circuits, such as MTI, IAGC, STC, and/or FTC, are included in the radar system under test, they should be disabled. The A-F-C circuitry, however, may be left operative. (An MDS measurement with and without the AFC in operation will test the effectiveness of this circuitry.) Proceed as follows:

1. Connect radar trigger-pulse output to trigger-input jack on FM signal generator. (Omit if internal sync is desired.)

2. Connect r-f input through coupling de-

vice to radar. (A directional coupler is preferable.)

3. Turn signal-width control to maximum (CW).

4. Adjust phase control for maximum klystron output as indicated on thermistor bridge.

5. Tune klystron (cavity) to approximate radar frequency, by adjusting the frequency meter to the frequency of the radar transmitter and tuning the klystron for a dip in the thermistor-bridge meter reading. (Since the klystron mode is fairly broad, extreme accuracy in tuning the klystron is not necessary. For example, the width of the flat portion of an X-band klystron is about 10 mc; therefore, the tuning accuracy required is ± 5 mc.)

6. If necessary, adjust phase control gain for maximum output. If a large adjustment is required, repeat Step 5 again.

7. Adjust uncalibrated attenuator for a 1-mw indication.

8. Set receiver gain control for a ¼-in. noise level on the A-scope.

9. Using a low attenuator setting, observe artificial echo pulse on radar A-scope. (If the radar has no A-scope, connect a synchroscope to the receiver output, and trigger it with the same pulse applied to the trigger input.)

10. If necessary, adjust phase control to position echo pulse in a target-free area.

11. Adjust signal-width control for desired echo-pulse width.

12. Increase attenuation until echo is just barely visible in the noise (see Fig. 12-17). This is the MDS level. (The echo pulse can be distinguished from the noise more easily, during the final adjustment of the attenuator, if the time delay is varied slightly.)

13. Find the total attenuation in decibels. The value obtained is the MDS in decibels below 1 mw (−dbm).

Total attenuation = coupling loss (db) + cable loss (db) + attenuator reading (db).

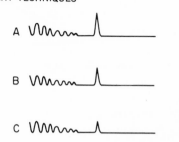

Fig. 12-17 Appearance of artificial echo on A-scope. Part A shows a strong signal; part B shows the same signal attenuated 10 db; part C shows the signal attenuated 5 db more. The last display is approaching the MDS level.

ELIMINATION OF LEAKAGE ERROR   In an MDS measurement, a high degree of attenuation (approximately 98 db for the average radar) and a very low power level (about 1 micro-microwatt) are involved. Because of these factors, very little r-f leakage can be tolerated or the amount of leakage signal picked up by the receiver will be appreciable compared to the signal fed through the attenuator. Since leakage signals are independent of the attenuator setting, very inaccurate MDS readings may be obtained when leakage is present. If the leakage signal reaches the receiver in phase with the signal through the attenuator, the MDS reading will be low, and thus will indicate that the receiver sensitivity is much better than it actually is. In such a case there is a strong possibility that a defective receiver may appear to be normal. On the other hand, if the leakage signal reaches the receiver out of phase with the signal through the attenuator, the MDS reading will be high, and thus will indicate that the receiver sensitivity is poorer than it actually is. In the construction of a signal generator, special attention is given to the problem of minimizing r-f leakage. The r-f oscillator is carefully shielded, and then it and the attenuator assembly are enclosed in a second shield which serves as the case. In addition, all connecting cables and couplings are provided with shields and close-fitting connectors. In spite of these precautions, however, a small amount of leakage exists, even in the most modern equipment.

The presence of leakage makes it imperative to locate all equipment associated with MDS tests outside the radar-antenna radiation field. In addition, the equipment should never be operated outside of its case, or with loose cable connections. Also, on early signal generators where a door is provided, on the front panel, for access to the oscillator adjustments, the door must be kept closed during measurements. If these precautions are not observed, erroneous results will be obtained.

The presence of leakage may be detected by the following method:

1. Determine the MDS level.
2. Rotate the test set to another position and determine the MDS level again.
3. If the MDS reading varies, leakage is present in one of the two positions. If leakage is found to be present, locate the test set as far from the radar antenna and receiver as possible. Find a position where a movement of the test set does not influence the MDS. In general, if rotation of the test set does not change the MDS level, leakage is not serious.

OVER-ALL RADAR-SYSTEM PERFORMANCE

Radar performance testing involves a series of measurements designed to indicate the ability of the radar system to detect targets. The combined results of all the performance tests indicate the over-all system performance. There are two distinct considerations in regard to radar performance: the *minimum range performance* and the *maximum range performance*.

Certain radar systems are designed to detect targets at close range: Examples of these are the radar systems used for fire control, aircraft interception, aircraft altitude indicators, and ground-controlled-approach systems. In these radar systems, the TR recovery time is an important factor in determining the *minimum range*. If a target has a range of 200 yd, the echo is returned to the

radar in about 1¼ microseconds (μsec) after the occurrence of the transmitter pulse. If the receiver is to respond to this echo, the TR switch must recover sufficiently during this short interval to allow passage of energy to the receiver. Since a near-by target returns a strong signal; the recovery need not be complete because the receiver will respond to a strong signal even at reduced sensitivity.

Minimum range performance is also influenced by the transmitter pulse width. Long-range search radars may use a pulse width of 2 μsec or over, which represents a free-space range of over 320 yd. Radars designed for close-range work have pulse widths as short as ¼ μsec, which represents only a little over 40 yd of free-space range. Furthermore, high-power radars may require the use of a pre-TR tube to prevent transfer of harmonic energy through the TR; as a result, the recovery period may correspond to 2000 yd of range or more.

The *maximum radar range* is determined by a great many factors, which may be generally classified in terms of three major controlling factors: target reflection, propagation factors, and radar-system performance. The first two factors are uncontrollable, but the third depends upon the condition of the radar system.

The energy reflected by a radar target is determined by the following factors:

1. Material of which the target is constructed
2. Surface area presented to radar
3. Configuration of surface presented to radar
4. Frequency of radar

In general, reflection from a target is so complicated that the reflected-signal strength cannot be predicted with any degree of accuracy. Hence, in cases where the reflected-signal strength is required, it is found by direct measurement.

Atmospheric conditions play a very important part in radar performance. Some of the more common factors which affect radar performance are

1. Duct formation
2. Temperature inversion and atmospheric refraction
3. Rain echoes and scattering
4. Atmospheric absorption

Duct formation occurs when there is a sharp discontinuity in the atmospheric condictions close to the ground. The discontinuity reflects a transmitted signal in about the same manner as a metallic surface, and thus directs the wave back to earth, where reflection occurs again. In effect, therefore, the space between earth and the discontinuity acts as a waveguide, and, as a result, an abnormally long radar range may be observed. This effect is most pronounced when operating over water.

Atmospheric refraction is the process by which radar waves are bent in the earth's atmosphere. Under normal conditions, the atmosphere is more dense at the surface of the earth and less dense as the altitude increases. As a result, electromagnetic energy travels more slowly at low altitudes and is effectively bent downward. The radar horizon is therefore extended about 15% beyond the mathematical horizon under normal conditions. This action may be enhanced by a condition known as *temperature inversion*, which is due to a warm air mass surmounting a colder air mass. The increased temperature at higher altitude further decreases normal atmospheric density compared to the surface density, and the radar horizon is greatly increased. Temperature inversion is very common where warm air masses from land move out over the cool air directly over a large body of water.

If the gradation of density is reversed, in that a colder air mass surmounts a warm air mass, refraction may cause the radar wave to be bent upward and thus greatly reduce the radar horizon.

Drops of moisture in the atmosphere may cause microwave signals to be either scattered or reflected, depending upon the size of the drops. If the drops are large, as in a heavy rain cloud, reflection occurs and causes an echo. This effect is very noticeable at the higher microwave frequencies. Smaller water drops may cause scattering rather than reflection; this effect will result in greatly reduced range.

A study of atmospheric absorption, which was discovered only recently, has led to many interesting developments. It has been found that atmospheric gases have the property of absorbing certain microwave frequencies. Each gas has its own absorption spectrum, and of the gases studied thus far, each is unique in regard to the absorption frequencies. For example, water vapor absorbs strongly above 10,000 mc, showing a peak at about 23,000 mc. Oxygen absorbs very strongly at about 60,000 mc, and ammonia gas at about 24,000 mc. The National Bureau of Standards has compiled a list of absorption spectra for the various gases to aid in gaseous analysis by absorption. Because the absorption characteristics of each gas are different from those of every other gas it is possible to analyze gases by means of their absorption spectra. As far as radar is concerned, the absorption effect is very undesirable because it results in reduced range at the frequencies of maximum absorption. Fortunately, this effect is not important in the X band and at lower frequencies, but it does make operation in the K band very unreliable.

In the radar test procedures described in this manual, the foregoing factors have no measurable effect. However, they have a very great effect on radar range. Because of the variableness of these factors, it is clear that the strength and range of permanent echoes do not give reliable indications of radar performance.

Radar-system performance is the only factor which may be controlled. It depends on such items as

1. Transmitter power
2. Transmitter frequency
3. Transmitter spectrum
4. Receiver sensitivity (MDS)
5. Receiver bandwidth
6. T-R recovery
7. A-F-C operation (if used)

All these items (with the exception of A-F-C operation) can be measured on an individual basis by the methods already discussed. This section seeks to provide an overall evaluation of these items under normal radar operating conditions.

SYSTEM SENSITIVITY System sensitivity (or the S-figure) is the ratio of the transmitted power encompassed by the receiver bandpass to the MDS power. A precise determination of system sensitivity, therefore, involves a check of both the transmitter spectrum and the receiver bandpass. Of course, if half the transmitted energy is

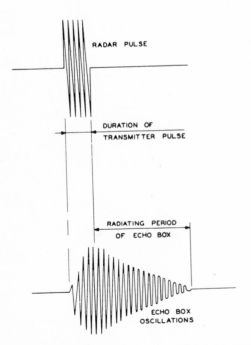

Fig. 12-18 Relationship between transmitter pulse and echo box ringing.

outside the receiver bandpass, the power is effectively cut in half.

The relationship of system sensitivity to maximum radar range is shown by the following proportionality:

$$\text{range (maximum)}: \sqrt[4]{\frac{P_t}{P_{\text{mds}}}}$$

where P_t = transmitter peak power output encompassed by receiver bandpass

P_{mds} = minimum discernible signal power.

Notice that the fourth root is taken rather than the square root. This is done because the inverse square law, as used to determine the strength of a transmitted signal over a given distance, is applied twice, once for the outward path and once for the echo return path.

If the transmitted power and MDS power are measured in units of watts, system sensitivity is calculated in terms of a power ratio by simple division. These two powers, however, are usually measured in dbm; in this case, the sensitivity is more conveniently calculated in db by means of the following formula:

system sensitivity (db) =

$$P_t\,(\text{dbm}) - P_{\text{mds}}\,(\text{dbm})$$

It should be noted here that MDS results in a negative dbm figure, and that a —dbm is subtracted from a +dbm by simply adding the two together. For example, with a transmitter power of 72.6 dbm and an MDS of —95 dbm, the system sensitivity is

$$72.6 - (-95) = 167.6\,\text{db}$$

The sensitivity of each radar system is specified by the manufacturer, and any decrease in sensitivity results in a corresponding loss in maximum range. The fourth-root equation preceding represents the maximum range-system sensitivity relationship for ideal propagation conditions.

The root actually varies according to these conditions, with the sixteenth root of P_t/P_{mds} representing the worst propagation conditions. The *mean* relationship is given by the eighth root of the S-figure.

EVALUATION WITH AN ECHO BOX   The echo box represents a simplified, self-contained instrument that is very useful for both system testing and troubleshooting. In basic form, the echo box is merely a tunable resonant circuit with a very high Q.

Any tuned circuit may be shock-excited by the sudden application of energy. When the excitation is removed, the tuned circuit will continue to oscillate for a length of time. The greater the Q of the resonant circuit, the greater the time of the oscillation. This action is very similar to that which occurs when a bell is struck. The bell will ring for a period of time following the shock excitation produced by the clapper. Because of the similarity of the two actions, the time of oscillation in a shock-excited tuned circuit is called *ringtime*. The relationship between an excitation pulse (transmitter pulse) and the resulting ringing of an echo box is shown in Fig. 12-18.

In the case of the echo box, part of the transmitted pulse is coupled into a tunable resonant cavity with a very high Q. The resultant signal produced by ringing action is visible on the radar A-scope, as shown in Fig. 12-19, and the ringtime is measured, in terms of either yards or microseconds, between the start of the transmitter pulse and the point where the ringing signal reaches the noise level of the radar receiver (see Fig. 12-20). The value of ringtime is influenced by the following:

1. Peak transmitter power
2. Receiver sensitivity
3. Coupling loss between echo box and radar
4. Transmitter pulse width
5. Q of echo box

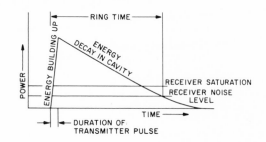

Fig. 12-19 Echo box ringtime curve.

Fig. 12-20 Ringtime on an A-scope.

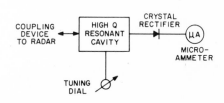

Fig. 12-21 Block diagram of modern echo box.

Notice that the first two factors provide a check of system sensitivity. This check is reliable, however, only if the other three factors are either known or kept constant.

Two refinements are applied to echo boxes to extend their usefulness a great deal. First, a meter and rectifier are used to monitor power (see Fig. 12-21), and the coupling to the rectifier is often made adjustable to allow for different operating conditions. Second, the frequency dial may be calibrated in absolute frequency, thus making accurate frequency measurements possible. The device is therefore comparable to a transmission-type frequency meter.

ECHO BOX CALIBRATION   An echo-box installation is calibrated as follows:

1. Orient the radar and pickup antennas

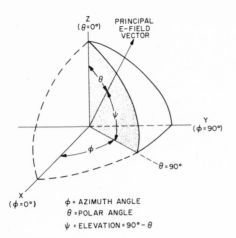

ϕ = AZIMUTH ANGLE
θ = POLAR ANGLE
ψ = ELEVATION = 90° − θ

Fig. 12-22 Polar coordinate system for defining antenna field measurements.

for maximum pickup. (This represents the final adjustment of the pickup antenna unless reflections are found to be present.)

2. Record settings of all radar controls that affect PRF and pulse width.

3. Adjust radar-receiver gain for about ¼ in. of noise on A-scope. (If no A-scope is used, connect a synchroscope to receiver output.)

4. Tune echo box for greatest ringtime as seen on A-scope.

5. Adjust coupling in echo box to give a standard meter reading (75% of full scale).

6. Carefully read ringtime. (Note temperature of echo box.)

7. Measure system sensitivity (determine P_t and P_{mds}) using standard test equipment and procedure. By means of the calibration procedure, ringtime is correlated with system sensitivity, so that future ringtime readings may be converted into sensitivity readings. The conversion is easy to make because the change in ringtime per db of change in sensitivity is specified for each echo box; a common value is about 100 yd per db. Thus if a radar has lost 1000 yd of ringtime, the sensitivity is down approximately 10 db. If the ringtime is found to be low, the meter reading is observed and compared to the calibrated reading. Since

the meter measures relative transmitter output, a low reading indicates transmitter trouble. With a low ringtime and a normal meter reading, however, trouble is indicated in the radar receiver.

PATTERN INTENSITY MEASUREMENTS

For the measurement of electromagnetic phase, polarization, and intensity in free space, certain optical conditions, as well as electronic and mechanical conditions, must be met. Although primarily directed to the study of radar antennas, this section presents techniques which are applicable to other r-f antenna systems with only minor modifications.

The *radiation pattern* of an antenna is a plot of the angular distribution of the energy radiated into space.

The *polarization* of an electromagnetic wave is the orientation of the electric field vector in space. A *linearly polarized* wave is one whose E vector is always pointed along a fixed line although the magnitude may change. The converse type of orientation —fixed magnitude, variable direction—is known as *circular polarization*. Variation in both magnitude and direction leads to *elliptical polarization*.

The characteristics of an antenna used as a receiver are identical to the characteristics of the antenna used as a transmitter.

Radiation patterns are most commonly plotted in either polar or rectangular coordinates. Polar coordinates are particularly advantageous because a polar plot quickly shows the range as a function of angle for the reception of a constant signal level. The three-dimension polar-coordinate system necessary for displaying polarization, as well as intensity and phase, is shown in Fig. 12-22.

Decibel units cannot be used for polar plots. The units should indicate only relative power or relative field intensity (volts/meter²).

PRIMARY PATTERNS Primary radiation patterns are associated with the antenna feed system, which is usually small enough to mount inside a laboratory area. *It is convenient to use the feed under transmitting conditions when determining primary patterns.*

Figure 12-23 shows the arrangement of the feed and pickup horn, along with the various reference axes which will be used throughout the discussion. The separation R of the two devices should be greater than

$$R = \frac{2b^2}{\lambda}$$

where b is the wide dimension of the feed aperture. The pickup horn should be highly directive and should be arranged so that the reflections from its mount are negligible. The various rotational directions required for pickup and feed are indicated in the figure. The entire apparatus should be located in an area that is as open as possible.

During the course of pattern measurements, it will be necessary to orient the principal E- and H-field planes so that one is vertical and the other horizontal. This can be approximately determined by examining the propagation mode in the feed in relation to the feed aperture dimensions (see the introductory section of Chapter 11). Either of the field planes can then be exactly oriented by mounting a small helical coil directly over the feed aperture. A sensi-

tive current or voltage indicator must be attached to the coil terminals. Rotate the feed about the system axis until the approximate location of the desired field is vertical. Then rotate the feed back and forth until the coil indicator reading is a maximum. At this point, the chosen field is oriented in the vertical direction. Before making measurements, the pickup horn should always be rotated about the system axis until the orientation of its aperture dimensions is the same as the feed orientation.

It is also necessary to locate the *center of feed* for the feed system. This is essentially a phase measurement, and the test setup is shown in Fig. 12-24. The pickup should be located at a fixed position and the probe moved until a minimum is located.

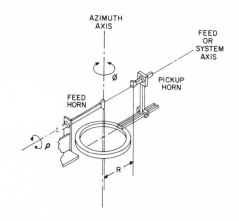

Fig. 12-23 Apparatus for primary pattern determination.

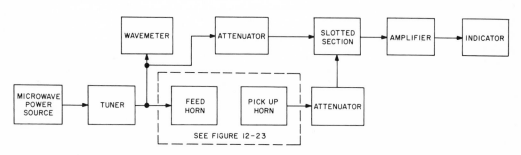

Fig. 12-24 Phase pattern and center-of-feed determinations.

The indicator reading at this position establishes a reference level. Lock the probe in place. Rotate the pickup about the azimuth axis by some arbitrary angle. Change the separation between feed and pickup until the reference level reading established above is repeated. Note the distance between pickup and feed. Then find a second pickup-feed separation which will repeat the reference level with the pickup at another arbitrary azimuth angle. When these measurements are completed, the location of the center of feed can be found by the geometric construction shown in Fig. 12-25. Point C in the diagram should be located with respect to the feed aperture in the physical system setup for future reference.

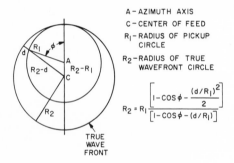

A – AZIMUTH AXIS
C – CENTER OF FEED
R_l – RADIUS OF PICKUP CIRCLE
R_2 – RADIUS OF TRUE WAVEFRONT CIRCLE

$$R_2 = R_l \frac{\left[1 - \cos\phi - \dfrac{(d/R_l)^2}{2} \right]}{\left[1 - \cos\phi - (d/R_l) \right]}$$

Fig. 12-25 Center-of-feed determination.

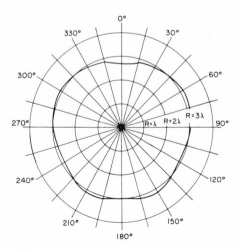

Fig. 12-26 Constant-phase wavefront (example).

If the separation between the pickup and feed does not have to be changed to repeat the reference level at the two arbitrary azimuth positions, the center of feed is located at the azimuth axis.

While the apparatus in Fig. 12-24 is set up, it will be convenient to make phase pattern determinations, if they are desired. Before proceeding, the center of feed should be placed at the azimuth axis. The same procedure and precautions described for phase determinations in Chapter 11 should be followed. Once the probe is located at a minimum for the 0° azimuth pickup location, it should be locked in place. The pickup can then be rotated about the azimuth axis through incremental angles until the full 360 degrees is encompassed. At each incremental angle position, the separation between pickup and feed should be changed until the reference minimum value is repeated. A plot of the pickup-feed separation versus azimuth angle will yield the phase front pattern as shown in Fig. 12-26. This pattern will be repeated at intervals of λ so that only one contour need be taken.

For reference, it is important to note that movement of the pickup horn by a distance ΔR is related to movement of the probe (ΔD) by

$$\Delta D = \frac{\Delta R \lambda_a}{\lambda}$$

The foregoing procedure establishes the phase pattern for either the principal E- or H-field—whichever is oriented in the horizontal direction. The alternate field pattern can be determined by rotating the feed (and pickup) 90 degrees about the system axis and repeating the process.

Relative field intensity measurements can be made with the setup shown in Fig. 12-27. Again, the center of feed must be located at the azimuth axis. With the pickup at 0 degrees azimuth find a reference minimum reading and lock the probe in position. Keeping the pickup-feed separation fixed,

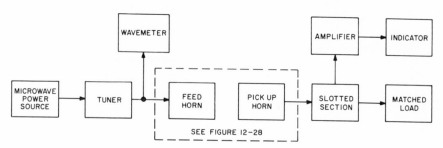

Fig. 12-27 Relative field strength determinations.

rotate the pickup about the azimuth axis incremental angles. At each point determine the relative field intensity by using the formula:

$$\text{relative field intensity} = \frac{\text{arbitrary reading}}{\text{reference reading}}$$

A plot of relative field intensity versus azimuth angle will yield the intensity pattern (see Fig. 12-28).

The foregoing procedure establishes the pattern for either the principal E- or H-field. To determine the pattern for the alternate field, rotate both the feed and pickup 90 degrees about the system axis and repeat the process.

Phase and intensity patterns can be plotted in reference planes other than the horizontal. This is accomplished by first setting the principal H-field in the horizontal direction. Then rotate the feed an arbitrary angle ρ about the feed axis. Determine the phase or intensity pattern as before. The process can be repeated for incremental values of ρ until the full range of 90 degrees is traversed. At each incremental value of ρ a pattern contour can be plotted.

SECONDARY PATTERNS Secondary patterns are associated with the over-all antenna system. Several such system patterns are shown in Fig. 12-29. Antenna designs are numerous—each for a specific operational application. *For secondary pattern determinations, the test antenna is used in its receiving function.*

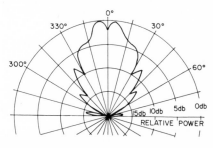

Fig. 12-28 Principal E-plane field intensity pattern (example).

The separation between the transmitting antenna and the test antenna should be greater than

$$R = \frac{2D^2}{\lambda}$$

where D is the maximum test antenna dimension. To eliminate ground interference, both antennas should be located at a height of

$$h = \frac{D^2}{d}$$

where d is the diameter of the transmitting dish.

A dish type of transmitting antenna is used to insure maximum directivity and focusing. The mount should provide rotation in the horizontal and vertical directions. A grating structure should be placed over the antenna aperture with the antenna polarization perpendicular to the grating slats. The slats should be spaced at intervals of $3\lambda/8$ and they should have a depth of $\lambda/4$.

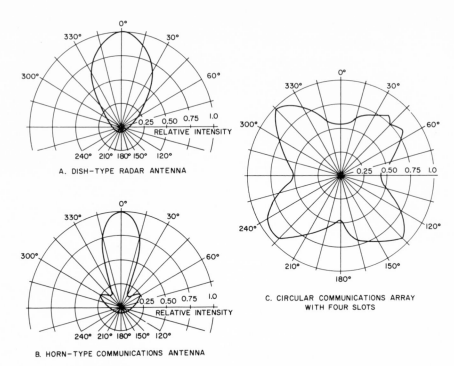

Fig. 12-29 Secondary patterns for various antenna configurations.

The test antenna should be mounted so that its principal E- or H-field (whichever is desired) is horizontal. It is more convenient to have a fixed transmitting antenna installation and to mount the test antenna so that it can be rotated in azimuth and elevation. For each position of the test antenna, the transmitting antenna should be focused to give maximum transfer of energy.

Phase and power measurements can be made at the test installation by the methods described in Chapter 11. These measurements can be made directly at the test antenna or can be arranged to include the performance of the over-all test system. In order to establish a reference power, the test antenna should be oriented to receive maximum power. It can then be returned to the 0 degree azimuth position and rotated through incremental azimuth angles. All powers should be related to the reference level so that data can be plotted in terms of relative values.

Complete space coverage can be deter-

mined by plotting patterns at different elevation angles. To minimize ground reflections, the antenna should be tilted only in the upward directions between the forward and reverse directions of the horizontal plane, and should be rotated only through the front 180 degrees of azimuth (90 degrees to either side of 0 degrees azimuth). The test antenna should then be inverted and the process repeated to establish the other half of the pattern.

ANTENNA GAIN MEASUREMENTS

In the determination of antenna patterns, only relative power levels and intensities were discussed. To make accurate performance determinations, it is necessary to place the radiation pattern on an absolute power basis. To do this, a knowledge of antenna gain, as well as radiation patterns, is required.

The directive gain of an antenna is defined for a transmitting antenna by

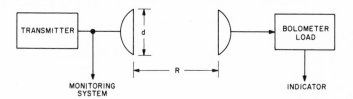

Fig. 12-30 Antenna calibration arrangement.

$$G_T = \frac{\text{peak power radiated/unit solid angle}}{\text{total power radiated}/4\pi}$$

and a receiving antenna by

$$G_R = \frac{\text{peak power received}}{\text{average power received}}$$

The approximate gain can be determined directly from the horizontal E- and H-patterns by:

$$G_R = \frac{\text{relative intensity at } 0° \text{ azimuth}}{\text{sum of areas enclosed by principal E- and H-patterns}}$$

The area required for the denominator is taken between 0 and 90 degrees azimuth. It can be found with the aid of a planimeter.

MEASUREMENTS OF DIRECTIVE GAIN   The actual experimental determination of G_R can be accomplished by comparing the power received by test antenna with that received by a calibrated antenna, which serves as a primary gain standard (G_S). The test antenna is first rotated and elevated until maximum power ($P_{\max}$) is received. It is then replaced by the standard antenna, which is also oriented in azimuth and elevation for maximum power reception (P_S). The gain is then given by

$$G_R = \frac{P_{\max}}{P_S} G_S$$

The same measurement system should be used for both determinations, and *the transmitter output must remain constant.*

The following conditions must exist in order to achieve accurate results:

1. The field distribution must be uniform.
2. The measurement systems and antennas must be matched.
3. The difference between G_R and G_S should be small (within 10 dbm).

CALIBRATION OF ANTENNA STANDARD   The calibration of the antenna standard requires that two identical antennas be set up as shown in Fig. 12-30. The calibration consists of determining the value of the following factors:

$$G_S = \frac{4\pi R}{\lambda}\sqrt{\frac{P_R}{P_T}}$$

If the measurement system is capable of indicating the ratio P_R/P_T directly, an accuracy of 5% can be achieved. This is very good accuracy considering the multitude of variable conditions which affect the measurement.

The procedure consists of measuring P_R at the receiving antenna and then moving the measuring system to the transmitting antenna to determine P_T. Usually this is repeated several times at various values of R, and the average value of G_S is obtained.

QUESTIONS

1 What is meant by the "resolving power" of a spectrum analyzer?

2 Describe the precautions to be taken against leakage in making MDS measurements.

3 Explain the use of an echo box in checking frequency.

4 Describe the procedure used to calibrate an antenna standard.

Radiac Equipment and Calibration Techniques 13

Radioactivity—the radiations and emanations of nuclear buildup and decay—cannot be detected by any of the human senses. For this reason, the detection and measurement of these quantities must be accomplished with special *radiac* equipment. This term is formed from the initial letters of the words "Radiation Activity, Detection, Identification, and Computation."

As stated in Chapter 3, the term *radiation* and its derivatives, as used in this manual, refer to the electromagnetic by-products of nuclear reactions, and the term *emanations* refers to the particles produced. These particles are often called *particulate* or *corpuscular* radiations in other references.

Instruments used to measure radioactivity depend upon the ionization of various media for their operation. Four classes of ionization media are in common use: (1) gases, (2) photographic emulsions, (3) radio-photoluminescent materials, (4) chemically decomposable materials.

Only survey and laboratory-type instruments are discussed in this manual since personnel-type instruments, such as the film badge and pocket dosimeter, are not precision devices.

PRINCIPLES OF DETECTION

The structure of the atom has been known since the first decade of the present century. Planetary electrons revolve about the central core, or nucleus, at *discrete* distances from the core. The orbits in which the electrons travel are nearly circular in nature and represent certain energy-level relationships. The more-distant orbits represent higher-energy electrons.

Although each electron orbit is considered to be a stationary level, it is possible for the electrons themselves to gain and lose energy. By so doing, it is possible for an electron to accomplish a transfer from one orbit (energy level) to another. A transfer of an electron to a higher-than-normal orbit represents an absorption of energy from some external source; transfer to a lower orbit, a release of energy to the surroundings.

Atoms whose electrons are in a transitional state are said to be *excited*. The transfers may occur in jumps of one orbit at a time or of several orbits simultaneously. Normally an electron which transfers to a higher orbit will remain there for only a short time before returning to its original level, thereby releasing the same amount of energy it initially absorbed.

This *atomic excitation* should not be confused with nuclear excitation—radioactivity—which is governed by entirely different principles.

IONIZATION   Figure 13-1 illustrates the principle of orbital transfer. As shown, the excited electron is absorbing energy so that it moves to higher energy levels (larger orbits). Finally, at some specific distance from the nucleus, the electron has a sufficient amount of energy to "break free" of all restraining forces and moves away from the atom as an individual particle. At this point, *ionization* occurs—the formerly neutral atom now has an excess positive charge. The freed electron may remain free or it may attach itself to a neutral atom depending upon surrounding conditions. If the latter occurs, a second ion is formed, since the previously neutral atom acquires an excess negative charge when the electron becomes attached. It is upon this production of ion-pairs—a positive and a negative ion—that radiac devices depend for their detection and measurement processes.

Ion-pairs are created either by a direct collision between the ionizing particle and the orbital electron or by a transfer of energy impulses from the rapidly moving ionizing particle to the electron, without actual contact. In the case of ionization due to radiations, the orbital electron acquires its excess energy through secondary effects of the electromagnetic radiation.

EMANATIONS The ionizing particles mentioned previously are the by-products of a nuclear reaction. These emanations have various structures and energies. The more commonly encountered emanations are (1) alpha particles, $_2He^4$; (2) beta particles, or electrons; and (3) neutrons.

Ionization by direct collision is shown in Fig. 13-2. The ionizing particle may produce

several ion-pairs as it travels along its path. Each production absorbs some of the initial energy contained by the emanation so that energy is lost at a specific rate.

Since this rate of energy transfer is inversely proportional to the velocity of the ionizing particle squared, fewer ion-pairs will be created by an emanation of higher velocity in a given volume of ionizing medium.

RADIATIONS The predominant, and therefore most important, radiations originating in the nuclei of matter are those in the gamma ray region of the electromagnetic spectrum. These radiations have a higher frequency (shorter wavelength) than X rays.

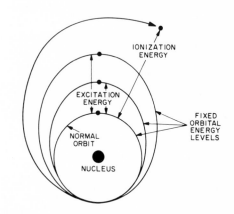

Fig. 13-1 Orbital transfer and freeing of orbital electrons.

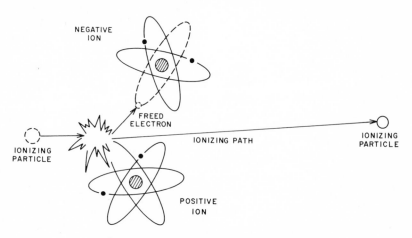

Fig. 13-2 Production of ion-pairs by collision.

All electromagnetic radiations travel as discrete bundles of energy, known as *photons,* with an energy content per photon given by

$$E = hf$$

where h is Planck's constant and f is the frequency of the radiation. Photons give up this energy to surrounding media through numerous complex processes. The three most important processes which account for the absorption of almost 100% of the photon energy are (1) the photoelectric effect, (2) the Compton effect, and (3) pair production.

The first two are reactions between photons and orbital electrons, whereas pair production is a reaction between a photon and an atomic nucleus. All three methods are illustrated in Fig. 13-3.

Figure 13-3A illustrates the photoelectric effect, which occurs for photons of less than 1 Mev energy but greater than the ionization energy of the medium involved. The photon energy in excess of the ionization potential is liberated in the form of kinetic energy associated with the freed electron.

When a photon with an energy in the vicinity of 1 Mev encounters atoms, part of the energy is used to free an orbital electron, and the remainder continues as another photon of lower frequency. This is shown in Fig. 13-3B.

Pair production, which occurs only if the photon has an energy of 1.02 Mev or greater, results in the emanation of two particles from the nucleus of the encountered atom. As shown in Fig. 13-3C, these particles are an electron and a positron (see Table 3-4). The positron eventually unites with a stray electron to form another photon (of lower energy than the first). The intricacies of matter-energy transformations, however, are beyond the scope of this manual. During pair production the atom remains neutral, but the electron which is emitted is capable of producing ionization just as any beta particle would be.

Figure 13-4 shows the relative amount of specific ionization produced by photons of various energies in two absorption media. In the region of 1 Mev, the ionization effect is about the same for all materials since the Compton effect is predominant at this point.

VISUAL TRACKS Although of lesser importance in quantitative measurements and calibrations, visual detection of emanations and radiations *can* be employed. The path of movement, as well as side effects, *can* be recorded photographically. Visual detection is accomplished by using a *cloud chamber,* similar to that originally used by C. T. R. Wilson.

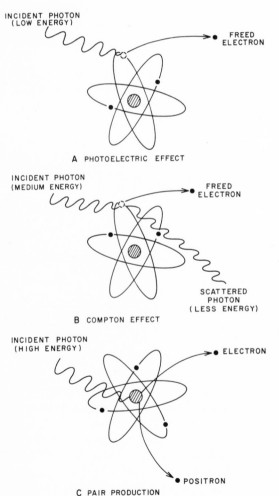

INCIDENT PHOTON
(LOW ENERGY)

FREED
ELECTRON

A PHOTOELECTRIC EFFECT

INCIDENT PHOTON
(MEDIUM ENERGY)

FREED
ELECTRON

SCATTERED
PHOTON
(LESS ENERGY)

B COMPTON EFFECT

INCIDENT PHOTON
(HIGH ENERGY)

ELECTRON

POSITRON

C PAIR PRODUCTION

Fig. 13-3 Gamma-atom reactions.

Figure 13-5 illustrates the basic principles of the cloud chamber. Dustfree air is saturated by the vapor of a liquid by rapidly withdrawing the piston. Ions which are formed in the air by the passage of emanations and radiations act as condensation nuclei, causing some of the vapor to condense. The close array of fine droplets, called a *cloud track*, traces out the path of the ionizing particle or radiation. A light beam directed through the chamber causes the cloud track to be visible as a white trace against the dark background of the piston.

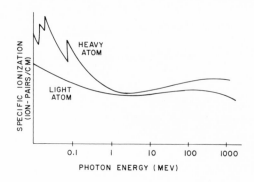

Fig. 13-4 Total ionization by gamma photon.

INSTRUMENT CONSTRUCTION AND OPERATION*

Under normal circumstances, negative ions will eventually lose their excess electrons and positive ions will gain back their lost electrons, thereby returning to the neutral state. If oppositely charged electrodes, however, are placed in the ionizing medium, the positive ions will migrate to one electrode and the negative ions to the other. The number of ion-pairs collected by the electrodes will be proportional to the potential applied to the electrodes, as shown in Fig. 13-6. The curve is a plot of current versus applied voltage. The current flows in the external circuitry between the electrodes and can be measured by a milliammeter. It consists of the excess electrons of positive ions given off at the anode where these ions collect. The curve shows three distinct regions of operation—a slight increase in region *OA*, linearity in region *AB*, and a rapid rise in region *BC*. Each of these regions is particularly suited for a specific type of measuring device.

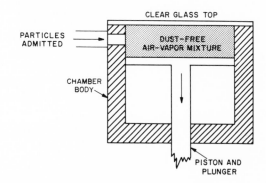

Fig. 13-5 Principles of Wilson cloud chamber.

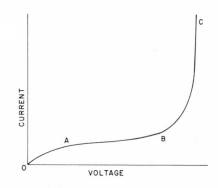

Fig. 13-6 Ionization chamber characteristic.

IONIZATION CHAMBERS   Although there are many sizes and shapes of counter-type ionization chambers, as well as different names for them, the principle of operation is the same for all. Figure 13-7 shows the basic elements

° Parts of this section are taken from James R. Spencer, "Radiac," *Philco TechRep Division Bulletin*, vol. 10, no. 2.

which make up a typical counter chamber. The chamber consists of a thin-wall metallic cylinder and a coaxially mounted anode wire. The cylinder is the cathode of the chamber. The chamber is enclosed in a thin-wall glass tube that is filled with a special gas and sealed. A typical gas used in counter chamber tubes is a mixture of approximately 90% neon

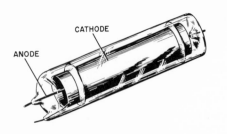

Fig. 13-7 Typical ionization chamber or Geiger-Muller tube.

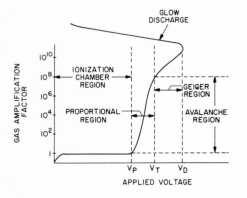

Fig. 13-8 Gas amplification factor versus applied voltage.

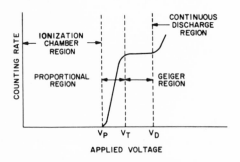

Fig. 13-9 Geiger-Muller tube characteristic curve.

and 10% amyl acetate at a pressure of about 10 cm of mercury. Such chamber tubes are commonly referred to as *Geiger-Muller tubes,* or *G-M tubes.*

One of the most important characteristics

of the G-M tube is known as the *gas amplification factor.* This factor is an expression of the inherent increase in ions associated with all gas-filled electronic tubes and is proportional to the potential applied to the electrodes.

It has already been stated that the ions produced in a gas-filled space between oppositely charged electrodes migrate toward the electrodes, where they will be collected. The velocity at which this migration occurs is dependent upon the electrode potential. If the electrodes have a large enough potential, the ions will be accelerated to such a degree that they will have sufficient kinetic energy to produce secondary ionization when they collide with other atoms of the ionizing medium.

The gas amplification factor is defined as the ratio of the number of electrons flowing from the anode to the number of electrons freed by the initial ionizing event.

Figure 13-8 is a plot of gas amplification factor versus applied voltage for a typical G-M tube. When a voltage less than V_P is applied to the G-M tube, the electrons and ions produced by the incoming radiation slowly drift to the anode and cathode. Their movement is too slow to produce any additional ionization by collision; therefore, the number of electrons flowing from the central anode equals the number initially produced. For this condition the tube has a gas amplification factor of 1, and *only the alpha particle has sufficient ionizing power to produce a recognizable current pulse.*

When the voltage across the tube is increased above V_P but kept below V_T, secondary ionization takes place as a result of electron-gas molecule collisions. This process is cumulative, and an *avalanche* of electrons reaches the central anode. For this condition, the amplitude of the resulting pulse is proportional to the number of electrons produced in the initial ionizing event.

If the voltage across the G-M tube is raised above V_T, the tube will enter a voltage region in which the size of the output pulse is independent of the number of ions formed in the initial ionizing event. The minimum voltage at which this occurs is called the *threshold voltage, V_T,* and the voltage region in which all pulses formed are of the same height is called the *Geiger region.*

Another way to illustrate the Geiger region is to plot the characteristic curve of a G-M tube. If a G-M tube is exposed to a constant radiation intensity and the number of pulses per second plotted against the applied voltage, a characteristic curve similar to the one shown in Fig. 13-9 results. As the voltage across the tube is raised through the proportional region, the counting rate increases until the threshold voltage, V_T, is reached.

Certain amplifying and counting circuitry must be used with the G-M tube in order to make useful the current impulses created by each ionization. The motion of positive and negative ions is relatively slow—1 or 2 cm/sec. This sluggishness is a result of the weight of the atoms. Since an electron weighs less than 1/1000 of the weight of the lightest monatomic gas, the mobility of these particles is correspondingly greater.

If the slower current pulses due to ion-electrode collisions were counted, the device would respond only to very slow radioactive disintegration processes. However, if the G-M tube or other appropriate ionization chamber is filled with a gas which does not allow the freed electrons to unite with neutral atoms to form negative ions, a much faster activity can be measured. Under these circumstances, ion-pairs are not produced. Each ionization consists, instead, of the production of a positive ion and a free electron. The latter particle speeds to the anode of the chamber tube to produce a current pulse.

The electrical energy, and therefore the amplitude, of each pulse is proportional to the number of ionizations produced by the individual particles or photons being counted. The rate at which the pulse increases (rise time) is dependent upon the direction of travel of the emanation or radiation relative to the chamber axis.

GEIGER-MULLER COUNTERS The Geiger-Muller (or simply Geiger) counter operates with the highest chamber-electrode voltages of any detector, as shown by the Geiger region in Fig. 13-8 and Fig. 13-9. When a particle or photon enters the chamber, the initial ionization triggers an electron avalanche which is so great in magnitude that the potential between the electrodes temporarily exceeds the discharge voltage V_D. This results in a continuous discharge through the chamber tube —all the gas in the tube is ionized. This action occurs in about 1 microsecond. Since the continuous discharge state represents the maximum current flow through the chamber tube, every pulse will be equal and will have the maximum possible amplitude. This independence of pulse height on the number of ionizations produced by each individual particle or photon is an advantage of the Geiger counter.

An immediate disadvantage results, however. As long as the G-M tube is in a totally ionized state, it is insensitive to further bombardment by particles or photons. This condition persists until the freed electrons and positive ions *recombine* to produce the original neutral gaseous state. The recombination time is on the order of 10^{-4} sec so that disintegrations occurring at a more rapid rate cannot be measured by the Geiger counter. This disadvantage can be partially overcome by using a *quenching circuit* such as the one shown in Fig. 13-10. This circuit imposes a square-wave voltage depression upon the chamber tube anode each time a pulse occurs. Self-quenching counter tubes

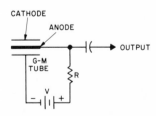

Fig. 13-10 Fundamental Geiger-Muller tube quenching circuit.

are also available. These ionization chambers employ special gaseous constituents to shorten the recombination time.

Figure 13-11A gives the functional block diagram of the Geiger counter; Fig. 13-11B shows a typical unit. The G-M tube produces a negative output pulse for each initial ionizing event. The amplified pulses are fed to the integrator and also to an earphone for aural monitoring. Each pulse produces a click in

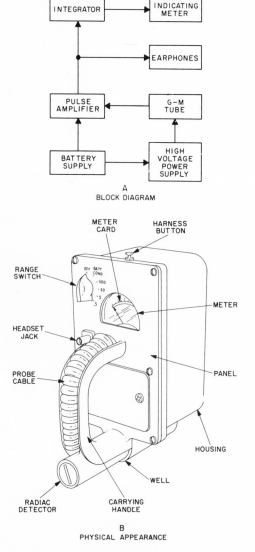

A
BLOCK DIAGRAM

B
PHYSICAL APPEARANCE

Fig. 13-11 Typical Geiger counter.

the earphone. The integrator averages the pulses into a varying d-c voltage which is proportional to the number of pulses created by the G-M tube. The indicating meter measures this varying voltage and is graduated to give direct readings in milliroentgens per hour.

Although capable of detecting almost every form of ionizing radiation and emanation, commercial Geiger counters are generally utilized for beta-particle and gamma-ray determinations. In order to exclude the alpha particles and heavier nuclides, the beta and gamma quantities are admitted to the G-M tube through a slitlike *window*. The window is a thin sheet of metal of sufficient thickness to stop the heavier nuclides before they reach the ionizing medium. Beta and gamma penetration power is such that these quantities are scarcely affected by the window material.

PROPORTIONAL COUNTERS When the ionization chamber is operated in the voltage region between V_T and V_D as shown in Fig. 13-8 and Fig. 13-9, the chamber with its associated circuitry is termed a *proportional counter*. Under this condition, the final number of electrons is equal to the initial number of electrons released multiplied by the gas amplification factor. The final indication of radioactivity then is greater than the actual value present by the same amount. The indicator scale is usually graduated in terms of the initial ionizing event in order to make it a direct-reading device.

Commercial proportional counters are generally designed to detect alpha and beta particles in the presence of high-intensity gamma rays and to distinguish between alpha and beta particles. In general, however, these devices will detect all forms of ionizing radioactivity.

The reliability of proportional counters and their ability to discriminate against undesired *background radioactivity*, as well as the shorter duration of the pulses produced, has resulted in widespread supplanting of the Geiger counter. Since the pulses produced by the proportional counter are on the order of

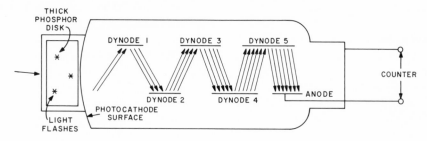

Fig. 13-12 Photomultiplier tube for scintillation counter.

only a few microseconds, this type of counter can detect reactions at a much higher rate than the Geiger counter.

SCINTILLATION COUNTERS

Scintillation is the liberation of photons of visible light frequencies when certain substances are struck by alpha and beta particles or gamma-frequency photons. The visible light photons are produced by normal atomic excitation as previously described. The orbital electrons of the fluorescent material absorb the impact energies of emanations and radiations and move to higher-energy orbits. Almost instantly the excited electrons drop back to their normal orbits and release their excess energy as visible light. Each impact produces a single flash of light.

Different substances fluoresce more for one type of nuclear emanation or radiation than for another. As a result, several different *phosphors* have been developed for various uses. For example, zinc sulfide fluoresces well for alpha particles; anthracene for beta particles; and thallium-activated sodium iodide for gamma rays. The emission properties of various phosphors are listed in Appendix C-11.

In actual applications, the phosphor is used in connection with a *photomultiplier tube,* as shown in Fig. 13-12. The light of a single scintillation—too feeble to measure, in itself—falls on the cathode of the multiplier tube. A number of electrons are released via normal photoelectric effects. This number is greatly increased by secondary emission from the successive stages, or *dynodes,* of the multiplier tube. Thus, a measurable current pulse is produced.

A scintillation counter is capable of responding to disintegration rates on the order of a million per second. For this reason it is indispensable in high-rate reaction determinations. Because of the high sensitivity of thallium-activated sodium iodide to gamma rays, this instrument is the most widely used radiac device for the detection and measurement of gamma radiation.

SPECIFIC COUNTING TECHNIQUES

ALPHA COUNTING Selective counting of alpha particles in the presence of other radioactivity depends upon the relatively large rate of energy loss compared to that of other emanations or radiations. Thus, a pulse discriminator can be used to pass only the higher-amplitude alpha pulses.

Scintillation counters are not particularly suited to selective alpha counting.

BETA COUNTING Selective counting of beta particles can be accomplished by excluding surrounding alpha particles with a sufficiently thick metal shield. The beta pulses will be larger than the gamma pulses so that the latter can be selectively eliminated. Proportional counters yield good results, although a certain percentage of lower-energy beta particles will not be counted.

Scintillation counters are ideally suited for determinations involving rapid rate reactions.

The electrons (beta particles), however, must have sufficient energy to produce light intensities greater than the inherent noise in photomultiplier tubes.

GAMMA COUNTING   Gamma detection is accomplished by the secondary effects of three processes—the photoelectric effect, the Compton effect, and pair-production—as previously explained. Materials of heavy atomic number Z must be used in the counter-tube walls. The ionizing gas must also have a high Z.

Selective gamma counting is accomplished by using shields of sufficient thickness to block any alpha or beta particles while offering negligible attenuation to the gamma radiation.

The principal problem in efficient gamma detection is the low rate of energy loss for gamma photons. This can be overcome, in part, by using a multiple-plate ionization chamber. A heavy gas under high pressure is utilized as the ionizing medium.

Scintillation counters are the most efficient devices for gamma determinations. As many as 28% of the total gamma photons will produce scintillations in a thallium-activated

sodium iodide plate 1 in. thick for 5-Mev photons. As many as 43% of 1-Mev photons will be counted in the same plate.

NEUTRON DETECTION AND COUNTING

Since they have no inherent charges, neutrons are not capable of producing direct ionization, nor do they create very many ions by colliding with orbital electrons. For these reasons, *direct* neutron detection and measurement by the previously discussed principles is impossible.

The lack of charge, however, allows neutrons to penetrate the electrostatic and electromagnetic fields surrounding all nuclei. This results in the fact that many neutrons enter into *nuclear reactions* with surrounding materials. The products of nearly all nuclear reactions include alpha and/or beta particles along with the possibility of gamma radiation. It is possible to relate the number of nuclear by-products to the original number of neutrons present, thereby providing an indirect method of neutron measurement using the instruments already discussed.

CALIBRATION TECHNIQUES

The indicating devices used with ionization chambers in radiac instruments must respond to the ionization currents produced or to a proportional current. These devices are electrometers, galvanometers, or micro-ammeters, all of which are described in Chapter 6. The latter two are used for relatively large currents.

The maximum ranges of emanations and radiations are of importance in calibration techniques. *Feather's rule* for beta particles gives the maximum range as

$$R = \frac{0.543E - 0.16 \text{ cm}}{\rho}$$

where E is the beta energy in Mev and ρ is the source density in gm/cm³. This equation gives an approximation for any type of absorbing material. Alpha emanations are

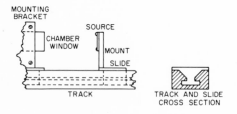

Fig. 13-13   Calibration track arrangement.

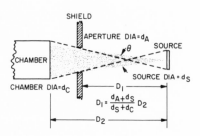

Fig. 13-14   Limiting scattering effects.

stopped by 2.5 cm of air and by thin sheets of solid material. Neutrons and gamma rays have a very large maximum range, depending upon their energy content. The energy content of these two radioactive by-products decreases inversely as the square of the distance they travel.

Errors introduced in counting techniques include the recombination of ion-pairs, *back-scattering effects,* and particle absorption (or gamma attenuation) in the walls of the ionization chamber. Each of these will be discussed as the need arises.

There will always be a small current flow in the detector circuit due to *background radiation.* Cosmic radiation will produce about three ion-pairs/cm³ in an unshielded ionization chamber at sea level. Local radioactivity in the earth itself may contribute as much as ten times this amount.

The calibration of field radiac devices is most easily accomplished by using a radioactive standard which produces the proper type of emanation or radiation. Since the standard source disintegrates at a known rate and since, ideally, each disintegration should produce one ion-pair, the efficiency of the device under test can be established and an appropriate correction factor can be calculated. A typical setup for making the calibration is shown in Fig. 13-13. In general, the correction factor is given by

$$C = \frac{A_s}{A_m d}$$

where A_s is the standard activity, A_m is the activity reading of the radiac meter, and d is the distance between the source and the detector. The correction factor C will contain several components because of the errors previously described as well as any error introduced by misadjustments within the detector circuitry. The variable resistors in the circuitry associated with the instrument range being calibrated can be adjusted until the value of C is a minimum.

The scattering error can be reduced by limiting the solid angle subtended by the counter chamber. This is accomplished by inserting a shield with a small aperture between the source and chamber. The relationship between the aperture opening and the shield position is shown in Fig. 13-14. The shield should be of sufficient thickness to stop the particles being counted.

The standard activity must be corrected to compensate for decay due to the half-life principle. This can be accomplished by consulting Fig. 4-12. The value of T depends upon the source material being used and will be specified by the distributor. To find the proper value along the horizontal axis in Fig. 4-12, divide the value of T by the length of time which has elapsed since the last certification of the source.

The precise determination of source activity depends upon *absolute counting methods,* which are beyond the scope of this manual.

The efficiency of the Geiger counter should be on the order of 98% for emanation counting. For gamma detection, the figure may be very low. Scintillation counter efficiency depends upon the phosphor used, as well as upon the efficiency of the photomultiplier tube. High percentages are usually encountered in emanation determinations, whereas gamma counting seldom exceeds 50%. Neutron detection is a low-efficiency process in all instances.

EXERCISE   Calibration of a Radiac Meter*

MATERIAL REQUIRED

1 Radiac set to be calibrated AN/PDR-27 or equivalent

2 Accurate radium source with minimum weight of 2 mg.

* Based on Navy calibration procedure.

3 Accurate measuring tape or rule

4 A special radiac set housing containing four holes which give access to the calibration controls

WARNING The calibration of this instrument requires the use of a radium source. Extreme caution should be exercised in the handling of this source. Follow all radiation safety precautions and wear a dosimeter. Perform the calibration as rapidly as possible to avoid prolonged exposure to the radiation.

PROCEDURE

The calibration must be performed in an area free of large metallic objects. This precaution is necessary to avoid inaccuracies caused by secondary radiation effects.

1 Remove the radiac set housing and replace with the special calibration housing. Check to see that the beta shield covers the end of the radiac detector, then slip the detector into the well of the radiac set.

2 Set up the equipment as shown in Fig. 13–15. The following is for a 2 mg. source. For a different source see Step 16.

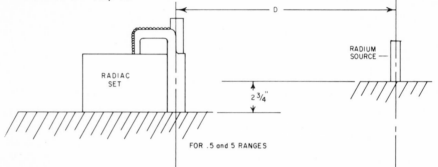

Fig. 13-15 For 0.5 and 5 ranges.

3 Set the RANGE switch on the radiac set to 0.5.

4 Adjust the spacing of D to 83.70 "± ¼."

5 The radiac meter should read within ±10% of 0.4 milliroentgen/hr. If not, adjust R 110 for the proper reading.

6 Set the RANGE switch on the radiac set to 5.

7 Adjust the spacing of D to 25.45 "± ¼."

8 The radiac meter should read within ± 10% of 4 milliroentgen/hr. If not, adjust R 104 for the proper reading.

9 Set up the equipment as shown in Fig. 13-16.

10 Set the RANGE switch on the radiac set to 50.

11 Adjust the spacing D to 7.620 "± ⅛."

12 The radiac meter should read within ± 10% of 40 milliroentgen/hr. If not, adjust R 106 for the proper reading.

13 Set the RANGE switch on the radiac set to 500.

14 Adjust the spacing D to 1.795 "± 0.025."

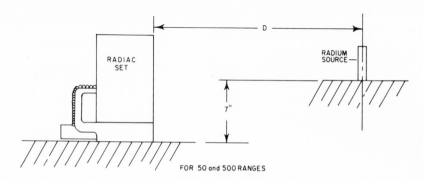

Fig. 13-16 For 50 and 500 ranges.

15   The radiac meter should read within ± 10% of 400 milliroentgen/hr. If not, adjust R 108 for the proper reading.

16   If the weight of the source is not 2 mg. use the following formula to find the relation between meter indication and distance between the radiac set and the radium soruce:

$$I = \frac{55,300 \times W}{D^2}$$

where   I = meter indication in milliroentgens per hour
             W = weight of the radium source in milligrams
             D = distance between the radiac set and the radium source in inches

17   Use the results of Step 16 and the procedure of Steps 3–15 for the calibration.

Appendix A

A-1 POWER RATIO UNITS

THE DECIBEL

The decibel, or db, is the unit which has been widely adopted in radio, sound amplification, and other branches of electronics to express logarithmically the ratio between two power or voltage levels, and less commonly the ratio between two current levels.

Although power, voltage, or current amplification, or the magnitude of a particular power, voltage, or current, relative to a given reference value, can be expressed as an ordinary ratio, the db has been adopted because of its much greater convenience.

Because the response of the human ear to sound waves is approximately proportional to the logarithm of the energy of the sound wave and is not proportional to the energy itself, the use of a logarithmic unit permits a closer approach to the reaction of the human ear. In other words, the impression gained by the human ear as to the magnitude of sound is roughly proportional to the logarithm of the actual energy contained in the sound; hence the logarithmic unit provides a convenient method for comparison. Thus, for example, a change in the gain of an amplifier, expressed in decibels, provides a much better index of the effect of the sound upon the ear than it does if expressed as a power or voltage ratio.

The small numbers which may be used to indicate in decibels the gain or loss which corresponds to large power, voltage, or current ratios, and the ease with which the db gains or losses may be added or subtracted are two additional important advantages in the use of the decibel.

The ratio, expressed in decibels, of two amounts of power, P_2 and P_1, is given by the following:

$$\text{db} = 10 \ \log_{10} \frac{P_2}{P_1}$$

The ratio, expressed in decibels, of two voltages, E_2 and E_1, or two currents, I_2 and I_1, is given by

$$\text{db} = 20 \ \log_{10} \frac{E_2}{E_1} , \quad \text{or} \quad \text{db} = 20 \log_{10} \frac{I_2}{I_1}$$

The decibel is based upon *power* ratios; hence the preceding formula for deriving decibel equivalents from voltage or current ratios is true *only if the impedance is the same for both values of voltage or current.* For example, if the preceding formulas were used, it would not be possible to obtain correct information on the gain of a given amplifier if the input impedance differed from that of the output. Hence, in circuits where the impedances differ, the expressions for decibel equivalents of voltage and current ratios become

$$\text{db} = 20 \ \log_{10} \frac{E_2 \sqrt{R_1}}{E_1 \sqrt{R_2}}$$

and $\quad \text{db} = 20 \ \log_{10} \dfrac{I_2 \sqrt{R_2}}{I_1 \sqrt{R_1}}$

It has been stressed that the decibel always refers to the *ratio* of two levels of power, voltage, or current. It is very often desirable, however, to express a single level or quantity of power, voltage, or current in decibels, as for example in transmission-line work.

VOLUME UNIT   Volume unit, abbreviated VU, is the name assigned to a unit which is used to measure relative volume of complex audio signals. Not to be confused with dbm, which is used in reference to a steady sine-wave audio signal, the volume unit is used in conjunction with such complex audio signals as voice, music, etc. A special meter calibrated in VU is used to measure volume-level changes. This meter, which is a root-mean-square type of instrument with a copper oxide rectifier, can be used to measure the volume of audio signals between 35 and 10,000 cps. When a steady sine-wave signal level is measured, the meter reading is in dbm.

OTHER UNITS

In addition to dbm, discussed previously, there are four other commonly used decibel units. These are dbw, dbv, dba, and dbRN.

1. DBW: Whereas the dbm unit has a "zero level" of 1 milliwatt, the dbw has a "zero level" of 1 watt. When the dbw unit is used, decibels above or below this level are termed $\pm$dbw. The following relationship exists between these units:

$$\text{dbw} = 30 \text{ dbm}$$

2. DBV: This unit expresses the response of a microphone at a given frequency in db. A reference level of 0 db is equal to 1 volt (dbv) when 1 dyne per square centimeter sound pressure is exerted on a microphone. When this unit is used, decibels above or below the reference level are termed $\pm$dbv.

3. DBA: This unit is used to express the relationship between the noise interference produced by a noise frequency (or a band of noise frequencies) and a standard reference-noise power level. Actually, two standard reference levels are used. One has been established as -90 dbm (10^{-12} watt) at a frequency of 1000 cycles, using a Western Electric Type 144 handset as the standard equipment. Another was established later as -85 dbm ($10^{-11.5}$ watt), using an improved handset, the Western Electric Type F1A. Therefore, the unit dba has two standard reference (zero) levels, -90 dbm and -85 dbm. When either is specified, the number of the handset used in conjunction with the dba value is given to distinguish the reference level.

4. DBRN: This unit is identical numerically to the dba, having a reference level of -90 dbm, as established using the 144 handset.

THE NEPER

The neper is a unit used to measure difference in power level, and in this respect performs the same function as the decibel; here, however, the similarity between these two units ends because they are based on different systems of logarithms. The decibel is based on common logarithms, to the base 10. The neper is based on Napierian logarithms, to the base ϵ, and is not generally used in English-speaking countries. The following conversion relationship exists between the two units:

$$1 \text{ db} = 0.115 \text{ neper}$$

$$1 \text{ neper} = 8.686 \text{ db}$$

A-2 ATTENUATOR AND MATCHING ARRANGEMENTS

Pad circuits can be computed using the network matching and attenuation nomograph. The following three examples illustrate how this nomograph may be used:

ATTENUATING PAD

Conditions: $Z_1 = Z_2$, and $R_a = R_b$

1. With straightedge, connect Z on scale A

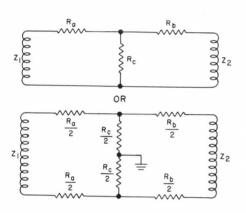

Fig. A-1 Attenuating pad.

to required db loss on scale C. Read R_c on scale F.

2. Connect Z on scale A to required db loss on scale D. Read $R_a + R_c$ on scale F.

3. Subtract R_c from the total, leaving R_a.

4. $R_a = R_b$.

MINIMUM LOSS MATCHING PAD

Conditions: $Z_1 > Z_2$, and $R_b = 0$

1. With straightedge, connect Z_1 on scale A to Z_2 on scale F. Read db loss on scale E.

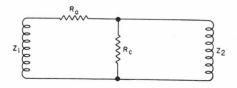

Fig. A-2 Minimum loss pad.

2. Connect Z_1 on scale B to Z_2 on scale F. Read $\sqrt{Z_1 Z_2}$ on scale A.

3. Connect $\sqrt{Z_1 Z_2}$ on scale A to db loss on scale C. Read R_c on scale F.

4. Connect Z_1 on scale A to db loss on scale D. Read $R_a + R_c$ on scale F.

5. Subtract R_c, leaving R_a.

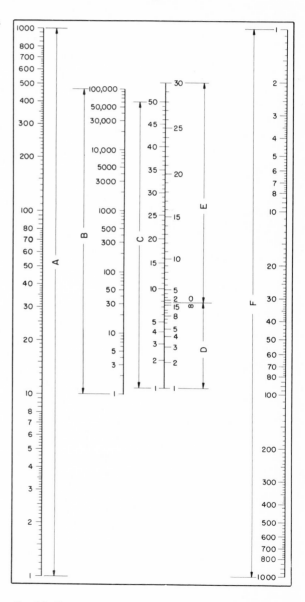

Fig. A-3 Nomograph for determining values of network matching and attenuating pads.

MATCHING AND ATTENUATING PAD

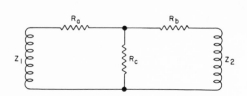

Fig. A-4 Dual-purpose pad.

Conditions: $Z_1 \neq Z_2$

1. With straightedge, connect Z_1 on scale F to Z_2 on scale B. Read $\sqrt{Z_1 Z_2}$ on scale A.

2. Connect $\sqrt{Z_1 Z_2}$ on scale A to required db loss on scale C. Read R_c on scale F.

3. Connect Z_1 on scale A to db on scale D. Read $R_a + R_c$ on scale F.

4. Subtract R_c, leaving R_a.

5. Connect Z_2 on scale A to db on scale D. Read $R_b + R_c$ on scale F.

6. Subtract R_c, leaving R_b.

MICROWAVE MATCHING

The standing-wave ratio (SWR) is the measure of the mismatch between the antenna (load) and the line, and is the ratio of instantaneous maximum current or voltage to the instantaneous minimum current or voltage. Thus,

$$\text{SWR} = \frac{i_{max}}{i_{min}} = \frac{e_{max}}{e_{min}}$$

If the SWR is known, the chart may be used to determine the length and placement of stubs in an r-f transmission line, when measuring from the I_{max} point nearest the load. A shorted stub, which is generally preferred, is placed toward the load from I_{max}; an open stub is placed toward the source from I_{max}. In the chart, A indicates the length of a shorted stub, B the length of an open stub, and P the location of the stub on the transmission line, measured from I_{max}.

A more complete discussion of microwave matching procedures is given in Appendix D-4.

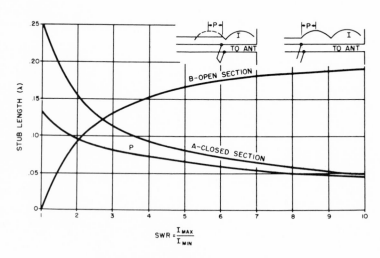

Fig. A-5 Chart for microwave matching stubs.

Appendix B

B-1 METRIC CONVERSION TABLE

Original Value	Desired value (move decimal)							
	Mega	Kilo	Units	Deci	Centi	Milli	Micro	Pico
Mega		+3	+6	+7	+8	+9	+12	+18
Kilo	−3		+3	+4	+5	+6	+9	+15
Units	−6	−3		+1	+2	+3	+6	+12
Deci	−7	−4	−1		+1	+2	+5	+11
Centi	−8	−5	−2	−1		+1	+4	+10
Milli	−9	−6	−3	−2	−1		+3	+9
Micro	−12	−9	−6	−5	−4	−3		+6
Pico	−18	−15	−12	−11	−10	−9	−6	

\+ move decimal to right.
− move decimal to left.

B-2 GENERAL CONVERSION FACTORS

To Convert		Multiply by	Conversely Multiply by
From	To		
Electrical and magnetic			
Ampere-hours	Coulombs	3.600×10^3	2.778×10^{-1}
Ampere turns	Gilberts	1.257	0.7958
Ampere turns/in.	Oersteds	0.495	2.02
Degrees (angle)	Radians	1.745×10^{-2}	57.30
Maxwells/sq in.	Gauss (maxwells/sq cm)	0.155	6.45
Webers	Maxwells	1.0×10^8	1.0×10^{-8}
Energy and heat			
BTU	Foot-pounds	778.3	1.285×10^{-3}
BTU	Joules	1.055×10^3	9.480×10^{-4}
BTU	Kilogram-calories	0.252	3.97
Ergs	Foot-pounds	7.367×10^{-8}	1.356×10^7
Horsepower (metric—542.5 ft-lb/sec)	BTU/min	41.83	2.390×10^{-2}
Horsepower (metric—542.5 ft-lb/sec)	Kilogram-calories/min	10.54	9.485×10^{-2}
Horsepower (550 ft-lb/sec)	BTU/min	42.41	2.357×10^{-2}
Joules	Foot-pounds	0.7376	1.356
Joules	Ergs	10^7	10^{-7}
Kilowatt-hours	BTU	3.413×10^3	2.930×10^{-1}
Lumens/sq ft	Foot-candles	1	1
Watts	BTU/min	5.689×10^{-2}	17.58
Watts	Ergs/sec	10^7	10^{-7}
Force and power			
Dynes	Pounds	2.248×10^{-6}	4.448×10^5
Foot-pounds	Horsepower-hours	5.05×10^{-7}	1.98×10^6
Foot-pounds	Kilowatt-hours	3.766×10^{-7}	2.665×10^6
Grams	Dynes	980.7	1.020×10^{-3}
Horsepower (550 ft-lb/sec)	Watts	745.7	1.341×10^{-3}
Horsepower (metric—542.5 ft-lb/sec)	Horsepower (550 ft-lb/sec)	0.9863	1.014
Nepers	Decibels	8.686	0.1151
Poundals	Dynes	1.383×10^4	7.233×10^{-5}
Watts	Foot-pounds/min	44.26	2.260×10^{-2}

To Convert		Multiply by	Conversely Multiply by
From	To		
Area, length, and volume			
Acres	Square feet	4.356×10^4	2.296×10^{-5}
Circular mils	Square centimeters	5.067×10^{-6}	1.973×10^5
Circular mils	Square mils	0.7854	1.273
Cubic feet	Gallons (liquid U.S.)	7.481	0.1337
Cubic feet	Liters	28.32	3.531×10^{-2}
Cubic feet	Tons (U.S. shipping)	0.025	40
Cubic inches	Cubic centimeters	16.39	6.102×10^{-2}
Cubic inches	Cubic meters	1.639×10^{-5}	6.102×10^4
Cubic meters	Cubic yards	1.308	0.7646
Fathoms	Feet	6.000	0.1667
Feet	Centimeters	30.48	3.281×10^{-2}
Gallons (liquid U.S.)	Cubic meters	3.785×10^{-3}	2.642×10^2
Gallons (liquid U.S.)	Gallons (liquid British)	0.8327	1.201
Inches	Centimeters	2.540	0.3937
Inches	Mils	1000	0.001
Kilometers	Feet	3281	3.048×10^{-4}
Leagues	Miles	3	0.33
Liters	Cubic centimeters	1000	0.001
Liters	Cubic inches	61.02	1.639×10^{-2}
Liters	Gallons (liquid U.S.)	0.2642	3.785
Meters	Yards	1.094	0.9144
Miles (nautical)*	Feet	6076.103	1.646×10^{-4}
Miles (nautical)*	Kilometers	1.852	0.5396
Miles (statute)	Feet	5280	1.894×10^{-4}
Miles (statute)	Kilometers	1.609	0.6214
Miles (statute)	Miles (nautical)*	0.8688	1.151
Square inches	Circular mils	1.273×10^6	7.854×10^{-7}
Square inches	Square centimeters	6.452	0.1550
Square miles	Acres	640	1.562×10^{-3}
Weight			
Grams	Ounces	3.527×10^{-2}	28.35
Kilograms	Tons, long (2240 lb)	9.842×10^{-4}	1016
Kilograms	Tons, short (2000 lb)	1.102×10^{-3}	907.2
Kilograms	Pounds	2.205	0.4536
Poundals	Pounds	3.108×10^{-2}	32.17
Slugs	Pounds	32.17	3.108×10^{-2}
Tons, long (2240 lb)	Tons, short (2000 lb)	1.120	0.8929
Velocity and acceleration			
Centimeters/sec	Feet/min	1.919	0.508
Centimeters/sec²	Feet/sec²	3.246×10^{-2}	30.8
Meters/min	Knots (nautical miles/hr*)	3.24×10^{-2}	30.866
Meters/min	Kilometers/hr	0.06000	16.67
Miles/hr	Feet/min	88	1.136×10^{-2}
Miles/hr	Knots (nautical miles/hr*)	0.8686	1.1508
Miles/hr	Kilometers/hr	1.609	0.6214
Miscellaneous			
Arc in degrees	Arc in mils	17.778	5.62×10^{-2}
Atmospheres	Pounds/sq in.	14.70	6.804×10^{-2}
Centigrade	Fahrenheit	$32 + (C° \times 9/5)$	$5/9 (F° - 32)$
Kelvin	Centigrade	$K° - 273$	$C° + 273$
Log_e N	Log_{10} N	0.4343	2.303
Rankine	Fahrenheit	$R° - 460$	$F° + 460$

* On July 1, 1954, the United States nautical mile was changed from 6080.20 ft to 6076.103 ft; hence it is now the same as the International Nautical Mile.

B-3 POWER TO DBM CONVERSION CHART

APPENDIX B-3
POWER TO DBM CONVERSION CHART

B-4 GRAVITATIONAL CORRECTIONS FOR MANOMETER CALIBRATION

Latitude (degrees)	g (m/sec^2)	Elevation (feet)	Subtract from g (m/sec^2)
0	9.78039	0	—
10	9.78195	1000	0.00094
20	9.78641	2000	0.00188
25	9.78960	3000	0.00282
30	9.79329	4000	0.00376
35	9.79737	5000	0.00470
40	9.80171	6000	0.00564
45	9.80621	7000	0.00658
50	9.81071	8000	0.00752
55	9.81507	9000	0.00846
60	9.81918	10000	0.00940

B-5 TEMPERATURE CORRECTIONS FOR BAROMETER CALIBRATION

Elevation (feet)	Mean atmospheric temperature, °C						
	−29	−17.8	−6.7	4.45	15.5	26.7	37.8
0	3.3	3.04	3.04	2.8	2.8	2.54	2.54
1000	3.04	3.04	2.8	2.8	2.54	2.54	2.54
2000	3.04	2.8	2.8	2.54	2.54	2.54	2.28
3000	2.8	2.8	2.54	2.54	2.54	2.28	2.28
4000	2.8	2.54	2.54	2.54	2.28	2.03	2.03
5000	2.54	2.54	2.54	2.28	2.28	2.03	2.03
6000	2.54	2.54	2.28	2.28	2.03	2.03	2.03
7000	2.54	2.28	2.28	2.28	2.03	2.03	2.03

B-6 PARTIAL STEM EMERSION CORRECTION FACTORS* (THERMO METER CALIBRATION)

MERCURY-IN-GLASS

Temperature $(T + T_0)/2$ (°C)	Glass Types				
	Verre dur	Jena† 16[III]	Jena‡ 59[III]	Jena 1565[III]	Jena combustion
50	0.000158	0.000158	0.000164	0.000172	0.000164
100	0.000158	0.000158	0.000164	0.000172	0.000164
150	0.000158	0.000158	0.000165	0.000173	0.000165
200	0.000159	0.000159	0.000167	0.000175	0.000167
250	—	0.000161	0.000170	0.000177	0.000171
300	—	0.000164	0.000174	0.000180	0.000174
350	—	—	0.000177	0.000184	0.000178
400	—	—	0.000182	0.000188	0.000182
450	—	—	0.000187	0.000194	0.000188
500	—	—	0.000195	0.000200	0.000195

OTHER LIQUID-IN-GLASS TYPES

Temperature $(T + T_0)/2$ (°C)	Liquid		
	Pentane	Toluene	Alcohol
−180	0.0009	—	—
−160	0.0009	—	—
−140	0.0009	—	—
−120	0.0010	—	—
−100	0.0010	—	—
−80	0.0010	0.0009	0.0010
−60	0.0011	0.0009	0.0010
−40	0.0012	0.0010	0.0010
−20	0.0013	0.0010	0.0010
0	0.0014	0.0010	0.0010
20	0.0015	0.0011	0.0010

* Taken from International Critical Tables, J. Opt. Soc. Am. and Rev. Sci. Inst., 6, (1922) 958.
† Data for Jena 16[III] glass may be used for Corning normal thermometer glass.
‡ Data for Jena 59[III] may be used for Corning borosilicate thermometer glass. For computations in Fahrenheit temperature, the correction factor is 5/9 of the tabulated value.

B-7   VSWR-REFLECTION COEFFICIENT CONVERSION CHART

(Courtesy, Narda Microwave Corporation)

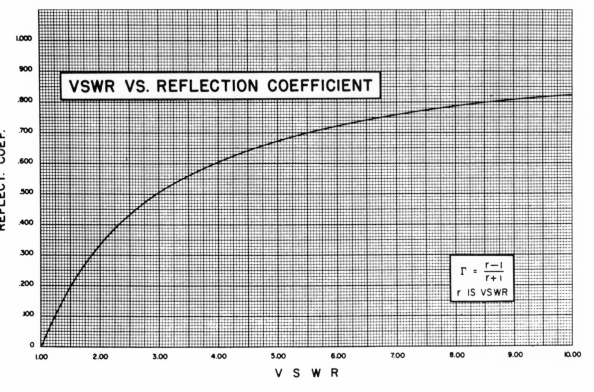

B-8   VOLTAGE, CURRENT AND POWER RATIO CONVERSION CHART

(Courtesy, Narda Microwave Corporation)

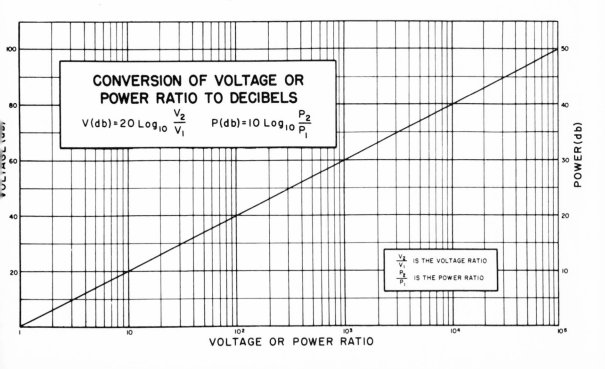

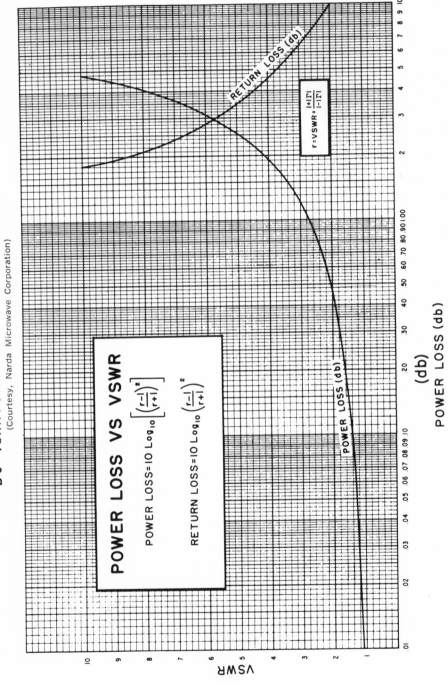

B-9 VSWR-POWER LOSS CONVERSION CHART
(Courtesy, Narda Microwave Corporation)

B-10 TIME LAG CORRECTIONS FOR RADIO TRANSMISSION
(Courtesy, Hewlett-Packard Company)

Accurate timekeeping depends upon (a) understanding oscillator behavior and (b) accurate time synchronization with a master timing source. Oscillator behavior, i.e., drift rate and change in drift rate, can be determined by inspecting the frequency or time plots. Absolute synchronization between two or more clocks presents a problem which has been solved in several ways:

A TRANSPORTING A MASTER CLOCK

Time synchronization accuracy to about ± 1 microsecond (μsec) or less can be made by transporting a master clock to each clock station. Achieved accuracy depends largely upon the comparison method. The rate (i.e., the daily time gain or loss) and acceleration (i.e., the change in rate) of the master clock must be accurately known and an appropriate correction must be made at each clock station.

B TWO-WAY RADIO TRANSMISSION

Time synchronization accuracy as good as ± 10 μsec can be made using a transponder at the clock station. The propagation delay which the timing pulse undergoes between the master transmitter and the clock station can be accurately determined at the master transmitter from the following relationship:

$$t_{\text{prop}} = \frac{2}{t_{\text{tot}} - t_{\text{tr}}}$$

where $t_{\text{prop}} =$ one-way propagation delay between master transmitter and clock station

$t_{\text{tot}} =$ total delay at master transmitter between transmission of timing signal and receipt of transponder signal

$t_{\text{tr}} =$ delay at the transponder between receipt of timing signal and retransmission of the signal

Time synchronization by this method requires special transmitting and receiving equipment at both the master time source and the station requiring synchronization and is therefore impractical for most time standard systems.

C ONE-WAY RADIO TRANSMISSION

Time synchronization accuracy to ± 1 millisec or less can be made using presently available standard time signals such as those transmitted by station WWV. With this method, the propagation delay between the transmitter and clock station must be determined and then applied as a correction to the clock reading. The principal factors which affect the propagation delay for hf signals are (a) the great circle distance between transmitter and receiver, (b) the transmission mode (i.e., the number of earth-to-ionosphere reflections between transmitter and receiver), and (c) the virtual height of the ionospheric reflection layers. Since lf and vlf transmissions are propagated for relatively great distances by ground wave, propagation delay for these frequencies can usually be found directly after computing the great circle distance. A detailed discussion of distance determination, transmission mode estimation, layer height estimation, and delay determination by graphic means, are given in the following paragraphs.

Once the propagation delay has been determined, the tick-phasing dial on the clock can be positioned to allow for the delay. The 1-sec clock ticks are then produced in synchronism with the transmitted master timing signal.

Example: A clock station (using oscillator-clock-oscilloscope system) located

3100 kilometers (about 10.80 millisec transmission delay) from WWV is required to synchronize its clock ticks with the WWV ticks as transmitted. Time-comparison readings are taken when the zero crossing of the second cycle of the received WWV tick is aligned with the vertical center-line of the CRT (1 millisec-per-centimeter sweep speed); the leading edge of the received WWV tick therefore occurs 4 millisec after the clock tick (which triggers the oscilloscope). Inspection of the smoothed curve on the time-comparison graph shows that for a particular day, the tick phasing dials on the clock should be set to 231,770 μsec for clock-tick coincidence with the received WWV tick. The tick phasing dial setting for synchronization with the transmitted WWV ticks on this day is determined as follows:

Time-comparison graph	231,770 μsec
Reading correction	+4,000
Transmission delay	−10,800
Final dial setting	224,970 μsec

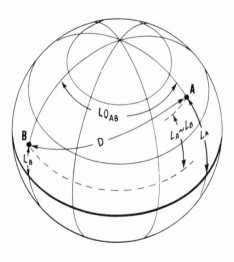

Fig. B-1 Great circle distance calculation.

GREAT-CIRCLE DISTANCE

The great circle distance between points A and B whose latitude and longitude are known can be rapidly determined from the following relationship (see Fig. B-1):

$$\text{hav } D = \cos L_A \cos L_B \text{ hav } Lo_{AB} + \text{hav } (L_A - L_B)$$

where $D =$ great circle distance A to B expressed in degrees of arc

$L_A =$ latitude of A

$L_B =$ latitude of B

$Lo_{AB} =$ difference of longitude between A and B

$(L_B \sim L_A) =$ the difference of L_A and L_B if A and B are on the same side of the equator or the sum of L_A and L_B if A and B are on opposite sides of the equator.

NOTE: The haversine of angle $\theta = 1/2$ versine $\theta = 1/2$ $(1 - \cos \theta) = \sin^2 1/2 \theta$; also hav $\theta =$ hav $(360° - \theta)$; thus, hav 210° = hav 150°.

Computations made using Tables B-1 and B-2 are sufficiently accurate for most skywave propagation delay estimates. Distance errors of as much as 10 to 20 miles contribute less error to the delay estimate than is expected to result from errors in estimating propagation mode and ionospheric height. A more extensive haversine table permitting distance calculations to within a mile, is given in Bowditch, *American Practical Navigator*, Part II, U.S. Government Printing Office, Washington 25, D.C.

Example: Find the distance between radio station WWV (point A), 39°00′ N 76°51′W, and Palo Alto, California (point B), 37°23′N 122°09′W.

$$L_A = 39°00′N$$

$$L_B = 37°23′N$$

$$Lo_{AB} = 45°18′$$

$$L_A \sim L_B = 1°37'$$

$$\log \cos L_A = \log \cos 39°00' = 9.8905 - 10$$
$$\log \cos L_B = \log \cos 37°23' = 9.9001 - 10$$
$$\log \text{hav } Lo_{AB} = \log \text{hav } 45°18' = 9.1712 - 10$$
$$\overline{8.9618 - 10}$$

Taking antilog from haversine table, log hav to nat hav:

$$\text{antilog } 8.9618 - 10 \qquad\qquad = 0.0916$$
$$\text{hav } (L_A \sim L_B) = \text{hav } 1°37' \qquad = 0.0002$$
$$\overline{0.0918}$$

$$D = \text{arc hav } 0.0918 = 35°17'.$$

Since 1 minute of arc = 1 nautical mile = 1.151 statute miles = 1.853 km, then 35°17' = 2117 nautical miles = 2439 statute miles = 3923 kilometers.

TRANSMISSION MODE

The ground-wave propagation path (most lf/vlf transmissions and short-distance hf transmissions) closely follows the great-circle route between the transmitter and receiver. However, hf transmissions over a distance of more than about 160 km follow sky-wave paths.

The maximum distance that can be spanned by a single hop (i.e., one reflection from the ionosphere) via the F2 layer is about 4000 km (Fig. B-2). Therefore, the fewest number of hops between transmitter and receiver is the next integer greater than the great-circle distance (in kilometers) divided by 4000. Transmission modes with one or two more hops than the minimum number of hops occur frequently (Fig. B-3), but modes of higher order are greatly attenuated during transmission and are of little concern.

Example 1: Find the minimum number of hops for a distance of 3923 km. Solution: A one-hop F2 mode is possible (3923 ÷ 4000 < 1).

Example 2: What modes are likely to be received at a distance of 7687 km? Solution: Two-hop, 3-hop, and 4-hop

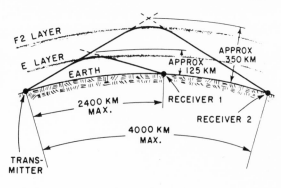

Fig. B-2 Single-hop sky-wave paths.

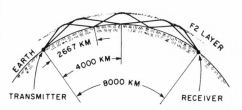

Fig. B-3 Multiple-hop transmission path.

F2 modes can be expected (7687 ÷ 4000 > 1, but < 2).

Useful transmissions via the E layer (daytime only) are usually limited to one-hop modes up to a distance of about 2400 km.

Remember that some locations may receive transmissions from both the E and F2 layers and that transmissions may be reflected occasionally from layers other than the E and F2.

The following approach should improve your estimate of propagation delay:

1. Determine which modes are possible at your location.

2. Tune to the highest frequency which provides consistent reception to reduce interference from high-order modes.

3. If several modes are being received (indicated by multiple tick reception or tick jitter between fairly constant positions), select the tick with earliest arrival time for measurements.

4. After plotting time measurements for

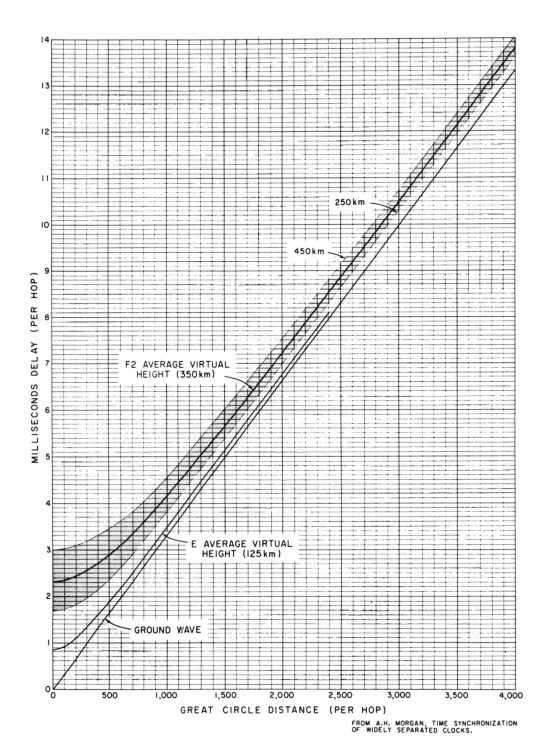

FROM A.H. MORGAN, TIME SYNCHRONIZATION
OF WIDELY SEPARATED CLOCKS.

Fig. B-4 Transmission delay graph.

several weeks, either disregard measurements which are conspicuously out of place, or correct the measurement to the more likely mode if the plot is mistimed by the difference in time between possible modes.

HEIGHT OF IONOSPHERE

Long-distance hf transmissions are usually reflected from the F2 layer, which varies in height from about 250 to 450 km. Experience has shown that the virtual height of the F2 layer averages about 350 km (Fig. B-2). Unless special studies permit determination of layer height at the point of reflection to high accuracy, an assumed height of 350 km can be used for delay estimation.

The E layer exists only during the daytime at a virtual height of about 125 km (Fig. B-2). One-hop E modes may provide very steady daytime reception at distances up to about 2400 km.

DELAY DETERMINATION

Once the transmitter-to-receiver distance, possible transmission modes, and layer heights have been determined, transmission delay can be found graphically from Fig. B-4. The shaded area along the F2 curve shows the possible extremes of height variation.

As shown in the following examples, the delay for a one-hop mode can be read directly from the transmission delay graph for a given distance and layer height.

Example 1: Find the one-hop delay for a distance of 3923 km. Solution: Ex-

pected F2 delay is about 13.60 millisec. No one-hop E mode is likely since the distance is greater than the usual limit of 2400 km for the one-hop E mode.

Example 2: Find the one-hop delay for a distance of 2200 km. Solution: Expected F2 delay is about 7.90 millisec; expected E delay is about 7.50 millisec.

For a multi-hop mode, (a) determine the distance covered by each hop, (b) find the delay for a single hop, then (c) multiply the single-hop delay by the number of hops to determine the total delay.

Example 3: Find the two-hop delay for a distance of 3923 km. Solution: Each 1962-km hop contributes a delay of about 7.15 millisec; the total delay is 7.15 × 2 or 14.30 millisec. Note that the two-hop delay for a 3923-km distance is 0.7 millisec greater than the one-hop delay for the same distance determined in Example 1.

Example 4: Find the three-hop delay for a distance of 7687 km. Solution: The delay contributed by each 2562-km hop is about 9.05 millisec; the total delay is 0.05 × 3 or 27.15 millisec.

Example 5: Find the four-hop delay for a distance of 7687 km. Solution: The delay contributed by each 1922-km hop is about 6.95 millisec; the total delay is 6.95 × 4 or 27.80 millisec. Note that the four-hop delay for a 7687-km distance is 0.65 millisec greater than the three-hop delay for the same distance determined in Example 4.

TABLE B-1 LOGARITHMS OF COSINE FUNCTION

(0° to 45°)

°	0'	10'	20'	30'	40'	50'	60'
0	0.0000	0.0000	0.0000	0.0000	0.0000	9.9999	9.9999
1	9.9999	9.9999	9.9999	9.9999	9.9998	9.9998	9.9997
2	9.9997	9.9997	9.9996	9.9996	9.9995	9.9995	9.9994
3	9.9994	9.9993	9.9993	9.9992	9.9991	9.9990	9.9989
4	9.9989	9.9989	9.9988	9.9987	9.9986	9.9985	9.9983
5	9.9983	9.9982	9.9981	9.9980	9.9979	9.9977	9.9976
6	9.9976	9.9975	9.9973	9.9972	9.9971	9.9969	9.9968
7	9.9968	9.9966	9.9964	9.9963	9.9961	9.9959	9.9958
8	9.9958	9.9956	9.9954	9.9952	9.9950	9.9948	9.9946
9	9.9946	9.9944	9.9942	9.9940	9.9938	9.9936	9.9934
10	9.9934	9.9931	9.9929	9.9927	9.9924	9.9922	9.9919
11	9.9919	9.9917	9.9914	9.9912	9.9909	9.9907	9.9904
12	9.9904	9.9901	9.9899	9.9896	9.9893	9.9890	9.9887
13	9.9887	9.9884	9.9881	9.9878	9.9875	9.9872	9.9869
14	9.9869	9.9866	9.9863	9.9859	9.9856	9.9853	9.9849
15	9.9849	9.9846	9.9843	9.9839	9.9836	9.9832	9.9828
16	9.9828	9.9825	9.9821	9.9817	9.9814	9.9810	9.9806
17	9.9806	9.9802	9.9798	9.9794	9.9790	9.9786	9.9782
18	9.9782	9.9778	9.9774	9.9770	9.9765	9.9761	9.9757
19	9.9757	9.9752	9.9748	9.9743	9.9739	9.9734	9.9730
20	9.9730	9.9725	9.9721	9.9716	9.9711	9.9706	9.9702
21	9.9702	9.9697	9.9692	9.9687	9.9682	9.9677	9.9672
22	9.9672	9.9667	9.9661	9.9656	9.9651	9.9646	9.9640
23	9.9640	9.9635	9.9629	9.9624	9.9618	9.9613	9.9607
24	9.9607	9.9602	9.9596	9.9590	9.9584	9.9579	9.9573
25	9.9573	9.9567	9.9561	9.9555	9.9549	9.9543	9.9537
26	9.9537	9.9530	9.9524	9.9518	9.9512	9.9505	9.9499
27	9.9499	9.9492	9.9486	9.9479	9.9473	9.9466	9.9459
28	9.9459	9.9453	9.9446	9.9439	9.9432	9.9425	9.9418
29	9.9418	9.9411	9.9404	9.9397	9.9390	9.9383	9.9375
30	9.9375	9.9368	9.9361	9.9353	9.9346	9.9338	9.9331
31	9.9331	9.9323	9.9315	9.9308	9.9300	9.9292	9.9284
32	9.9284	9.9276	9.9268	9.9260	9.9252	9.9244	9.9236
33	9.9236	9.9228	9.9219	9.9211	9.9203	9.9194	9.9186
34	9.9186	9.9177	9.9169	9.9160	9.9151	9.9142	9.9134
35	9.9134	9.9125	9.9116	9.9107	9.9098	9.9089	9.9080
36	9.9080	9.9070	9.9061	9.9052	9.9042	9.9033	9.9023
37	9.9023	9.9014	9.9004	9.8995	9.8985	9.8975	9.8965
38	9.8965	9.8955	9.8945	9.8935	9.8925	9.8915	9.8905
39	9.8905	9.8895	9.8884	9.8874	9.8864	9.8853	9.8843
40	9.8843	9.8832	9.8821	9.8810	9.8800	9.8789	9.8778
41	9.8778	9.8767	9.8756	9.8745	9.8733	9.8722	9.8711
42	9.8711	9.8699	9.8688	9.8676	9.8665	9.8653	9.8641
43	9.8641	9.8629	9.8618	9.8606	9.8594	9.8582	9.8569
44	9.8569	9.8557	9.8545	9.8532	9.8520	9.8507	9.8495

Note: Append −10 to each logarithm.

TABLE B-1 LOGARITHMS OF COSINE FUNCTION (CONT'D)

(45° to 90°)

°	0′	10′	20′	30′	40′	50′	60′
45	9.8495	9.8482	9.8469	9.8457	9.8444	9.8431	9.8418
46	9.8418	9.8405	9.8391	9.8378	9.8365	9.8351	9.8338
47	9.8338	9.8324	9.8311	9.8297	9.8283	9.8269	9.8255
48	9.8255	9.8241	9.8227	9.8213	9.8198	9.8184	9.8169
49	9.8169	9.8155	9.8140	9.8125	9.8111	9.8096	9.8081
50	9.8081	9.8066	9.8050	9.8053	9.8020	9.8004	9.7989
51	9.7989	9.7973	9.7957	9.7941	9.7926	9.7910	9.7893
52	9.7893	9.7877	9.7861	9.7844	9.7828	9.7811	9.7795
53	9.7795	9.7778	9.7761	9.7744	9.7727	9.7710	9.7692
54	9.7692	9.7675	9.7657	9.7640	9.7622	9.7604	9.7586
55	9.7586	9.7568	9.7550	9.7531	9.7513	9.7494	9.7476
56	9.7476	9.7457	9.7438	9.7419	9.7400	9.7380	9.7361
57	9.7361	9.7342	9.7322	9.7302	9.7282	9.7262	9.7242
58	9.7242	9.7222	9.7201	9.7181	9.7160	9.7139	9.7118
59	9.7118	9.7097	9.7076	9.7055	9.7033	9.7012	9.6990
60	9.6990	9.6968	9.6946	9.6923	9.6901	9.6878	9.6856
61	9.6856	9.6833	9.6810	9.6787	9.6763	9.6740	9.6716
62	9.6716	9.6692	9.6668	9.6644	9.6620	9.6595	9.6570
63	9.6570	9.6546	9.6521	9.6495	9.6470	9.6442	9.6418
64	9.6418	9.6392	9.6366	9.6340	9.6313	9.6286	9.6259
65	9.6259	9.6232	9.6205	9.6177	9.6149	9.6121	9.6093
66	9.6093	9.6065	9.6036	9.6007	9.5978	9.5948	9.5919
67	9.5919	9.5889	9.5859	9.5828	9.5798	9.5767	9.5736
68	9.5736	9.5704	9.5673	9.5641	9.5609	9.5576	9.5543
69	9.5543	9.5510	9.5477	9.5443	9.5409	9.5375	9.5341
70	9.5341	9.5306	9.5270	9.5235	9.5199	9.5163	9.5126
71	9.5126	9.5090	9.5052	9.5015	9.4977	9.4939	9.4900
72	9.4900	9.4861	9.4821	9.4781	9.4741	9.4700	9.4659
73	9.4659	9.4618	9.4576	9.4533	9.4491	9.4447	9.4403
74	9.4403	9.4359	9.4314	9.4269	9.4223	9.4177	9.4130
75	9.4130	9.4083	9.4035	9.3986	9.3937	9.3887	9.3837
76	9.3837	9.3786	9.3734	9.3682	9.3629	9.3575	9.3521
77	9.3521	9.3466	9.3410	9.3353	9.3296	9.3238	9.3179
78	9.3179	9.3119	9.3058	9.2997	9.2934	9.2870	9.2806
79	9.2806	9.2740	9.2674	9.2606	9.2538	9.2468	9.2397
80	9.2397	9.2324	9.2251	9.2176	9.2100	9.2022	9.1943
81	9.1943	9.1863	9.1781	9.1697	9.1612	9.1525	9.1436
82	9.1436	9.1345	9.1252	9.1157	9.1060	9.0961	9.0859
83	9.0859	9.0755	9.0648	9.0539	9.0426	9.0311	9.0192
84	9.0192	9.0070	8.9945	8.9816	8.9682	8.9545	8.9403
85	8.9403	8.9256	8.9104	8.8946	8.8783	8.8613	8.8436
86	8.8436	8.8251	8.8059	8.7857	8.7645	8.7423	8.7188
87	8.7188	8.6940	8.6677	8.6397	8.6097	8.5776	8.5428
88	8.5428	8.5050	8.4637	8.4179	8.3668	8.3088	8.2419
89	8.2419	8.1627	8.0658	7.9408	7.7648	7.4637	———

Note: Append −10 to each logarithm.

TABLE B-2 HAVERSINES

(0° to 44°)

°	0' Nat	0' Log	10' Nat	10' Log	20' Nat	20' Log	30' Nat	30' Log	40' Nat	40' Log	50' Nat	50' Log
0	.0000	—	.0000	6̄ .3254	.0000	6̄ .9275	.0000	5̄ .2796	.0000	5̄ .5295	.0001	5̄ .7233
1	.0001	5̄ .8817	.0001	.0156	.0001	.1316	.0002	.2339	.0002	.3254	.0003	.4081
2	.0003	.4837	.0004	.5532	.0004	.6176	.0005	.6775	.0005	.7336	.0006	.7862
3	.0007	.8358	.0008	.8828	.0008	.9273	.0009	.9697	.0010	.0101	.0011	.0487
4	.0012	.0856	.0013	.1211	.0014	.1551	.0015	.1879	.0017	.2195	.0018	.2499
5	.0019	.2794	.0020	.3078	.0022	.3354	.0023	.3621	.0024	.3880	.0026	.4132
6	.0027	.4376	.0029	.4614	.0031	.4845	.0032	.5071	.0034	.5290	.0036	.5504
7	.0037	.5714	.0039	.5918	.0041	.6117	.0043	.6312	.0045	.6503	.0047	.6689
8	.0049	.6872	.0051	.7051	.0053	.7226	.0055	.7397	.0057	.7566	.0059	.7731
9	.0062	.7893	.0064	.8052	.0066	.8208	.0069	.8361	.0071	.8512	.0073	.8660
10	.0076	.8806	.0079	.8949	.0081	.9090	.0084	.9229	.0086	.9365	.0089	.9499
11	.0092	.9631	.0095	.9762	.0097	.9890	.0100	.0016	.0103	.0141	.0106	.0264
12	.0109	.0385	.0112	.0504	.0115	.0622	.0119	.0738	.0122	.0852	.0125	.0966
13	.0128	.1077	.0131	.1187	.0135	.1296	.0138	.1404	.0142	.1510	.0145	.1614
14	.0149	.1718	.0152	.1820	.0156	.1921	.0159	.2021	.0163	.2120	.0167	.2217
15	.0170	.2314	.0174	.2409	.0178	.2504	.0182	.2597	.0186	.2689	.0190	.2781
16	.0194	.2871	.0198	.2961	.0202	.3049	.0206	.3137	.0210	.3223	.0214	.3309
17	.0218	.3394	.0223	.3478	.0227	.3561	.0231	.3644	.0236	.3726	.0240	.3807
18	.0245	.3887	.0249	.3966	.0254	.4045	.0258	.4123	.0263	.4200	.0268	.4276
19	.0272	.4352	.0277	.4427	.0282	.4502	.0287	.4576	.0292	.4649	.0297	.4721
20	.0302	.4793	.0307	.4865	.0312	.4935	.0317	.5006	.0322	.5075	.0327	.5144
21	.0332	.5213	.0337	.5281	.0343	.5348	.0348	.5415	.0353	.5481	.0359	.5547
22	.0364	.5612	.0370	.5677	.0375	.5741	.0381	.5805	.0386	.5868	.0392	.5931
23	.0397	.5993	.0403	.6055	.0409	.6116	.0415	.6177	.0421	.6238	.0426	.6298
24	.0432	.6358	.0438	.6417	.0444	.6476	.0450	.6534	.0456	.6592	.0462	.6650
25	.0468	.6707	.0475	.6764	.0481	.6820	.0487	.6876	.0493	.6932	.0500	.6987
26	.0506	.7042	.0512	.7096	.0519	.7150	.0525	.7204	.0532	.7258	.0538	.7311
27	.0545	.7364	.0552	.7416	.0558	.7468	.0565	.7520	.0572	.7572	.0578	.7623
28	.0585	.7674	.0592	.7724	.0599	.7774	.0606	.7824	.0613	.7874	.0620	.7923
29	.0627	.7972	.0634	.8021	.0641	.8069	.0648	.8117	.0655	.8165	.0663	.8213
30	.0670	.8260	.0677	.8307	.0684	.8354	.0692	.8400	.0699	.8446	.0707	.8492
31	.0714	.8538	.0722	.8583	.0729	.8629	.0737	.8673	.0744	.8718	.0752	.8763
32	.0760	.8807	.0767	.8851	.0775	.8894	.0783	.8938	.0791	.8981	.0799	.9024
33	.0807	.9067	.0815	.9109	.0823	.9152	.0831	.9194	.0839	.9236	.0847	.9277
34	.0855	.9319	.0863	.9360	.0871	.9401	.0879	.9442	.0888	.9482	.0896	.9523
35	.0904	.9563	.0913	.9603	.0921	.9643	.0929	.9682	.0938	.9721	.0946	.9761
36	.0955	.9800	.0963	.9838	.0972	.9877	.0981	.9915	.0989	.9954	.0998	.9992
37	.1007	.0030	.1016	.0067	.1024	.0105	.1033	.0142	.1042	.0179	.1051	.0216
38	.1060	.0253	.1069	.0289	.1078	.0326	.1087	.0362	.1096	.0398	.1105	.0434
39	.1114	.0470	.1123	.0505	.1133	.0541	.1142	.0576	.1151	.0611	.1160	.0646
40	.1170	.0681	.1179	.0716	.1189	.0750	.1198	.0784	.1207	.0819	.1217	.0853
41	.1226	.0887	.1236	.0920	.1246	.0954	.1255	.0987	.1265	.1020	.1275	.1054
42	.1284	.1087	.1294	.1119	.1304	.1152	.1314	.1185	.1323	.1217	.1333	.1249
43	.1343	.1282	.1353	.1314	.1363	.1345	.1373	.1377	.1383	.1409	.1393	.1440
44	.1403	.1472	.1413	.1503	.1424	.1534	.1434	.1565	.1444	.1596	.1454	.1626

Note: Characteristics of the logarithms are omitted.

TABLE B-2 HAVERSINES (CONT'D)

(45° to 89°)

°	0' Nat	0' Log	10' Nat	10' Log	20' Nat	20' Log	30' Nat	30' Log	40' Nat	40' Log	50' Nat	50' Log
45	.1464	.1657	.1475	.1687	.1485	.1718	.1495	.1748	1506	.1778	.1516	.1808
46	.1527	.1838	.1537	.1867	.1548	.1897	.1558	.1926	.1569	.1956	.1579	.1985
47	.1590	.2014	.1601	.2043	.1611	.2072	.1622	.2101	.1633	.2129	.1644	.2158
48	.1654	.2186	.1665	.2215	.1676	.2243	.1687	.2271	.1698	.2299	.1709	.2327
49	.1720	.2355	.1731	.2382	.1742	.2410	.1753	.2437	.1764	.2465	.1775	.2492
50	.1786	.2519	.1797	.2546	.1808	.2573	.1820	.2600	.1831	.2627	.1842	.2653
51	.1853	.2680	.1865	.2706	.1876	.2732	.1887	.2759	.1899	.2785	.1910	.2811
52	.1922	.2837	.1933	.2863	.1945	.2888	.1956	.2914	.1968	.2940	.1979	.2965
53	.1991	.2991	.2003	.3016	.2014	.3041	.2026	.3066	.2038	.3091	.2049	.3116
54	.2061	.3141	.2073	.3166	.2085	.3190	.2096	.3215	.2108	.3239	.2120	.3264
55	.2132	.3288	.2144	.3312	.2156	.3336	.2168	.3361	.2180	.3384	.2192	.3408
56	.2204	.3432	.2216	.3456	.2228	.3480	.2240	.3503	.2252	.3527	.2265	.3550
57	.2277	.3573	.2289	.3596	.2301	.3620	.2314	.3643	.2326	.3666	.2338	.3689
58	.2350	.3711	.2363	.3734	.2375	.3757	.2388	.3779	.2400	.3802	.2412	.3824
59	.2425	.3847	.2437	.3869	.2450	.3891	.2462	.3913	.2475	.3935	.2487	.3957
60	.2500	.3979	.2513	.4001	.2525	.4023	.2538	.4045	.2551	.4066	.2563	.4088
61	.2576	.4109	.2589	.4131	.2601	.4152	.2614	.4173	.2627	.4195	.2640	.4216
62	.2653	.4237	.2665	.4258	.2678	.4279	.2691	.4300	.2704	.4320	.2717	.4341
63	.2730	.4362	.2743	.4382	.2756	.4403	.2769	.4423	.2782	.4444	.2795	.4464
64	.2808	.4484	.2821	.4504	.2834	.4524	.2847	.4545	.2861	.4565	.2874	.4584
65	.2887	.4604	.2900	.4624	.2913	.4644	.2927	.4664	.2940	.4683	.2953	.4703
66	.2966	.4722	.2980	.4742	.2993	.4761	.3006	.4780	.3020	.4799	.3033	.4819
67	.3046	.4838	.3060	.4857	.3073	.4876	.3087	.4895	.3100	.4914	.3113	.4932
68	.3127	.4951	.3140	.4970	.3154	.4989	.3167	.5007	.3181	.5026	.3195	.5044
69	.3208	.5063	.3222	.5081	.3235	.5099	.3249	.5117	.3263	.5136	.3276	.5154
70	.3290	.5172	.3304	.5190	.3317	.5208	.3331	.5226	.3345	.5244	.3358	.5261
71	.3372	.5279	.3380	.5297	.3400	.5314	.3413	.5332	.3427	.5349	.3441	.5367
72	.3455	.5384	.3466	.5402	.3483	.5419	.3496	.5436	.3510	.5454	.3524	.5471
73	.3538	.5488	.3	.5505	.3566	.5522	.3580	.5539	.3594	.5556	.3608	.5572
74	.3622	.5589	.36	.5606	.3650	.5623	.3664	.5639	.3678	.5656	.3692	.5672
75	.3706	.5689	.3720	.5705	.3734	.5722	.3748	.5738	.3762	.5754	.3776	.5771
76	.3790	.5787	.3805	.5803	3819	.5819	.3833	.5835	.3847	.5851	.3861	.5867
77	.3875	.5883	.3889	.5899	.3904	.5915	.3918	.5930	.3932	.5946	.3946	.5962
78	.3960	.5977	.3975	.5993	.3989	.6009	.4003	.6024	.4017	.6039	.4032	.6055
79	.4046	.6070	.4060	.6086	.4075	.6101	.4089	.6116	.4103	.6131	.4117	.6146
80	.4132	.6161	.4146	.6176	.4160	.6191	.4175	.6206	.4189	.6221	.4203	.6236
81	.4218	.6251	.4232	.6266	.4247	.6280	.4261	.6295	.4275	.6310	.4290	.6324
82	.4304	.6339	.4319	.6353	.4333	.6368	.4347	.6382	.4362	.6397	.4376	.6411
83	.4391	.6425	.4405	.6440	.4420	.6454	.4434	.6468	.4448	.6482	.4463	.6496
84	.4477	.6510	.4492	.6524	.4506	.6538	.4521	.6552	.4535	.6566	.4550	.6580
85	.4564	.6594	.4579	.6607	.4593	.6621	.4608	.6635	.4622	.6648	.4637	.6662
86	.4651	.6676	.4666	.6689	.4680	.6703	.4695	.6716	.4709	.6730	.4724	.6743
87	.4738	.6756	.4753	.6770	.4767	.6783	.4782	.6796	.4796	.6809	.4811	.6822
88	.4826	.6835	.4840	.6848	.4855	.6862	.4869	.6875	.4884	.6887	.4898	.6900
89	.4913	.6913	.4927	.6926	.4942	.6939	.4956	.6952	.4971	.6964	.4985	.6977

Note: Characteristics of the logarithms are omitted.

TABLE B-2 HAVERSINES (CONT'D)

(90° to 134°)

°	0′ Nat	0′ Log	10′ Nat	10′ Log	20′ Nat	20′ Log	30′ Nat	30′ Log	40′ Nat	40′ Log	50′ Nat	50′ Log
90	.5000	.6990	.5015	.7002	.5029	.7015	.5044	.7027	.5058	.7040	.5073	.7052
91	.5087	.7065	.5102	.7077	.5116	.7090	.5131	.7102	.5145	.7114	.5160	.7126
92	.5174	.7139	.5189	.7151	.5204	.7156	.5218	.7175	.5233	.7187	.5247	.7199
93	.5262	.7211	.5276	.7223	.5291	.7235	.5305	.7247	.5320	.7259	.5334	.7271
94	.5349	.7283	.5363	.7294	.5378	.7306	.5392	.7318	.5407	.7329	.5421	.7341
95	.5436	.7353	.5450	.7364	.5465	.7376	.5479	.7387	.5494	.7399	.5508	.7410
96	.5523	.7421	.5537	.7433	.5552	.7444	.5566	.7455	.5580	.7467	.5595	.7478
97	.5609	.7489	.5624	.7500	.5638	.7511	.5653	.7523	.5667	.7534	.5681	.7545
98	.5696	.7556	.5710	.7567	.5725	.7577	.5739	.7588	.5753	.7599	.5768	.7610
99	.5782	.7621	.5797	.7632	.5811	.7642	.5825	.7653	.5840	.7664	.5854	.7674
100	.5868	.7685	.5883	.7696	.5897	.7706	.5911	.7717	.5925	.7727	.5940	.7738
101	.5954	.7748	.5968	.7759	.5983	.7769	.5997	.7779	.6011	.7790	.6025	.7800
102	.6040	.7810	.6054	.7820	.6068	.7830	.6082	.7841	.6096	.7851	.6111	.7861
103	.6125	.7871	.6139	.7881	.6153	.7891	.6167	.7901	.6181	.7911	.6195	.7921
104	.6210	.7931	.6224	.7940	.6238	.7950	.6252	.7960	.6266	.7970	.6280	.7980
105	.6294	.7989	.6308	.7999	.6322	.8009	.6336	.8018	.6350	.8028	.6364	.8037
106	.6378	.8047	.6392	.8056	.6406	.8066	.6420	.8075	.6434	.8085	.6448	.8094
107	.6462	.8104	.6476	.8113	.6490	.8122	.6504	.8131	.6517	.8141	.6531	.8150
108	.6545	.8159	.6559	.8168	.6573	.8177	.6587	.8187	.6600	.8196	.6614	.8205
109	.6628	.8214	.6642	.8223	.6655	.8232	.6669	.8241	.6683	.8250	.6696	.8258
110	.6710	.8267	.6724	.8276	.6737	.8285	.6751	.8294	.6765	.8302	.6778	.8311
111	.6792	.8320	.6805	.8329	.6819	.8337	.6833	.8346	.6846	.8354	.6860	.8363
112	.6873	.8371	.6887	.8380	.6900	.8388	.6913	.8319	.6927	.8405	.6940	.8414
113	.6954	.8422	.6967	.8430	.6980	.8439	.6994	.8447	.7007	.8455	.7020	.8464
114	.7034	.8472	.7047	.8480	.7060	.8488	.7073	.8496	.7087	.8504	.7100	.8513
115	.7113	.8521	.7126	.8529	.7139	.8537	.7153	.8545	.7166	.8553	.7179	.8561
116	.7192	.8568	.7205	.8576	.7218	.8584	.7231	.8592	.7244	.8600	.7257	.8608
117	.7270	.8615	.7283	.8623	.7296	.8631	.7309	.8638	.7322	.8646	.7335	.8654
118	.7347	.8661	.7360	.8669	.7373	.8676	.7386	.8684		.8691	.7411	.8699
119	.7424	.8706	.7437	.8714	.7449	.8721	.7462	.8729		.8736	.7487	.8743
120	.7500	.8751	.7513	.8758	.7525	.8765	.7538	.8772	.7550	.8780	.7563	.8787
121	.7575	.8794	.7588	.8801	.7600	.8808	.7612	.8815	.7625	.8822	.7637	.8829
122	.7650	.8836	.7662	.8843	.7674	.8850	.7686	.8857	.7699	.8864	.7711	.8871
123	.7723	.8878	.7735	.8885	.7748	.8892	.7760	.8898	.7772	.8905	.7784	.8912
124	.7796	.8919	.7808	.8925	.7820	.8932	.7832	.8939	.7844	.8945	.7856	.8952
125	.7868	.8959	.7880	.8965	.7892	.8972	.7904	.8978	.7915	.8985	.7927	.8991
126	.7939	.8998	.7951	.9004	.7962	.9010	.7974	.9017	.7986	.9023	.7997	.9030
127	.8009	.9036	.8021	.9042	.8032	.9048	.8044	.9055	.8055	.9061	.8067	.9067
128	.8078	.9073	.8090	.9079	.8101	.9085	.8113	.9092	.8124	.9098	.8135	.9104
129	.8147	.9110	.8158	.9116	.8169	.9122	.8180	.9128	.8192	.9134	.8203	.9140
130	.8214	.9146	.8225	.9151	.8236	.9157	.8247	.9163	.8258	.9169	.8269	.9175
131	.8280	.9180	.8291	.9186	.8302	.9192	.8313	.9198	.8324	.9203	.8335	.9209
132	.8346	.9215	.8356	.9220	.8367	.9226	.8378	.9231	.8389	.9237	.8399	.9242
133	.8410	.9248	.8421	.9253	.8431	.9259	.8442	.9264	.8452	.9270	.8463	.9275
134	.8473	.9281	.8484	.9286	.8494	.9291	.8505	.9297	.8515	.9302	.8525	.9307

Note: Characteristics of the logarithms are omitted.

TABLE B-2 HAVERSINES (CONT'D)

(135° to 180°)

°	0' Nat	0' Log	10' Nat	10' Log	20' Nat	20' Log	30' Nat	30' Log	40' Nat	40' Log	50' Nat	50' Log
135	.8536	.9312	.8546	.9318	.8556	.9323	.8566	.9328	.8576	.9333	.8587	.9338
136	.8597	.9343	.8607	.9348	.8617	.9353	.8627	.9359	.8637	.9364	.8647	.9369
137	.8657	.9374	.8667	.9379	.8677	.9383	.8686	.9388	.8696	.9393	.8706	.9398
138	.8716	.9403	.8725	.9408	.8735	.9413	.8745	.9417	.8754	.9422	.8764	.9427
139	.8774	.9432	.8783	.9436	.8793	.9441	.8802	.9446	.8811	.9450	.8821	.9455
140	.8830	.9460	.8840	.9464	.8849	.9469	.8858	.9473	.8867	.9478	.8877	.9482
141	.8886	.9487	.8895	.9491	.8904	.9496	.8913	.9500	.8922	.9505	.8931	.9509
142	.8940	.9513	.8949	.9518	.8958	.9522	.8967	.9526	.8976	.9531	.8984	.9535
143	.8993	.9539	.9002	.9543	.9011	.9548	.9019	.9552	.9028	.9556	.9037	.9560
144	.9045	.9564	.9054	.9568	.9062	.9572	.9071	.9576	.9079	.9580	.9087	.9584
145	.9096	.9588	.9104	.9592	.9112	.9596	.9121	.9600	.9129	.9604	.9137	.9608
146	.9145	.9612	.9153	.9616	.9161	.9620	.9169	.9623	.9177	.9627	.9185	.9631
147	.9193	.9635	.9201	.9638	.9209	.9642	.9217	.9646	.9225	.9650	.9233	.9653
148	.9240	.9657	.9248	.9660	.9256	.9664	.9263	.9668	.9271	.9671	.9278	.9675
149	.9286	.9678	.9293	.9682	.9301	.9685	.9308	.9689	.9316	.9692	.9323	.9695
150	.9330	.9699	.9337	.9702	.9345	.9706	.9352	.9709	.9359	.9712	.9366	.9716
151	.9373	.9719	.9380	.9722	.9387	.9725	.9394	.9729	.9401	.9732	.9408	.9735
152	.9415	.9738	.9422	.9741	.9428	.9744	.9435	.9747	.9442	.9751	.9448	.9754
153	.9455	.9757	.9462	.9760	.9468	.9763	.9475	.9766	.9481	.9769	.9488	.9772
154	.9494	.9774	.9500	.9777	.9507	.9780	.9513	.9783	.9519	.9786	.9525	.9789
155	.9532	.9792	.9538	.9794	.9544	.9797	.9550	.9800	.9556	.9803	.9562	.9805
156	.9568	.9808	.9574	.9811	.9579	.9813	.9585	.9816	.9591	.9819	.9597	.9821
157	.9603	.9824	.9608	.9826	.9614	.9829	.9619	.9831	.9625	.9834	.9630	.9836
158	.9636	.9839	.9641	.9841	.9647	.9844	.9652	.9846	.9657	.9849	.9663	.9851
159	.9668	.9853	.9673	.9856	.9678	.9858	.9683	.9860	.9688	.9863	.9693	.9865
160	.9698	.9867	.9703	.9869	.9708	.9871	.9713	.9874	.9718	.9876	.9723	.9878
161	.9728	.9880	.9732	.9882	.9737	.9884	.9742	.9886	.9746	.9888	.9751	.9890
162	.9755	.9892	.9760	.9894	.9764	.9896	.9769	.9898	.9773	.9900	.9777	.9902
163	.9782	.9904	.9786	.9906	.9790	.9908	.9794	.9910	.9798	.9911	.9802	.9913
164	.9806	.9915	.9810	.9917	.9814	.9919	.9818	.9920	.9822	.9922	.9826	.9924
165	.9830	.9925	.9833	.9927	.9837	.9929	.9841	.9930	.9844	.9932	.9848	.9933
166	.9851	.9935	.9855	.9937	.9858	.9938	.9862	.9940	.9865	.9941	.9869	.9943
167	.9872	.9944	.9875	.9945	.9878	.9947	.9881	.9948	.9885	.9950	.9888	.9951
168	.9891	.9952	.9894	.9954	.9897	.9955	.9900	.9956	.9903	.9957	.9905	.9959
169	.9908	.9960	.9911	.9961	.9914	.9962	.9916	.9963	.9919	.9965	.9921	.9966
170	.9924	.9967	.9927	.9968	.9929	.9969	.9931	.9970	.9934	.9971	.9936	.9972
171	.9938	.9973	.9941	.9974	.9943	.9975	.9945	.9976	.9947	.9977	.9949	.9978
172	.9951	.9979	.9953	.9980	.9955	.9981	.9957	.9981	.9959	.9982	.9961	.9983
173	.9963	.9984	.9964	.9985	.9966	.9985	.9968	.9986	.9969	.9987	.9971	.9987
174	.9973	.9988	.9974	.9989	.9976	.9989	.9977	.9990	.9978	.9991	.9980	.9991
175	.9981	.9992	.9982	.9992	.9983	.9993	.9985	.9993	.9986	.9994	.9987	.9994
176	.9988	.9995	.9989	.9995	.9990	.9996	.9991	.9996	.9992	.9996	.9992	.9997
177	.9993	.9997	.9994	.9997	.9995	.9998	.9995	.9998	.9996	.9998	.9996	.9998
178	.9997	.9999	.9997	.9999	.9998	.9999	.9998	.9999	.9999	.9999	.9999	.9999
179	.9999	.9999	.9999	.9999	1.0000	.0000	1.0000	.0000	1.0000	.0000	1.0000	.0000
180	1.0000	.0000										

Note: Characteristics of the logarithms are omitted.

Appendix C

C-1 MATHEMATICAL AND ELECTRONIC CONSTANTS

Symbol or name	Numerical value	Symbol or name	Numerical value
π	3.1416	ϵ	2.7183 (base of natural logarithms)
$\dfrac{1}{\pi}$	0.3183	$\dfrac{1}{\epsilon}$	0.3679
π^2	9.8696	ϵ^2	7.389
$\dfrac{1}{\pi^2}$	0.1013	$\sqrt{\epsilon}$	1.649
$(2\pi)^2$	39.4784	$\log_{10}\epsilon$	0.4343
$\dfrac{1}{(2\pi)^2}$	0.0253	$\sqrt{2}$	1.414
π^3	31.0062	$\dfrac{1}{\sqrt{2}}$	0.7071
$\dfrac{1}{\pi^3}$	0.0322	$\sqrt{3}$	1.732
		$\sqrt{5}$	2.236
$\sqrt{\pi}$	1.7725	g	Acceleration due to gravity at sea level, 40° latitude is 32.1578 ft/sec/sec
$\dfrac{1}{\sqrt{\pi}}$	0.5642	$\sqrt{2g}$	8.020
$\sqrt[3]{\pi}$	1.4646	h	6.62 × 10⁻²⁷ erg-sec (Planck's constant)
$\dfrac{1}{\sqrt[3]{\pi}}$	0.6818	j	$\sqrt{-1}$
$\log_{10}\pi$	0.4971	e	1.602 × 10⁻¹² erg (electron volt)
$\log_{10}\pi^2$	0.9943	μ	0.001 millimeter (micron)
$\log_{10}\sqrt{\pi}$	0.2486	m	9.11 × 10⁻²⁸ gram (electron mass)
radian	57.2959° or $\dfrac{180°}{\pi}$	k	1.38 × 10⁻¹⁶ erg/deg C (Boltzmann's constant)
360°	2π radians	c	2.9979 × 10⁸ meters/sec or 186,284 miles/sec in a vacuum (speed of light)
arc 1°	0.0175 radian		
arc 1°	17.78 mils		

C-2 MATHEMATICAL SYMBOLS

Symbol	Definition	Symbol	Definition	Symbol	Definition	Symbol	Definition
$+$	Plus, positive, add	$\|n\|$	Absolute value of n	$>$	Greater than	$\mathrm{Log}_{10}X$	Logarithm of X to base 10
$-$	Minus, negative, subtract	$\angle$	Angle	$>>$	Much greater than	$\mathrm{Log}_{\epsilon}X$	Logarithm of X to base ϵ
$\times$ or $\cdot$	Multiplied by	$°$	Degree	$\leqq$	Less than or equal to	j	Square root of minus one
		$'$	Minutes of a degree; feet				
$\div$ or $/$	Divided by			$<$	Less than		
$:$	Ratio	$''$	Seconds of a degree; inches	$<<$	Much less than	ϵ	Base of natural logarithms (2.71828)
				$\therefore$	Therefore		
$=$ or $::$	Equals	$\int$	Integration	$\perp$	Perpendicular to		
$\equiv$	Identical with	$\triangle$	Increment of	$\parallel$	Parallel to	( ) or [ ] or —	Indicate a term to be treated as a single number
$\neq$	Not equal to	$\propto$	Varies as				
$\cong$ or $\approx$	Approximately equal to	$!$	Factorial	$\sqrt{}$	Square root		
		∞	Infinity				
$\geqq$	Greater than or equal to	Σ	Summation	$\sqrt[3]{}$	Cube root	$\%$	Hundredths, percentage
				$\sqrt[n]{}$	nth root		

C-3 THERMAL PROPERTIES OF MATERIALS

(at 70° F unless otherwise noted)

Materials	Density (ρ = lb per cu ft)	Specific heat (cρ = Btu per lb per deg)	Conductivity (K = Btu per hr per °F per in. thickness)	Melting Point (°F)	Heat of fusion (Btu per lb)
Metals:					
Aluminum	167	0.22	1,415	1220	156
Brass	530	0.09	750	....	...
Copper	550	0.095	2,690	1982	75
Iron, gray cast	445	0.13	340	2400	40
Iron, pure	490	0.107	440	2795	65
Lead	710	0.030	239	621	10
Magnesium	108	0.24	1,100	1203	130
Nickel	550	0.105	406	2650	131
Platinum	1,335	0.032	482	3200	...
Silver	656	0.056	2,950	1762	47
Steel, structural	485	0.11	400	2550	...
Tin	455	0.055	430	449	25
Zinc	445	0.093	770	787	46
Building Materials and Other Solids:					
Brick, common	110	0.22	5.0		
Brick, hard (face brick)	130	0.24	9.2		
Coal, solid	100	0.3			
Concrete, stone	140	0.16	12		
Firebrick	140	0.26	9		
Glass, window	160	0.16	6		
Ice	57	0.52			
Plaster	95	0.25	3.3		
Stone, building	150	0.2	12.5		
Wood, oak	45	0.55	1.2		
Wood, pine or hemlock	30	0.65	0.8		
Insulating Materials:					
Asbestos, millboard	60	0.2	1.0		
Corkboard	10	0.45	0.30		
Fiberboard	15	0.5	0.33		
Fiber (or hair) blanket	6	0.5	0.27		
Mineral wool	10	0.2	0.27		
Insulating Furnace Brick	28	0.2	0.8		
85% magnesia pipe covering	15	0.2	0.5		

Gases (at atmospheric pressure):	Density	Specific heat	Conductivity	Boiling Point (°F)	Latent heat of vaporization (Btu)	Freezing Point (°F)
Air, 70°	0.075	0.24	0.16			
Air, 200°	0.0602	0.242	0.20			
Air, 1000°	0.0272	0.25	0.33			
Carbon dioxide	0.0724	0.20	0.095			
Hydrogen	0.0052	3.4	1.1			
Steam, 212°	0.037	0.49	0.15			
Liquids:						
Alcohol, ethyl	49	0.56	1.26	173	370	− 150
Gasoline, motor	46	0.55	1	...	140	...
Glycerin	79	0.58	2.0	554	...	...
Kerosene	50	0.5	1.05	...	110	...
Mercury	845	0.033	50	675	120	− 38
Oil, lubricating	53	0.5	1.15	...	...	...
Water, 70°	62.2	1.0	4.0	212	970	32
Water, 210°	59.9	1.0	5.0			

C-4 THERMAL RADIATION FACTORS

Table C–1 Emissivities

Surface	ϵ	Surface	ϵ
Small hole in furnace enclosure	0.97 to 0.99	Dull metals	0.20–0.30
Black nonmetallic surfaces	0.90 to 0.98	Polished metals (brass, copper, etc.)	0.02–0.05
Glass (window)	0.90 to 0.95		
Aluminum paint	0.40 to 0.60	Polished metals (aluminum, chromium, etc.)	0.02–0.04

Table C-2 Radial Emittance Factors*

Separation	F — value
D	0.2
D/2	0.4
D/4	0.6
D/8	0.8

*For parallel surfaces.

C-5 REFERENCE TEMPERATURES °C

Material	Equilibrium point	
	Solid and liquid	Liquid and vapor
Helium		−271.4
Hydrogen		−252.75
Neon		−245.92
Nitrogen		−195.78
Oxygen	−218.8	−182.97
Krypton	−157	
Chlorine	−101	
Razdon	− 71	
Mercury	− 38.87	
Water	0	100.
Gallium	29.75	
Sodium	98.	
Sulfur	119.	444.6
Tin	231.9	
Lead	327.3	
Zinc	419.5	
Aluminum	660.1	
Copper	1083.	
Platinum	1769.	
Tungsten	3880.	

C-6 RESISTIVITIES OF COMMON CONDUCTORS

(Ohms per Circular mil-foot at 20°C)

Material	Resistivity
Silver	9.56
Copper (annealed)	10.37
Aluminum	17.0
Tungsten	34.0
Brass	42.0
Nickel	60.0
Platinum	60.0
Iron	61.0
Manganin	264.0
Constantan	294.0
Cast Iron	435.0
Nichrome	675.0
Carbon	22,000.0

C-7 TEMPERATURE COEFFICIENTS OF RESISTANCE (AT 20°C)

Material	α_{20}	Material	α_{20}
Aluminum	0.0039	Zinc	0.0040
Antimony	0.0036	Brass	0.0015
Bismuth	0.004	Bronze	0.0020
Copper	0.00393	German silver	0.0004
Gold	0.0034	Manganin	±0.000015
Lead	0.00387	Monel	0.00019
Mercury	0.00072	Nichrome	0.00017
Platinum	0.003	Silver	0.0038
Steel, soft	0.0016	Tungsten	0.005

C-8 CIRCULAR WAVEGUIDE CUT-OFF FREQUENCIES

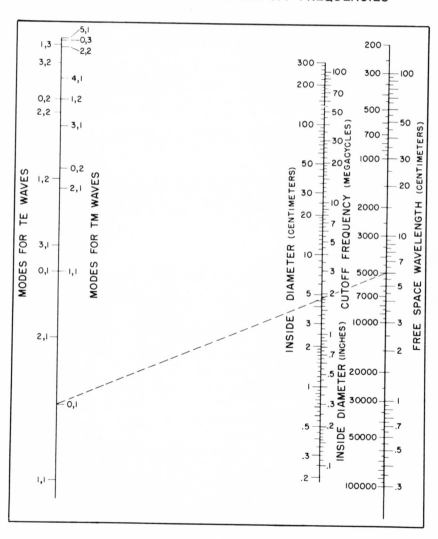

C-9 SQUARE WAVEGUIDE ATTENUATION (TE$_{01}$ MODE)

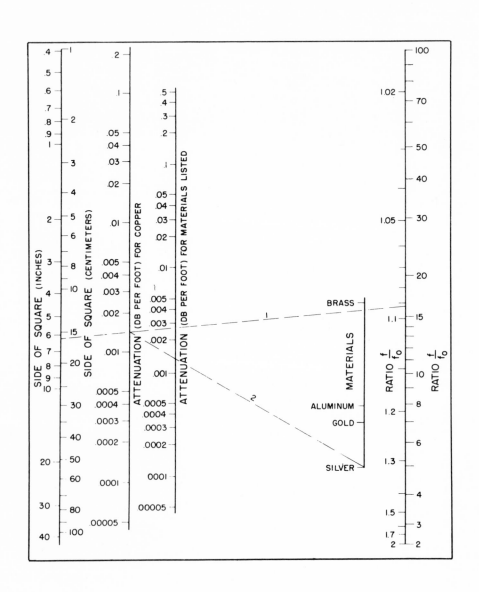

C-10 DUTY FACTOR (CYCLE) NOMOGRAPH

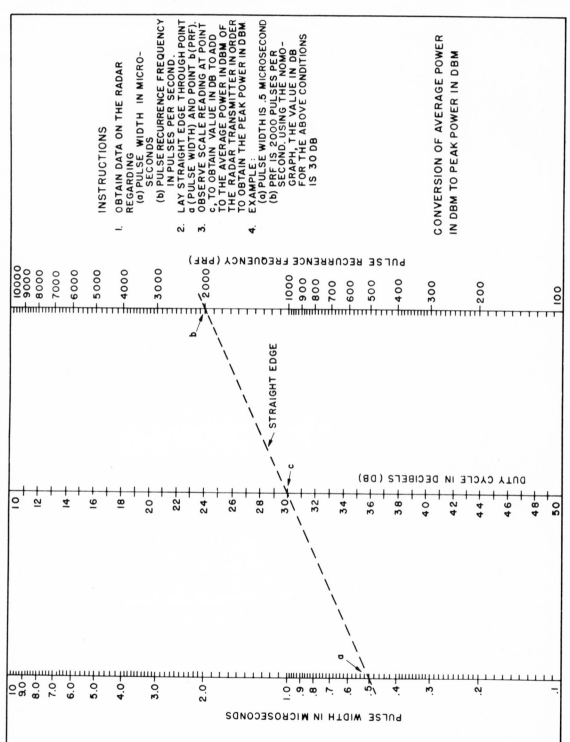

INSTRUCTIONS

1. OBTAIN DATA ON THE RADAR REGARDING
   (a) PULSE WIDTH IN MICRO-SECONDS
   (b) PULSE RECURRENCE FREQUENCY IN PULSES PER SECOND.
2. LAY STRAIGHT EDGE THROUGH POINT a (PULSE WIDTH) AND POINT b (PRF).
3. OBSERVE SCALE READING AT POINT c, TO OBTAIN VALUE IN DB TO ADD TO THE AVERAGE POWER IN DBM OF THE RADAR TRANSMITTER IN ORDER TO OBTAIN THE PEAK POWER IN DBM.
4. EXAMPLE:
   (a) PULSE WIDTH IS .5 MICROSECOND
   (b) PRF IS 2000 PULSES PER SECOND. USING THE NOMO-GRAPH, THE VALUE IN DB FOR THE ABOVE CONDITIONS IS 30 DB

CONVERSION OF AVERAGE POWER IN DBM TO PEAK POWER IN DBM

PULSE RECURRENCE FREQUENCY (PRF)

DUTY CYCLE IN DECIBELS (DB)

PULSE WIDTH IN MICROSECONDS

STRAIGHT EDGE

C-11 RADIATION EMISSION PROPERTIES OF SCINTILLATION PHOSPHORS

Phosphor	Maximum emitted wavelength (Angstrom)	Particle pulse strength (anthracene = 1.0)
Inorganic:		
Zinc Sulfide		
(Silver activated)	4,500	1.0
Sodium iodide		
(Tellurium activated)	4,100	2.1
Calcium tungstate	4,300	0.36
Cadmium tungstate	5,300	1.0
Organic:		
Anthracene	4,440	1.0
Stiblene	4,080	0.6
p-terphenyl:		
(in xylene)	4,050	0.2
(in phenyl-cyclo-hexane)	4,500	0.35
(in toluene)	4,150	0.42
(in polystyrene)	4,450	0.39

C-12 APPARENT (WAVEGUIDE) WAVELENGTH CHART

(Courtesy, Narda Microwave Corporation)

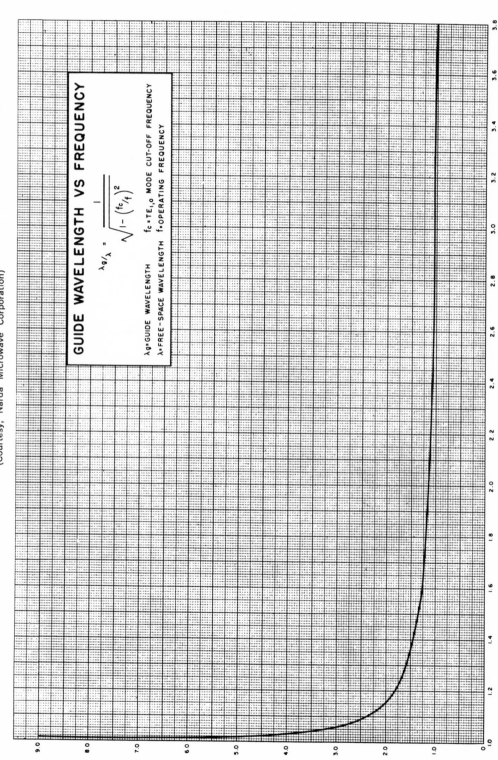

GUIDE WAVELENGTH VS FREQUENCY

$$\lambda g/\lambda = \frac{1}{\sqrt{1 - (f_c/f)^2}}$$

$f_c = TE_{1,0}$ MODE CUT-OFF FREQUENCY
$f = $ OPERATING FREQUENCY

$\lambda g = $ GUIDE WAVELENGTH
$\lambda = $ FREE-SPACE WAVELENGTH

C-13 CHARACTERISTIC IMPEDANCE OF AIR-FILLED COAXIAL LINE

(Courtesy, Narda Microwave Corporation)

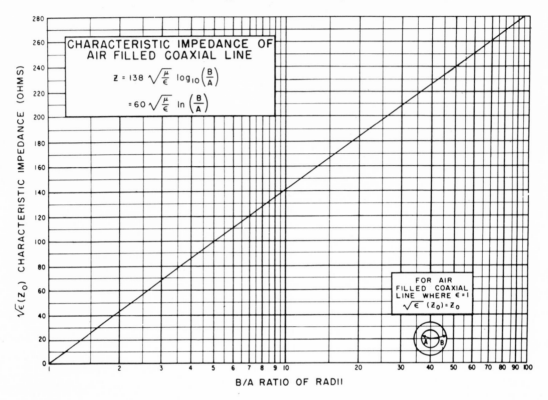

CHARACTERISTIC IMPEDANCE OF
AIR FILLED COAXIAL LINE

$$Z = 138 \sqrt{\frac{\mu}{\epsilon}} \ \log_{10}\left(\frac{B}{A}\right)$$

$$= 60 \sqrt{\frac{\mu}{\epsilon}} \ \ln\left(\frac{B}{A}\right)$$

FOR AIR
FILLED COAXIAL
LINE WHERE $\epsilon = 1$
$\sqrt{\epsilon} \ (Z_0) = Z_0$

B/A RATIO OF RADII

Appendix D

D-1 ALTERNATING CURRENT AND VOLTAGE VALUES

EFFECTIVE (R-M-S) VALUE

Since the ordinate (amplitude value) of an alternating waveform varies from instant to instant, an *effective* numerical value has been established for application to all waveshapes. Since the heating effect of a current is independent of the direction in which the current flows, this effect has become the basis for this technique of comparing waveforms.

An alternating current has an *effective value* of 1 amp if it produces heat in a given number of ohms of resistance at the same rate as heat is produced in an equal resistance value by 1 amp of continuous (direct) current.

Since the heating value of direct current is equal to i^2R, the heating value of an alternating current must be computed from the i^2 curve of the alternating waveform. Figure D-1 shows the i^2 curve for a sine wave. It is obtained by squaring a sufficient number of ordinates along the i curve and then drawing a smooth curve through the i^2 ordinates. Note that the i^2 curve lies entirely above the $i = 0$ axis. This is always

true, since the square of a negative value is positive. The i^2 curve will also have a frequency (or repetition rate) equal to twice the frequency of the i curve, if the i curve has both positive and negative values.

The i^2 curve will be symmetrical about some axis with a value $(i_{avg})^2$ equal to the average of all the i^2 values. This $(i_{avg})^2$ value represents the heating effect of the current and the square root of this value is the desired effective value of the waveform.

Since this process involves the square root of an average (mean) value, it is referred to as the "root-mean-square" or r-m-s value. This term is used more frequently than "effective" value.

The exact procedure for determining the r-m-s value of any alternating waveform involves the following steps:

1. Plot a waveform whose ordinates are equal to the squares of the original waveform ordinates.

2. Find the average ordinate by dividing the area under one cycle of the squared wave by the base (duration of one cycle).

3. Determine the square root of the average ordinate.

This may be stated compactly by

$$\text{r-m-s value} = \frac{\text{area (one cycle) of } i^2 \text{ curve}}{\text{base (one cycle) of } i^2 \text{ curve}}$$

The area required may be obtained from the mathematically plotted graph, or an oscilloscopic photograph of the i^2 curve with a planimeter. The r-m-s value can also be computed (if the original current waveform equation is known) from the definite integral:

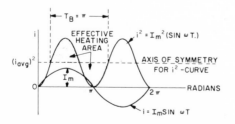

Fig. D-1 Graphical relations for determining the effective value of a sine wave.

315

$$\text{r-m-s value} = \sqrt{\frac{1}{T_B} \int_0^{T_B} i^2 \, dt}$$

For the sine wave, $i = I_m \sin \omega t$ and

$$\text{r-m-s value} = \sqrt{\frac{1}{\pi} \int_0^{\pi} I_m^2 \, (\sin \omega t)^2 \, dt}$$

which has a value of $0.707 \, I_m$.

Figure D-2 shows a pulse waveform similar to that of the pulse from a radar transmitter. The computation of the r-m-s value is shown. The r-m-s value is equal to the peak value of the pulse. This result is logical since the r-m-s value is the d-c heating equivalent of the original current, and in the case of this pulse, the peak value may be considered to be a direct current during this time interval, $0 < t < T_B$. This is true of all pulse waveforms with constant amplitude and very rapid (theoretically, zero) rise time and fall time.

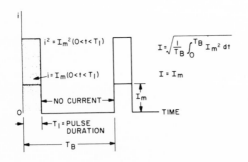

Fig. D-2 Effective value of radar pulse.

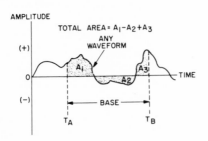

Fig. D-3 Determining the average value of an a-c waveform.

Notice that the r-m-s value is equal to a constant times the peak value. This factor is called the r-m-s "multiplying factor," M. For the sine wave, $M_s = 0.707$ and for the pulse, $M_p = 1$. For a triangular waveform, $M_t = 0.577$, or

$$\text{r-m-s value (triangular)} = 0.577 \, I_m$$

AVERAGE VALUE

The average value of any alternating waveform is the value found by adding the ordinates of the waveform between two bounding values (T_A and T_B) and dividing by the base ($T_B - T_A$). (See Fig. D-3.)

$$\text{average value} = \frac{\text{area between } T_A \text{ and } T_B}{(T_B - T_A)}$$

Generally, all waveforms are started at zero for purposes of analysis so that $T_A = 0$ and the average is taken over one cycle. Again, the area may be determined with a planimeter or by a definite integral, whereby the equation takes the form:

$$\text{average value} = \frac{\int_{T_A}^{T_B} F(t) \, dt}{(T_B - T_A)}$$

where $F(t)$ is the equation of the waveform valid for $T_A < t < T_B$.

For the sine wave, the average value is given by

$$\text{average value} = \frac{\int_0^{2\pi} I_m \sin \omega t \, (dt)}{2\pi}$$

which is equal to $0.637 \, I_m$. Consulting Fig. D-2, the average value for one cycle of a radar pulse is given by

$$\text{average value} = \frac{\int_0^{T_1} I_m \, dt}{T_B} = \frac{I_m T_1}{T_B}$$

As with the r-m-s value, the average value is equal to a constant times the peak value. This constant is the average multiplying factor, M_A. For the sine wave, $M_{A(S)} = 0.637$. For the pulse, the value is $M_{A(p)} = T_1/T_B$ = duty cycle. The term "duty cycle" is commonly applied to pulse waveforms for the value of M_A.

INSTRUMENT CORRECTIONS

The scales of most voltage and current indicating devices are calibrated from the r-m-s value of a pure sine wave (the heating effect of an equivalent d-c current). Hence, the readings obtained will be valid as long as the applied signal is a sine wave of a frequency within the specified range. If such instruments are used to make nonsinusoidal measurements, certain corrections based on the multiplying factors must be made. For accurate measurements it is necessary that the harmonic content of the nonsinusoidal waveform (see Appendix D-3) fall within the frequency range of the meter.

For example, if it were necessary to determine the effective value of a triangular waveform with a common-type VTVM, this instrument would be calibrated on the basis:

$$\text{r-m-s value} = 0.707 \, I_m$$

Since the r-m-s value of a triangular waveform is given by $0.577 \, I_m$, the measured value would be equal to the sinusoidal reading times the ratio of the triangular r-m-s multiplying factor to the sinusoidal r-m-s multiplying factor:

$$\frac{M_T}{M_S}(\text{VTVM reading}) = 0.816 \, (\text{VTVM reading})$$

The relationship:

$$\frac{M_X}{M_S} \, (\text{VTVM reading})$$

holds true for all types of waveforms with M_X as the r-m-s multiplying factor for the nonsinusoidal waveform and M_S for the sine wave. A similar relationship holds true for

Table D-1 Average and r-m-s multiplying factors for six common waveforms.

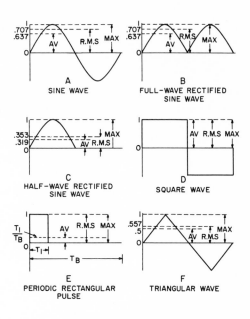

average reading instruments except that M_X and M_S become the average multiplying factors.

A listing for the more common waveforms is given in Table D-1. The waveforms shown in this table have a peak value of 1 (volt or ampere). The values given must, in general, be multiplied by I_M, the peak value of the waveform in question.

Additional considerations may be involved when the waveform is a periodic rectangular pulse, as represented by waveform (e) in the table. Generally, the d-c component is removed by blocking capacitors present in the input circuit of most vacuum-tube voltmeters. The waveform then applied to the rectifier of the instrument has the same shape, but the positive and negative swings of potential are based on an average-value reference given by the dotted line. Hence, the areas above and below this reference are equal, but the peak values and the durations of these loops are vastly different. If the detector circuit is arranged so that the meter is actuated by the positive portion of the waveform only, the factor M will have the value stated in the table. The factor M_A of an average-value instrument employing a blocking capacitor will be unaffected by reversal of the input leads, since the average value of either loop is the same, but a peak-responding instrument will provide an entirely different reading if the leads are reversed. This change, known as *turnover*, arises from the different peak value of the loops. The values given in (e) of Table D-1 are based on the true r-m-s voltage of the actual waveform, not the smaller value of the rectangular wave that results when the d-c component is removed.

Frequently, complex waveforms containing many harmonics are applied to average-reading instruments. Reversing the leads will often cause a turnover effect in such cases, since the phase relationships of the harmonics affect the average values of either of the two half cycles considered separately.

Instruments, such as thermocouples, dynamometers and square-law VTVM's, indicate r-m-s values for *any waveform* so that corrections need not be made. The harmonic content of the waveform, however, must be within the frequency range of the instrument.

D-2 FORM FACTOR

The form factor for any waveshape is defined by

$$\text{form factor} = F = \frac{\text{effective value}}{\text{average value}}$$

This relationship is a constant value for a particular type of waveshape and, for this reason, is frequently used for comparing a nonsinusoidal waveform with a sinusoidal (or several nonsinusoidal waveforms with each other). It is also utilized to determine the peak amplitude of one waveform necessary to have the same heating effects as another waveform.

For the sine wave,

$$F = \frac{0.707\ I_M}{0.637\ I_M} = 1.11$$

and for the radar pulse, Fig. D-2 (Appendix D-1), $F = T_B/T_1$

Close scrutiny of the defined equation will show that the form factor calculation reduces to

$$F = \frac{M}{M_A}$$

since I_M is common to both values. Here, M and M_A are the r-m-s and average multiplying factors respectively.

D-3 WAVEFORM ANALYSIS

By a technique first formulated by Fourier in 1812, any periodic waveform can be mathematically represented by, or physically synthesized from, a series of harmonically related sinusoidal functions. In theory, an infinite number of such pure sinewaves may be needed. Physical limitations of circuitry, however, generally cause the representation to require only a finite number of sinusoids. It is these physical limitations which permit Fourier analysis to be applied to alternating waveforms on a practical basis. Harmonic and spectrum presentations are the most common applications of the Fourier technique.

It is also possible to extend this technique to include nonperiodic and randomly generated waveforms. Such application, however, is beyond the scope of this manual.

FOURIER-SERIES ANALYSIS

The two techniques commonly employed for representing waveforms are shown diagrammatically in Fig. D-4. Part A shows the familiar amplitude-time plane; part B shows the amplitude-frequency plane (wave spectrum). The second technique is essential to design considerations, such as bandwidth and distortion, and has become more popular as the art of *information theory* has advanced to its present state. The harmonic spectrum of a periodic waveform can be determined from purely mathematical techniques or from experimentally determined waveform records (oscillograph or oscilloscope).

The Fourier expression for any periodic waveform is given by

$$y = A_1 \sin \omega t + A_2 \sin 2\omega t + A_3 \sin 3\omega t + \dots$$
$$+ A_n \sin n\omega t + B_1 \cos \omega t + B_2 \cos \quad 2\omega t$$
$$+ B_3 \cos 3\omega t + \dots + B_n \cos n\omega t + B_o$$

This is an infinite series of sinusoids based on a fundamental frequency, $f = 1/T$ where T is the interval of one period of the original waveform. The term B_o represents a d-c value which may or may not be present in order to complete the alternating waveform presentation.

For most practical applications completion of the series to the seventh harmonic $(n = 7)$ is sufficient to represent electrically generated waveforms.

An application of mathematical symmetry further reduces the number of sinusoidal terms needed to represent a periodic waveform. Figure D-5 shows an "even" and "odd" waveform (function of time). The even function is symmetrical about the vertical axis. Mathematically, this is stated by

$$f(t) = f(-t)$$

where $f(t)$ is the equation of the waveform. Thus, the amplitude of an even function is the same for specific positive and negative

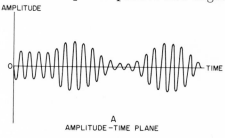

AMPLITUDE

TIME

A
AMPLITUDE –TIME PLANE

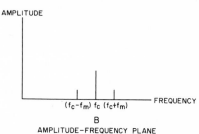

AMPLITUDE

FREQUENCY

$(f_c - f_m)$ f_c $(f_c + f_m)$

B
AMPLITUDE–FREQUENCY PLANE

Fig. D-4 Two common methods of plotting a-c waveforms (applied to single-tone AM sinusoid).

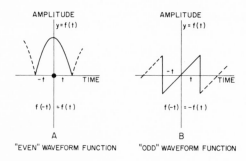

Fig. D-5 Illustrating "even" and "odd" functions.

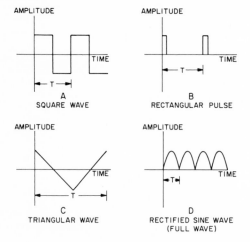

Fig. D-6 Repetition time for several waveforms.

values of t. The odd function has an amplitude equal in numerical value but opposite in sign for positive and negative values of t, or

$$f(-t) = f(t)$$

The Fourier series for an even function contains only the cosine terms.

$$y = f(t) \text{ "even"} = B_1 \cos \omega t + B_2 \cos 2\omega t + B_3 \cos 3\omega t + \ldots + B_n \cos n\omega t$$

For the odd function, only the sine terms are present:

$$y = f(t) \text{ "odd"} = A_1 \sin \omega t + A_2 \sin 2\omega t + A_3 \sin 3\omega t + \ldots + A_n \sin n\omega t$$

If the equation for the waveform $f(t)$ is known, the coefficients for the series (A_n and B_n) can be evaluated from the definite integrals:

$$B_o = \frac{1}{T} \int_0^T f(t)\, dt$$

$$A_n = \frac{2}{T} \int_0^T f(t) \sin \left(\frac{2n\pi t}{T} \right) dt$$

$$B_n = \frac{2}{T} \int_0^T f(t) \cos \left(\frac{2n\pi t}{T} \right) dt$$

If it is not possible to use the preceding integrals, the coefficients may be determined

Table D-2 Fourier series expressions for six common waveforms.

FULL-WAVE RECTIFIED SINE WAVE

$$y = \frac{2}{\pi} + \frac{4}{\pi}\left[\frac{1}{3}\cos 2f - \frac{1}{15}\cos 4f + \frac{1}{35}\cos 6f - \cdots\cdots + \frac{(-1)^{n+1}}{4n^2-1}\cos 2nf + \cdots\right]$$

HALF-WAVE RECTIFIED SINE WAVE

$$y = \frac{1}{\pi} + \frac{1}{2}\cos f + \frac{2}{\pi}\left[\frac{1}{3}\cos 2f - \frac{1}{15}\cos 4f + \frac{1}{35}\cos 6f - \cdots\cdots + \frac{(-1)^{n+1}}{4n^2-1}\cos 2nf + \cdots\right]$$

SQUARE WAVE

$$y = \frac{4}{\pi}\left[\sin f + \frac{1}{3}\sin 3f + \frac{1}{5}\sin 5f \cdots\cdots + \frac{1}{2n+1}\sin(2n+1)f + \cdots\right]$$

PERIODIC RECTANGULAR PULSE

$$y = \frac{T_1}{\pi} + \frac{2}{\pi}\left[\sin T_1 \cos\frac{1}{T_B} + \frac{\sin 2T_1}{2}\cos 2\frac{1}{T_B} + \frac{\sin 3T_1}{3}\cos 3\frac{1}{T_B} + \cdots + \frac{\sin nT_1}{n}\cos n\frac{1}{T_B} + \cdots\right]$$

TRIANGULAR WAVE

$$y = \frac{8}{\pi^2}\left[\sin f - \frac{1}{9}\sin 3f + \frac{1}{25}\sin 5f - \frac{1}{49}\sin 7f + \cdots\cdots + \frac{(-1)^n}{(2n+1)^2}\sin(2n+1)f + \cdots\right]$$

SAWTOOTH WAVE

$$y = \frac{2}{\pi}\left[\sin f - \frac{1}{2}\sin 2f + \frac{1}{3}\sin 3f - \frac{1}{4}\sin 4f + \cdots\cdots + \frac{(-1)^{n+1}}{n}\sin nf + \cdots\right]$$

from an experimental plot of the waveform in the amplitude-time plane. Of course, for even functions only the B_o and B_n terms need be computed, and for the odd function, only the A_n terms are needed. There are several graphical techniques for determining these coefficients on a strictly arithmetic basis.* The process, however, requires considerable time to perform.

Table D-2 gives the Fourier series expression for some commonly encountered waveforms. Most electrical waveforms have symmetry of one form or another so that the series reduces to only sine terms or only cosine terms (plus a d-c component, occasionally). Notice that each term follows a set pattern so that it can be expressed for any value of n.

The frequency of the fundamental must be computed. Since there is one cycle of the fundamental within one repetition of the nonsinusoidal waveform, the frequency must be given by

$$f = \frac{1}{T}$$

This is shown in Fig. D-6 for several of the waveshapes. The harmonic frequencies are multiples of f.

As stated previously, the accuracy of the representation depends on the number of harmonics used. The greater the number of harmonics, the more accurate the representation. This is shown in Fig. D-7. The amplitudes for most of the terms listed in Table D-2 diminish rather rapidly so that only a few terms will be required for a practical representation of the waveform.

The frequency-amplitude spectrum for the sawtooth wave is shown in Fig. D-8. This is the spectrum of a pure sawtooth wave. If both sine and cosine terms are present, the amplitude (C_n) for the spectrum plot is determined for each harmonic as

$$C_n = \sqrt{A_n^2 + B_n^2}$$

* Frank A. Laws, *Electrical Measurements* (New York, McGraw-Hill, 1938), pp. 677–92. (Many other engineering texts also include these methods.)

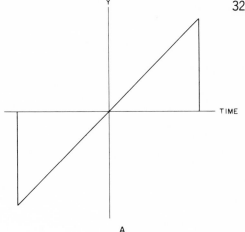

A
PURE SAWTOOTH WAVEFORM

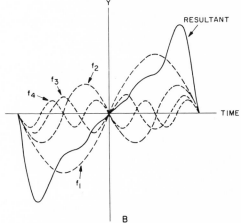

B
SAWTOOTH SYNTHESIZED BY FOUR TERMS OF FOURIER SERIES

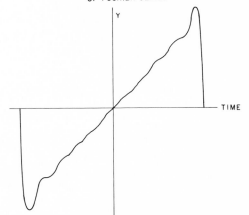

C SAWTOOTH SYNTHESIZED BY TEN TERMS OF FOURIER SERIES

Fig. D-7 Synthesis of waveform by harmonic addition.

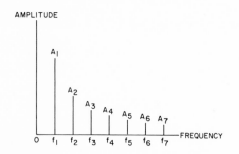

Fig. D-8 Spectrum of sawtooth wave showing seven harmonics.

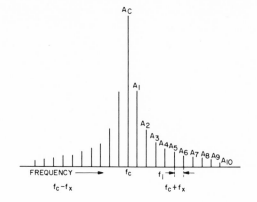

Fig. D-9 Spectrum for sinusoidal carrier amplitude-modulated by sawtooth.

In order to plot the spectrum for a sine-wave carrier f_c which is amplitude-modulated by a sawtooth, a slightly different technique must be used. The carrier frequency f_c will represent a center frequency of amplitude A_c and the harmonics will be equally spaced above and below f_c. (See Fig. D-9.)

D-4 USE OF THE SMITH CHART

The Smith Chart (Fig. D-10) is an especially constructed graph designed to provide rapid solutions for microwave problems concerning impedance, *VSWR*, matching, etc. The chart serves such calculations in the same manner that a slide rule serves the mathematical operations for which it is designed.

Notice that the horizontal axis is marked RESISTANCE or CONDUCTANCE COMPONENT and is graduated from one to zero from the center of the chart toward the left and from one to infinity from the center toward the right. Circles drawn through this axis represent *constant resistance or conductance circles* as shown in the figure. The values along this axis represent normalized resistance (R/Z_o) and conductance (G/Y_o).

The chart also contains circular segments above and below the horizontal axis and tangent to the horizontal axis at the right hand end. These curves are portions of *constant reactance (or susceptance) circles.*

Again, the values are normalized (jX/Z_o and jB/Y_o). The upper half of the chart represents positive values; the lower half, negative values.

A circle drawn with its center at the center of the Smith Chart represents a constant *VSWR* circle or, since,

$$|K| = \frac{VSWR - 1}{VSWR + 1}$$

a constant reflection coefficient circle. The numbers along the right-hand half of the horizontal axis serve as a *VSWR* axis so that the circle shown in Fig. D-10 represents a *VSWR* of 1.4 ($K = 0.167$, magnitude only).

The periphery of a Smith Chart is marked with three scales. One represents distance toward the load (away from the source) along the transmission line or waveguide and increases in a counterclockwise direction. The second represents distance *toward the generator* (away from the load) and in-

IMPEDANCE OR ADMITTANCE COORDINATES

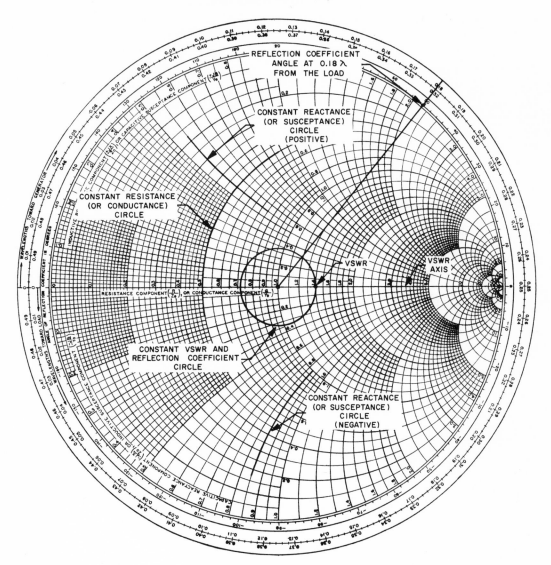

Fig. D-10 Smith chart components.

creases in the clockwise direction. These two scales are complementary and are both included for convenience. Computations can thus be made with respect to either end of the line or waveguide. Both scales are in terms of wavelength and start at the left-hand end of the horizontal axis. A complete circuit of these scales represents a distance of 0.5 λ along the transmission medium. Distances greater than 0.5 λ represent multiple circuits of the chart.

The third scale represents the angle associated with the reflection coefficient at various points along a transmission medium. A line drawn from the center of the chart to a point representing distance along the medium intersects this scale at the proper angle. The magnitude is determined from the previous formula. The line shown in Fig. D-10 represents a reflection coefficient of 0.167 $\diagup$ 50° at a point 0.18 λ from the load end of the medium.

CALCULATION OF LOAD IMPEDANCE AND ADMITTANCE

In order to determine the load with the Smith Chart, two quantities must be known —the VSWR and the point at which a voltage minimum occurs. Assume that the measured VSWR in a certain waveguide is 1.8. A voltage minimum is found at 5 cm from the load. The system is operating at 9 kmc.

The constant VSWR circle is drawn in Fig. D-11. It is now necessary to locate the voltage minimum on the chart. First, determine the wavelength.

$$\lambda = \frac{c}{f} = \frac{2.998 \times 10^{10} \text{ cm/sec}}{9 \times 10^9 \text{ cycles/sec}} = 3.33 \text{ cm}$$

The distance of 5 cm then represents

$$\frac{5}{3.33} \lambda = 1.55 \lambda$$

Since this distance is *away* from the load, we use the "wavelengths toward generator" scale. A distance of 1.55 λ is slightly over *three half waves* which represents three circuits of the chart plus an additional portion of a circuit. Since the fourth circuit would represent 2 λ (four half waves) the portion of the fourth circuit is given by

$$2 \lambda - 1.55 \lambda = 0.05 \lambda$$

This is marked on the chart.

A line drawn from the center of the chart to 0.05 λ intersects the constant VSWR circle at point A in Fig. D-11. This point of intersection represents the normalized load impedance. The resistive and reactive components are determined as shown. This results in a normalized load of 0.6 + j.22 ohms. If the characteristic impedance (Z_o) for the

medium were 40 ohms, the actual load impedance would be

$$40 (0.6 + j.22) = 24 + j8.8 \text{ ohms}$$

If the load admittance were desired, the line from the center of the chart would be extended to intersect the constant VSWR circle at point B–diametrically opposite point A. The conductance and susceptance components at this point yield a normalized load admittance of: 1.5 − j0.525 mhos. Assuming a characteristic admittance of:

$$\frac{1}{Z_o} = \frac{1}{40} = 0.025 \text{ mhos}$$

the load admittance is given by:
0.025 (1.5 − j0.525) = 0.0375 − j0.0131 mhos

CALCULATION OF INPUT IMPEDANCE AND ADMITTANCE

Once the load point and VSWR circle have been located on the Smith Chart it is possible to determine the input impedance to the transmission medium. The only information required is the length of the medium. This is shown in Fig. D-11. Point A (the load) is the reference point.

Assume that the length of the transmission medium is 37.13 cm which, in terms of wavelengths at 9 kmc, is

$$\frac{37.13}{3.33} = 11.1 \lambda$$

This represents twenty-two complete circuits of the chart along the "wavelengths toward generator" scale (from point A to 0.05 λ) plus an additional part (0.1 λ) of the twenty-third circuit. Hence,

$$0.05 \lambda + 0.1 \lambda = 0.15 \lambda$$

which is point E in Fig. D-11.

The input impedance (normalized) is read at point C and the normalized input admittance at point D, diametrically opposite.

When the input value and VSWR (or voltage minimum) are known, the load

IMPEDANCE OR ADMITTANCE COORDINATES

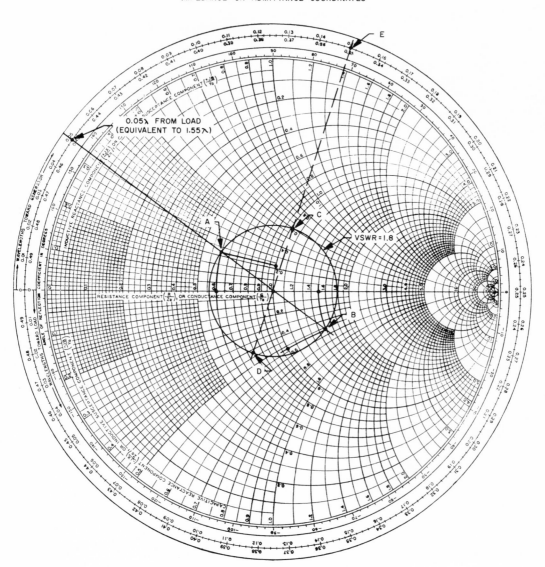

Fig. D-11 Load impedance and admittance determination.

values can be found by reversing the procedures described above.

MATCHING (SHORT-CIRCUIT STUB)

Figure D-12 shows the procedure for matching the load to the characteristic impedance

of a transmission medium. The stub (attached branch) is terminated in a short circuit. By varying the length of the stub (d_s) and its distance from the load (d_L) it is possible to cancel the reactive component of the load and alter the resistive component to make it equal to Z_o. *The characteristic im-*

pedance of the stub medium should be the same as that of the main transmission medium. The value of d_s and d_L can be readily found from a Smith Chart.

With the short-circuit stub it is most convenient to use the chart in terms of admittance rather than impedance. The admittance of the load in Fig. D-12 is: 0.1375 − j 0.0131 mhos. This is normalized by dividing the characteristic admittance, 0.025 mhos to produce a normalized admittance of 1.5 − j 0.525 which is located at point A in Fig. D-13. The constant *VSWR* circle is then drawn through point A and the intersection with the unity constant conductance circle is labeled point B. The difference in conductance between point A and point B represents the amount of conductance which must be added to the load to produce a normalized conductance of 1 (which corresponds to a load conductance equal to the characteristic conductance). The length of transmission medium needed to acomplish this (d_L) is determined by constructing lines from the center of the chart through points

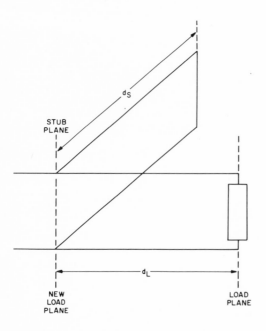

Fig. D-12 Short-circuit stub.

A and B and measuring the distance between the two lines along the *wavelengths toward generator scale.* In Fig. D-13, this distance is computed by

$$0.352\,\lambda - 0.298\,\lambda = 0.054\,\lambda$$

If the frequency is 9 kmc as in the previous example the stub must be located

$$0.054\,(3.33\text{ cm}) = 0.178\text{ cm}$$

from the load.

The foregoing procedure has physically translated the load plane (Fig. D-12) from its original position to a new position corresponding to the stub plane. Everything to the right of the new load plane is now the load for the transmission medium. This new load has a conductance equal to the characteristic admittance of the transmission medium. However, a normalized susceptance of − j0.6 still exists. To obtain a perfect match this susceptance must be canceled. This cancellation is accomplished by the length of the stub.

Canceling a normalized susceptance of − j 0.6 means adding a normalized susceptance of + j 0.6. On the Smith Chart, this is accomplished by locating the end of the + j 0.6 susceptance curve (point C in Fig. D-13). A line drawn through the center of the chart and point C intersects the "wavelengths toward generator" scale at 0.086 λ. A short circuit represents an infinite admittance. The infinite admittance point on the chart is at point D in the figure. The distance between point C and point D represents the required length of the stub

$$0.25\,\lambda + 0.086\,\lambda = 0.336\,\lambda$$

With a frequency of 9 kmc, this is a length of

$$d_s = 0.336\,(3.33\text{ cm}) = 1.119\text{ cm}$$

The match produced by this stub occurs along the transmission medium at all points to the left of the stub (new load) axis.

IMPEDANCE OR ADMITTANCE COORDINATES

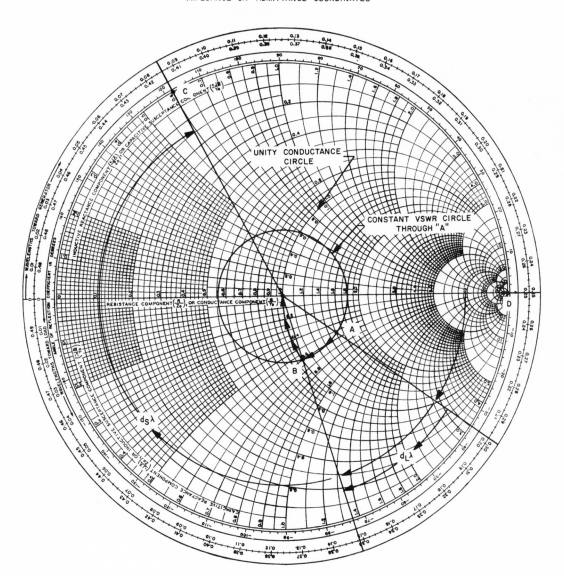

Fig. D-13 Short-circuit stub matching.

MATCHING (OPEN-CIRCUIT STUB)

A load can also be matched by using an open-circuit stub as shown in Fig. D-14. The procedure is the same as for a short-circuit stub—the original load plane is translated to the stub plane which alters the load resistance until it is equal to the characteristic

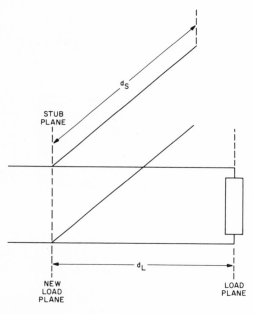

Fig. D-14 Open-circuit stub.

impedance. The length of the stub is then adjusted to cancel the reactive component of the load. As with the short-circuit stub, the characteristic impedance of stub and main medium must be the same.

Open-circuit stub matching with a Smith Chart is most easily accomplished in terms of admittance. The normalized admittance of the load shown in Fig. D-14 is

$$\frac{0.0416 + j\,0.0114}{0.02} = 2.08 + j\,0.57$$

This is point A in Fig. D-15. The constant VSWR circle through this point intersects the unity resistance circle at point B. The distance between A and B along the "wavelengths toward generator" scale is given by

$$0.5\,\lambda - (0.224\,\lambda - 0.154\,\lambda) = 0.43\,\lambda$$

Notice that this is almost one complete circuit of the chart.

To cancel the $+j\,0.57$ reactance component, the stub must have a $-j\,0.57$ reactance. This point is indicated at C in the figure. The open-circuit stub represents a load admittance of zero magnitude which is indicated at point D. The distance between C and D measured along the "wavelengths toward generator" scale is read directly as $0.419\,\lambda$. This is the length of the stub.

IMPEDANCE OR ADMITTANCE COORDINATES

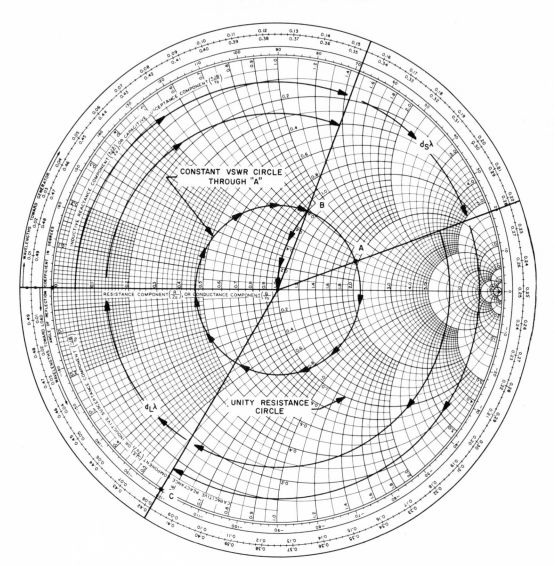

Fig. D-15 Open-circuit stub matching.

Bibliography

Colvin, Fred H., and Frank A. Stanley, **American Machinist's Handbook**. New York: McGraw-Hill, 1940.

Davis, Harmer E., G. E. Troxell, and C. T. Wiskocil, **The Testing and Inspection of Engineering Materials**. New York: McGraw-Hill, 1941.

Dawes, Chester L., **Electrical Engineering**, Vol. I, **Direct Currents**. New York: McGraw-Hill, 1952.

Fairchild, C. O., J. D. Hardy, R. B. Sosman, and H. T. Wensel, **Temperature, Its Measurement and Control In Science and Industry**. New York: Reinhold Publishing Corp., 1941.

Glasstone, Samuel, **Sourcebook On Atomic Energy**. Princeton, N. J.: D. Van Nostrand, 1950.

Golding, E. W., **Electrical Measurements and Measuring Instruments**. London: Pitman Sons, 1940.

Lapp, R. E., and H. L. Andrews, **Nuclear Radiation Physics**. Englewood Cliffs, N. J.: Prentice-Hall, Inc., 1954.

Laws, Frank A., **Electrical Measurements**. New York: McGraw-Hill, 1938.

Manning, Kenneth V., Robert L. Weber, and Marsh W. White, **College Physics**. New York: McGraw-Hill, 1959.

Page, Leigh, and N. I. Adams, Jr., **Principles of Electricity**. Princeton, N. J.: D. Van Nostrand, 1958.

Ryder, John D., **Networks, Lines, and Fields**. Englewood Cliffs, N. J.: Prentice-Hall, 1955.

Schneider, Walter A., and Lloyd B. Hann, **Experimental Physics for Colleges**. New York: Macmillan, 1942.

Shoop, Charles F., and G. L. Turve, **Mechanical Engineering Practice**. New York: McGraw-Hill, 1941.

Smith, A. W., and M. L. Wiedenbeck, **Electrical Measurements**. New York: McGraw-Hill, 1959.

Sweeny, R. J., **Measurement Techniques in Mechanical Engineering**. New York: John Wiley & Sons, 1959.

Tang, K. Y., **Alternating-Current Circuits**. Scranton, Pa.: International Textbook, 1951.

Terman, F. E., and J. M. Pettit, **Electronic Measurements**. New York: McGraw-Hill, 1952.

Wind, Moe (ed.), **Handbook of Electronic Measurements**, Vol. I, II. New York: Interscience Publishers, 1956.

————, **Handbook of Microwave Measurements**, Vol. I, II. New York: Interscience Publishers, 1954.

Answers to Problems

CHAPTER 2

1	2.5–1	12	19.375 v	23	0.775 v
2	55 v	13	9.625 v	24	0.775 v
3	55 v	14	13.75 v	25	0.385 v
4	77.5 v	15	13.75 v	26	0.385 v
5	77.5 v	16	2.75 v	27	0.55 v
6	38.5 v	17	2.75 v	28	0.55 v
7	38.5 v	18	3.875 v	29	0.1375 v
8	55 v	19	1.925 v	30	0.1937 v
9	55 v	20	2.75 v	31	0.096 v
10	13.75 v	21	0.55 v	32	0.1375 v
11	19.375 v	22	0.55 v		

CHAPTER 4

1	−40°F	3	1761.44°F	5	373°K
2	790.0°K	4	1292.28°R	6	90.03°K

CHAPTER 5

1	9.79329	4	450 in.–oz.	7	2690
2	9.81166	5	0.90–0.95	8	6
3	0.000379	6	0.02–0.04	9	0.27

CHAPTER 6

1	27 ohms/ft	5	55.5 mv	9	100,000 ohms
2	24.6 ma	6	30 in.	10	50,000 ohms
3	2.25 ohm/in.	7	885 μv	11	40,000 ohms
4	67.5 ohms	8	60,000 ohms	12	2.722 ohms

Index